The Symptom–Context Method

Symptoms as Opportunities in Psychotherapy

LESTER LUBORSKY

The American Psychological Association
WASHINGTON, DC

Published by the
American Psychological Association
750 First Street, NE
Washington, DC 20002

Copies may be ordered from
APA Order Department
P.O. Box 2710
Hyattsville, MD 20784

In the United Kingdom and Europe, copies may be ordered from
American Psychological Association
3 Henrietta Street
Covent Garden, London
WC2E 8LU England

Typeset in Goudy by PRO-IMAGE Corporation, Techna-Type Div., York, PA

Printer: United Book Press, Inc., Baltimore, MD
Cover designer: Mike Fender Design, Arlington, MA
Technical/production editor: Valerie Montenegro

Library of Congress Cataloging-in-Publication Data
Luborsky, Lester, 1920–
    The symptom-context method : symptoms as opportunities in
psychotherapy / by Lester Luborsky.
        p.   cm.
    Includes bibliographical references and index.
    ISBN 1-55798-354-2 (cb : acid-free paper)
    1. Psychology, Pathological.   2. Symptomatology.
3. Psychotherapy.   I. Title.
    [DNLM: 1. Psychotherapy—methods.   2. Mental Disorders—diagnosis.
3. Mental Disorders—therapy.   4. Psychophysiologic Disorders—
diagnosis.   5. Psychophysiologic Disorders—therapy.   WM 420 L929s
1996]
RC454.4.L83   1996
616.89'075—dc20
DNLM/DLC
for Library of Congress   96-4876
                                                                            CIP

British Library Cataloguing-in-Publication Data
A CIP record is available from the British Library.

Printed in the United States of America
First edition

CONTENTS

ACKNOWLEDGMENTS

Sources of Support and Supportiveness

Beginning in 1946 with the study of the context for an ulcer patient's recurrent stomach pains in the course of psychotherapy, I began to mull over ideas leading to the symptom-context method. I was blessed by having Raymond Cattell to work with, for he was the primary idea-maker and grand encourager for single-case studies by his P-technique method for factor analysis of repeated measures within each person. Then, the idea for the at-the-time novel focus on the systematic analysis of the context of particular symptoms came to me through my experiences with this ulcer patient's psychotherapy.

Providently, survival-sustaining support for some of my symptom-context studies came from the recurrent modest sums from the Luborsky Bio-psychosocial Foundation as well as from the 27 years of indispensable steady salary support by the Research Scientist Awards from the National Institute of Mental Health (NIMH) Research Development Program from 1968 to 1992 (MH-40710), which was continued by the National Institute on Drug Abuse (NIDA) in 1992 and still continues (DA-00168). Since July 1990, this work has also been supported in part by NIMH Clinical Research Center Grant P50 MN-45178 and NIDA Coordinating Center Grant U18-DA07090 (to Paul Crits-Christoph).

A number of my dear friends, dear family, dear colleagues, and combinations of these, have been facilitators. Ruth Samson Luborsky, as always, has been the foremost helpmate in my immediate and broad context. Ellen Luborsky, my psychologist daughter, has been a long-term, brilliant critiquer and collaborator. Lise Luborsky, my lawyer daughter, has been a resourceful legal consultant, and Peter Luborsky, my linguist son, has been always knowledgeable about translations. Miranda Outman, my writer granddaughter, has been a rigorously helpful editor for this and past books. Alexander Outman, my historian grandson, has been a supportive discussant of the philosophy of science context of my research.

Marshall Edelson, my steadfast old friend, got through to me that "it's time now" to finish this book. Linda Book's advice has also been a good focuser: to reconsider the relative worth of the nonessential distractors from work on this book. Many associates have been active in seeing the book through to completion, including Laura Dahl, who helped with editing; Majorie Cohen; Nona Sachdeva; Yvonne Burnett, who helped with transcription; and Joyce Bell, who zipped through and kept on top of the mountain of drafts of the book chapters with her magical computer and general management. In the last two years Louis Diguer's advice and support with the multiple reanalyses helped to shape and reshape each and every chapter so the work could sail along faster and safer. Roberta Bailey Harvey, Donald Phoenix, Shirley H. Heineman, Ellen Luborsky, Suzanne Johnson, Joyce Bell, Karen Burns, Amy Horn, Monica Bishop, and David Seligman helped me to chisel away on the gradual refashioning of the chapters, with Amanda Horn and David Seligman most involved in the last lap. Louis Diguer, James McKay, and Robert Rosenthal, helped along by Suzanne Johnson and David Seligman, were indispensable guides to statistical wisdom. George Stricker, distinguished professor at the Derner Institute of Adelphi University, contributed as an overall evaluator. John Cacciola's diagnostic expertise has fortified the *DSM-IV* diagnostic correctness of all chapters. David Seligman has concentrated for the past year on the refinement and execution of the voluminous data analyses in each chapter. Robert Rosenthal and his Harvard associates, Don Rubin and Douwe Yntema, held a vital, marathon, curative review session with me on the book's design and statistics just in time before the book was finished.

Gary VandenBos (APA, Executive Director of Publications and Communications), as far back as a decade ago, encouraged me to pull together and extract the essence of my symptom-context research into one book. A year ago I was happy to sign on with APA Books to do this. The staff at APA Books have been warmly supportive; Julia Frank-McNeil has been a reliable helpful arranger of all publication issues, and Peggy Schlegel, development editor, has been a clear-visioned, extensive developer of the book's logical organization and a navigator of its course through its publication cycle. In its final stages, Valerie Montenegro has done a superbly careful editing check of the entire text.

Some of the coauthored chapters had already come out in earlier form because these coauthors had usually been participants with me in the original research or articles. They have been acknowledged by keeping them as part of the current authorship. However, I am responsible for all of the present revisions—the often extensive alterations, new material, new analyses and reanalyses, and implications for future research and practice.

Many patients' records and tape recordings were obtained in an era in which written releases from patients were not required practice. All one had to do was to deal with the data in a way that caused no injury to the patient. I have done that, as well as changed all names and places in the chapters. I think it now would be an injury to the patients to contact them after so many years, and many would not recognize my name, because I did not have anything to do with their treatment.

And, as with the earlier books, the Augusts of 1994 and 1995 on Martha's Vineyard were each a tranquil respite from the routines of city life and gave me opportunities to build, plane, sand, and trial-launch the earlier constructions to make them more solidly seaworthy.

PROJECT PARTICIPANTS

Keith Alexander, PhD
Bensalem, PA

Gerald Aronson, MD
Los Angeles, CA

Arthur H. Auerbach, MD
University of Pennsylvania

Jacques P. Barber, PhD
University of Pennsylvania

Paul Crits-Christoph, PhD
University of Pennsylvania

Louis Diguer, PhD
Laval University
Quebec, Canada

John P. Docherty, MD
Cornell Medical Center
Westchester Division, NY

Louis A. Gottschalk, MD, PhD
University of California
Irvine, CA

John Hartke, PhD
Fairmount Institute
Philadelphia, PA

Roberta Bailey Harvey
Scott Paper Company

Ellen Gay, PhD
Wilmington, DE

Suzanne Johnson
Temple University
Philadelphia, PA

Ellen Luborsky, PhD
Riverdale Mental Health Center
Riverdale, NY

Rachel Kabasakalian-McKay, PhD
Chestnut Hill College

A. Thomas McLellan, PhD
University of Pennsylvania

Jim Mintz, PhD
University of California at Los
    Angeles

Kelly Ann Schmidt
George Washington University

Martin E. P. Seligman, PhD
University of Pennsylvania

David A. Seligman
University of Pennsylvania

Barton Singer, PhD
Rutgers University

Thomas C. Todd, PhD
Illinois School of Professional
    Psychology
Chicago, IL

I

GUIDE TO THE
SYMPTOM-CONTEXT
METHOD

1

THE SYMPTOM-CONTEXT METHOD: ITS ORIGINS AND USES AND WHY CLINICIANS AND RESEARCHERS NEED IT

LESTER LUBORSKY

On a bright spring day in 1963, I was doing my usual listening to a patient in psychotherapy when she suddenly stopped short in the midstream of talking, paused, and explained, "Oh, I just forgot a thought. I just had it in mind. What was it?" She paused again. "Oh, yes, now it has returned. Here it is. . . ." She then recovered a memory about being rejected by others, a theme that seemed to fill her thoughts each time she experienced momentary forgetting. At the moment she recovered her thought, a serendipitous idea came to me for an apt research method for searching out the onset conditions of psychological symptoms. It was a newer version of an idea that had come to me first years before (Luborsky, 1953).

THE START OF THE METHOD

With this method, one would begin by looking at a set of actual episodes of a patient's momentary forgetting and continue by focusing on the context in which the forgetting repeatedly occurred. The context would take in the patient's thoughts and behaviors both before and after the forgetting. The potential advantage of this method would be that therapists and researchers could identify those thoughts that tended to come

3

before symptoms and that might, therefore, be preconditions for dysfunctional memory symptoms.

Clinicians and researchers need such a method. Much of what clinicians do in treatment is aimed at finding out what has been hindering patients from reaching their goals. Often it is the symptoms, and so the therapist joins the patient in trying to resolve them (using the clinical methods detailed in chap. 15 in this book). The new method would have the added virtue of an expanded view from the multiple vantage points of different observers: the patient's, while going through the experience of the symptom; the therapist's, while also present and observing the experience; and other observers', while replaying the experience on an audiotape or a videotape—all as firsthand witnesses of a symptom's eruption within its context over the course of many sessions.

Developing the method first required finding nodal points in psychotherapy sessions when a symptom had appeared and then examining, both clinically and quantitatively, the context of the thoughts and behaviors before and after the symptom's appearance. It was also necessary to select control nodal points where the symptom did not appear, to provide a means of comparison with the real nodal points. This method was suitably named the *symptom-context method* because of its focus on the symptom in its context as begun in Luborsky (1953, 1964, 1970) and Luborsky and Auerbach (1969).

Through this method, theories of symptom formation could also be tested within a collection of symptoms that were actually observed at the moment they occurred, rather than by the usual retrospective method of relying on the patient's recall of the earlier appearance of a symptom. The hunch that came to me at that moment when my patient lost her train of thought gave me the idea that led to a restudy of the conditions for the formation of current psychological and psychosomatic symptoms. For many decades, the field has been based almost entirely on recall of the conditions associated with various symptoms. Such reliance on retrospection to locate the conditions of symptoms is natural because it is so hard to find occasions in which a symptom is recorded along with its context. How often can one record a series of symptoms (for example, for a patient who precipitously becomes depressed) at the exact onset of depression, and to record the patient's thoughts and behaviors around the depression as well?

Ideas Leading to the Creation of the Symptom-Context Method

Freud's Clinical Method

From a historical perspective, the symptom-context method is a logical extension of Freud's clinical method for understanding symptoms.

Again and again he showed that he was attentive to the context of meanings in which symptoms appeared. This is illustrated, for example, in his (1895/1955) early studies on hysteria, and then in his Dora case of hysteria (Freud, 1901/1953). He had examined the context of meanings in Dora's recurrent cough and in her recurrent aphonia and concluded, "It quite regularly happens that a single symptom corresponds to several meanings simultaneously" (p. 53). He used a similar method in his studies of the meanings of the phobia in his famous Little Hans case (Freud, 1909/1955; see also chap. 6). Freud's early collaborators continued this interest; for example, Ferenczi (1902/1912) examined the meaning of transient symptoms during psychotherapy sessions.

A Control Method: Discriminating Symptom Versus Nonsymptom Segments

Use of the symptom-context method combines examining the meanings of the thoughts and behaviors in the context of symptoms that reappear in the sessions and using controlled clinical and quantitative analyses, especially the comparison with nonsymptom segments of sessions as a necessary baseline. The latter control method has not been used by Freud and others. The only example of this symptom-context control design was offered by Margaret Brenman-Gibson in Brenman, Gill, and Knight (1952), which I must have seen and decided to adopt. These researchers examined states in hypnosis by comparing two contexts—when the patient said "I am going deeper" with when the patient did not make that statement. This design became the model for the nonsymptom control segments. A fuller account of the symptom-context method is given in chapter 2.

The P-Technique

In later years, in thinking over the preconditions for my germinal idea for this method, it became clearer to me that my first revelatory experience was multiply overdetermined and was prefigured. I already had had the idea in a similar form and had used it during collaborative research with Raymond Cattell from 1945 to 1949. He had contributed by involving me in his search for the main dimensions of fluctuations in personality states over time. Our search led to the first longitudinal intra-individual factor analysis (P-technique) of a patient in psychotherapy (Cattell & Luborsky, 1950; Luborsky, 1953, 1995; see also chap. 7). I had conducted the psychotherapy sessions and a test battery immediately preceding every session. During some psychotherapy sessions I noticed that the patient reported recurrent intrusions into his awareness of a stomach pain located at the site of a partially healed ulcer. So, with the help of a version of the symptom-context method, I examined the larger state conditions in which these pains were reported.

Psychosomatic Research Method

Some psychosomatic researchers continued to use Freud's method, as is illustrated in studies by Gottschalk (1956) of the meaning of recurrent epileptic symptoms in an 8-year-old boy and of the recurrent context for grand mal seizures in a young soldier (Gottschalk, 1955).

Clinical Theories of Symptom Formation

In contrast to the limited quantitative research on the conditions for recurrent symptoms, there are many clinical theories of symptom formation. Five representative classical theories are reviewed in chapter 16: those of Freud (1926/1959); Engel and Schmale (1965); Goldstein (1939); Angyal (1965); and Seligman (1975). The general idea that runs through these classical theories and that fits the clinical example at the beginning of this chapter, on momentary forgetting, is that a particular thought appears and is reacted to with anxiety and helplessness so that a symptom emerges to help a person cope with it. One of the goals of this book is to compare and contrast these theories with the symptom-context theory.

Five Views That Have Hindered Research on Theories of Symptom Formation

Five longstanding clinical and research views have slowed research on theories of symptom formation. These are merely listed here, but they are expanded in Luborsky and Spence (1978). The first is the prevalent view of some clinicians that traditional clinical methods, such as those used in treating patients through psychotherapy, have sufficient power to offer research support for the theories and that no other methods are necessary. This was Freud's view for most of his career (Holt, 1965). The second view is that quantitative methods cannot increase our power to understand psychotherapy data, or, that the methods only inform us of what we already know (Waelder, 1960). This was Freud's view also, after he broke off with his number-oriented friend Wilhelm Fleiss and came to believe that clinical methods were sufficient, although quantitative methods could "do no harm," as he wrote to Saul Rosenzweig (cited in Luborsky & Spence, 1978). A third related clinical view is that quantitative methods fatally distort the clinical data, rather than having the power to clarify the clinical data. Fourth, the common limited view that was attractive to psychologists for so long was that cross-sectional methods with aggregates of patients is the method of choice, as compared with intra-individual methods. Fifth is the mistaken view that appropriate and convenient intra-individual methods applicable to clinical data are unavailable.

Not only these views, but also a lack of appropriate data for examining symptom contexts, have held back research. What is lacking, specifically, since Freud's time (1926/1959) are collections of the actual words and behaviors of patients before various symptoms appear. The explanation for the lack of appropriate data so far is obvious—researchers have not been present very often before recurrent symptoms appear and in circumstances where tape recording can be done.

Happily, there are some signs of the waning of the weight of these views. There has been a special section devoted to intra-individual P-technique studies in the *Journal of Consulting and Clinical Psychology* (Russell, 1995). And this book presents the only collection of symptom-context data that is suitable for a clinical–quantitative examination of theories of symptom formation.

THE LOGIC OF THE SELECTION OF CASES AND OF THE BOOK'S FRAMEWORK

It is important that the reader know from the start that this book does not offer only selected cases from a larger collection—there is no larger collection! For every one of the seven symptom studies in the book, I chose the *only* appropriately data-based cases available to ensure some basic uniformity of design even though the studies were done over a span of nearly 50 years (1946–1995); I did not arbitrarily select among cases and present only one or another. As an example, for the momentary forgetting case I took the only one with a sufficiently large number of momentary forgettings—the other 16 of these cases had very few examples of forgettings per case and therefore did not lend themselves to symptom-context analysis. Even for the three available absence epilepsy episode cases, only one was a case in psychotherapy and, therefore, that one was chosen for special symptom-context analyses. Finally, the diversity of symptoms prevents the results from reflecting only a single type of symptom.

I will give a quick tour of the framework of the book to explain the logic of its construction. In this chapter, I have looked over the origins of the ideas leading to the symptom-context method and the basis for its appeal to clinicians and researchers. The details of the method are described in chapter 2. The book continues with symptom-context analyses of recurrent psychological symptoms: momentary forgetting (chaps. 3 and 4), depressive mood shifts (chap. 5), and phobias (chap. 6).

The next four chapters bear on the question of whether the onset conditions found for recurrent psychological symptoms can also be found for recurrent somatic symptoms: stomach ulcer pains, migraine-like headaches, absence epilepsy (petit mal) episodes, and premature ventricular contractions of the heart (chaps. 7, 8, 9, and 10). Because the latter two recurrent symptoms were directly measured, they offer an opportunity for a comparison with self-reported symptoms.

Another logical question is then confronted in the chapters on laughing, crying, and touching (chaps. 11, 12, 13, and 14): Would the onset conditions for symptoms be similar to the onset conditions for recurrent behaviors that are not usually considered symptoms? If so, maybe the conditions before recurrent symptoms do not differ from the conditions before recurrent behaviors.

The final three chapters of the book (chaps. 15, 16, and 17) offer three types of overviews: a guide to everyday diagnostic and therapeutic uses of the symptom-context method, a review of some classical theories of symptom formation, and, as the book's finale, a presentation of a new symptom-context theory that is based on comparisons of symptom-context studies with the classical theories.

REFERENCES

Angyal, A. (1965). E. Hanfman & R. M. Jones (Eds.). Neurosis and treatment: A holistic theory. New York: Wiley.

Brenman, M., Gill, M., & Knight, R. (1952). Spontaneous fluctuations in depth of hypnosis and their implications for ego-function. *International Journal of Psycho-analysis, 33*, 22–33.

Cattell, R. B., & Luborsky, L. B. (1950). P-technique demonstrated as a new clinical method for determining personality structure. *Journal of General Psychology, 42*, 3–24.

Engel, G., & Schmale, A. (1967). Psychoanalytic theory of somatic disorders: Conversion, specificity and the disease onset situation. *Journal of the American Psychoanalytic Association, 15*, 344–365.

Ferenczi, S. (1912). On transitory symptom-constructions during the analysis. In S. Ferenczi (Ed.), *Sex in psychoanalysis* (pp. 164–180). New York: Dover. (Original work published 1902)

Freud, S. (1953). Fragment of an analysis of a case of hysteria. In J. Strachey (Ed. and Trans.), *The standard edition of the complete psychological works of Sigmund Freud* (Vol. 7, pp. 15–122). London: Hogarth Press. (Original work published 1901)

Freud, S. (1955). Psychotherapy of hysteria. In J. Breuer & S. Freud, *Studies on hysteria* (Vol. 2). In J. Strachey (Ed. and Trans.), *The standard edition of the complete psychological works of Sigmund Freud* (pp. 255–305). London: Hogarth Press. (Original work published 1895)

Freud, S. (1955). Analysis of a phobia in a five-year-old boy. In J. Strachey (Ed. and Trans.), *The standard edition of the complete psychological works of Sigmund Freud* (Vol. 10, pp. 5–149). London: Hogarth Press. (Original work published 1909)

Freud, S. (1959). Inhibitions, symptoms and anxiety. In J. Strachey (Ed. and Trans.), *The standard edition of the complete psychological works of Sigmund Freud*

(Vol. 20, pp. 87–174). London: Hogarth Press. (Original work published 1926)

Goldstein, K. (1939). *The organism*. New York: American Books.

Gottschalk, L. (1955). Psychologic conflict and electroencephalographic patterns. *Archives of Neurological Psychiatry, 73*, 656–662.

Gottschalk, L. (1956). The relationship of psychologic state and epileptic activity: Psychoanalytic observations on epileptic child. In *Psychoanalytic study of the child* (Vol. 11, pp. 352–380). New York: International Universities Press.

Holt, R. R. (1965). Freud's cognitive style. *American Imago, 22*, 163–179.

Janis, I. L. (1958). *Psychological stress*. New York: Wiley.

Luborsky, L. (1953). Intraindividual repetitive measurements (P-technique) in understanding symptom structure and psycho-therapeutic change. In O. H. Mowrer (Ed.), *Psychotherapy: Theory and research* (pp. 389-413). New York: Ronald Press.

Luborsky, L. (1964). A psychoanalytic research on momentary forgetting during free association. *Bulletin of the Philadelphia Association for Psychoanalysis, 14*, 119–137.

Luborsky, L. (1970). New directions in research on neurotic and psychosomatic symptoms. *American Scientist, 58*, 661–668.

Luborsky, L. (1995). The first trial of P-technique in psychotherapy research—A still-lively legacy. *Journal of Consulting and Clinical Psychology, 63*, 6–14.

Luborsky, L., & Auerbach, A. H. (1969). The symptom-context method: Quantitative studies of symptom formation in psychotherapy. *Journal of the American Psychoanalytic Association, 17*, 68–99.

Luborsky, L., & Spence, D. (1978). Quantitative research on psychoanalytic therapy. In S. L. Garfield & A. E. Bergin (Eds.), *Handbook of psychotherapy and behavior change* (Rev. ed., pp. 331–368). New York: Wiley.

Russell, R. (1995). Introduction to the special section on multivariate psychotherapy process research: Structure and change in the talking cure. *Journal of Consulting and Clinical Psychology, 63*, 3–5.

Seligman, M. (1975). *Helplessness: On depression, development and death*. New York: Freeman.

Waelder, R. (1960). *Basic theory of psychoanalysis*. New York: International Universities Press.

2

A GUIDE TO THE SYMPTOM-CONTEXT METHOD

LESTER LUBORSKY

This chapter offers the nuts and bolts of the symptom-context method. It is a how-to manual for clinicians to use in their practice and for researchers to use in their symptom-context studies.

I begin by describing the core principles that support the use of the symptom-context method, then I explain the steps of the method, and I end with two limitations of the method. The studies referred to throughout the chapter—all known symptom-context and related studies—are listed in the Appendix to this chapter.

PRINCIPLES SUPPORTING THE USE OF THE SYMPTOM-CONTEXT METHOD

The symptom is present at the moment. The symptom, together with its context, is caught for observation at the moment it actually appears. Because the symptom is current, the researcher need not rely on a patient's retrospective memory to find the conditions that surround the appearance of the symptom.

The symptom segments require a within-subject baseline. Comparisons are made between the symptom-context and control context as an essential base-rate comparison. This ingenious method came from a study by Brenman, Gill, and Knight (1952).

The natural temporal sequence for understanding a session is to examine the context before, during, and after the symptom. The full temporal sequence before, during, and after the symptom is vital for inferring factors responsible for symptom formation, because temporal contiguity implies associative linkage. This reasoning derives from Freud's (1895/1955; 1926/1959) clinical understanding of temporal contiguity. When a patient has an intrusive symptom, such as being seized by a pain in the stomach or having a disruptive forgetting experience while thinking and speaking a thought, particularly a thought that has just slipped out and then come back into the patient's awareness, clinicians have learned to look for determinants of the symptom in the patient's experiences just before the symptom appeared. The symptom-context method depends on this premise of the association theory that *ideas and behaviors are associatively linked thematically.*

The main rule for understanding, according to Freud (1900/1953, p. 353) is based on "context." As was restated by Erdelyi (1985), ". . . the correct interpretation (of a symbol) can only be arrived at on each occasion from context" (p. 95). Thus, a patient's flow of language in clinical interviews, especially in free association sessions (Janis, 1958), provides an excellent medium for analyzing for the factors that might be associated with the symptom outbreak. As will be seen in the example of Ms. Apfel (see chap. 3), the context of her forgetting included the idea of being rejected, which was linked associatively with memories of her helpless state and linked temporally with the appearance of the momentary forgetting.

Multilevels are continually assessed. A multilevel approach enables researchers to broaden their knowledge of the context for each symptom. The levels include use of clinical review, rating methods, scoring methods (both psychological and physiological), and background context methods. The initial qualitative approach of the clinical review helps inform the subsequent choice of quantitative methods, such as the ratings and scorings. Then the user can better understand the ratings and scorings by referring back to the qualitative clinical analysis. Finally, the combination offers more than a single method.

These levels have much in common with the multilevel approaches recommended by Sargent (1961) and Kächele, Thomä, and Schaumberg (1975): clinical case study, systematic clinical description, guided clinical judgment, and computer-assisted linguistic and text analysis. The research enterprise also includes examining two other levels: the immediate and the broad background context. The immediate context consists of the thoughts and behaviors close around a symptom and the broader background context consists of the whole session and contiguous psychotherapy sessions as well as repeated tests.

The person is the primary unit of study. The person, as assessed on repeated occasions, is the unit of study. More than one patient can be studied as long as each patient is analyzed intra-individually. The set of studies in this book follow this principle of qualitative and quantitative single-case design (recommended by Edelson, 1988), as opposed to the more conventional cross-sectional aggregate designs.

Psychotherapy is an appropriate and conceptually generative medium. Psychotherapy, as the contextual medium, has special assets for studying symptom formation. It was the medium through which Freud's concepts of symptom formation originally had been derived; therefore, systematic tests of the theories are appropriately based on psychotherapy data. It is also a practical and convenient context within which to collect symptoms because the patient and therapist regularly meet together, their exchange can be easily recorded, and symptoms appear from time to time within psychotherapy.

An understanding of symptom contexts has obvious clinical use for treatment. The clinical utility of knowledge of the symptom context is most clearly shown for patients who have serious recurrent symptoms in the course of psychotherapy (such as in the example of the patient with phobic behavior in chap. 6).

STEPS IN THE SYMPTOM-CONTEXT METHOD

The steps in the method are diagrammed in Figure 1. This diagram helps the reader to see how the major parts of the method operate together; the technical details of the method are as follows:

Step 1. Choose a Symptom or Behavior

The method is called the symptom-context method because it was first applied to symptoms, yet it can be applied as well to any recurrent behaviors that occur in psychotherapy or in other continuously recorded verbal contexts. Therefore, although the method could be described by the broader term, the behavior-context method, it is better to stay with the more familiar original term. Whatever the label for the method, the first step in using it is to choose as its nodal point either a recurrent symptom or a recurrent behavior. The psychological symptoms chosen should usually be consistent with those in the *Diagnostic and Statistical Manual* (American Psychiatric Association, 1994), but the primary basis for choice should be how it fits with the general definition of a symptom as an impairment of a usual function (as is explained in chap. 16).

Session timeline: |←----------→|←----------→|←----------→|←----------→|←----------→|←----------→|

Context studied	Background context	Immediate context before symptom	Content during symptom	Immediate context after symptom	Background context
Symptom context	Whole session, series of sessions, and CCRTs	Patient's and therapist's words and other behaviors	Symptom or other behavior	Patient's and therapist's words and other behaviors	Whole session, series of sessions, and CCRTs
Nonsymptom control context	Same as above	Same as above	Control point in the same or other session in which the symptom or other behavior is *not* present	Same as above	Same as above

Figure 1. Diagram of the basic components of the symptom-context method applied in psychotherapy or other types of sessions.

The beginning and end points of the nodal symptom or behavior must then be demarcated in the text of the session; the more clearly doable this is, the better. To help with this, criteria for locating the beginning and ending must be decided on for each symptom. To collect an adequate sample, it is helpful to choose a symptom or behavior that appears not too infrequently or not too frequently. For example, stuttering may occur too frequently to allow for a scorable and separable pre- and then post-symptom-context; momentary forgetting appears so infrequently that data collection requires a prolonged search to find occurrences.

Step 2. Decide on the Length of the Symptom Context

Analysis of the context is intended to reveal the temporal course of the significant qualities of the context in which the target behavior develops. Figure 1 shows that the symptom-context data are temporally partitionable into three parts: the words and other behaviors before a symptom, the selected nodal event—a symptom or other behaviors—and the words and other behaviors subsequent to this symptom. The standard symptom-context methods of discerning the temporal course are to mark off before and after the appearance of the symptom or behavior either units of time or units of a patient's words. The user needs to choose the type of unit, the size of the units, and the number of units before and after the symptom. The choices about these units do not need to be based on hunch alone, but can be informed by previous studies. The units often used are convenient but arbitrary—numbers of patient's words, such as 50- or 100-word units. The total extent of a usual immediate context may be a total of 500 words before and 500 words after the appearance of the symptom. An alternative type of unit is a single "thought unit," as it is defined by Benjamin (1986), which has the virtue of being a meaningful unit.

Step 3. Select Controls to Establish a Base Rate

In this vital step the user selects nonsymptom segments to provide a base rate for comparing the frequency of variables in nonsymptom contexts versus symptom contexts. The base rate controls show that even variables highly evident in the symptom segments, such as anxiety and depression, may also be highly evident in the nonsymptom segments. It must, therefore, be found out for each patient just how different such variables are for symptom contexts versus for control contexts.

Each instance of a symptom context is paired with one or several nonsymptom control contexts. The user should select controls using an unbiased procedure, such as selecting parts of the same session or parts of another session that have none of the target symptoms. The selection rule for pairing symptom sessions with control sessions is purposely arbitrary;

for example, a control session is designated as three sessions before or three sessions after the symptom session. Within the control session a control point is located at a time in the session that is as far temporally into the control session as the symptom is in the paired symptom session. The reason for pairing with controls selected in terms of time into the session is that the symptom or behavior itself may have a time-into-the-session basis. Then word units (or time units or thought units) of context are similarly marked off just before and just after the control points. The judges doing the scoring are kept blind to the distinction between symptom segments and control segments, because the segments are not distinguished on their copy of the transcripts; even the type of symptom itself could be deleted. The control data are evaluated in the same way as are the symptom data.

Step 4. Select the Variables to Be Rated and Scored

The variables that have usually been used in symptom-context studies were derived from the theories of symptom formation by Freud (1926/ 1959) and the other theorists described in chapter 16. In the symptom-context studies, the clinical review was the most generative procedure, for it very often suggested variables to be rated and scored. The variables that were used were mostly the same or similar from study to study. The ones that were most commonly used were the 12 rated variables that are listed in Table 2 of chapter 17: Helplessness, Hopelessness, Anxiety, Feeling Blocked, Concern about Supplies, Hostility to Therapist, Hostility to Others, Involvement with Therapist, Depression, Separation Concern, Lack of Control, and Guilt (and self-blame). These are mostly defined with the rating scales cited in the Appendixes to chapters 3 and 10. The scored variables that were most commonly used are listed in Table 3 of chapter 17: Reference to Therapist, Cognitive Disturbance, Speech Disturbance, Helplessness, Anxiety, Hostility-Outward, Overt Hostility, Covert Hostility, Total Affect, Hostility-Inward, Hostility-Ambivalent, Schizophrenia, and Cognitive Impairment.

Step 5. Make a Multilevel Assessment of the Symptom and Control Contexts

In each of the studies, varied forms of assessment of the context are represented, and they are presented in a preferred sequence—the clinical review, the rating of variables, the scoring of variables, the biological variables, and the broad background context.

Clinical Review

Such reviews are a good beginning for the assessment of the symptom context. Whatever the mysterious process that creates understanding, it is known to be pushed ahead by reading and rereading the transcript and by listening to some of the tape recordings from before and after the appearance of the symptom.

Rating Methods

The clinical review helps to generate the variables to be rated. Also, a sorting method (see chap. 7) can suggest variables to be rated. Additional variables can also be selected from previous research on symptom formation, such as from Freud (1926/1959); Engel and Schmale (1967); Luborsky, Docherty, and Penick (1973); and other studies summarized in this book (see chap. 17).

Scoring Methods

Some of the rated variables can generate content analysis codes as guides to even more reliable scoring. Ratings of Involvement with Therapist can be supplemented by scoring References to Therapist. Ratings of Depression, for example, can then be compared with content coding scoring measures for depression, such as the ones offered by Gottschalk and Gleser (1969). For the ratings and for the scorings, the independent judges are not told that some of the instances are control segments.

Broad Background Context Methods

In most of the studies conducted by my colleagues and me, we have assessed the broad background context. It is most often defined as the remainder of the session beyond the immediate symptom context. Sometimes the broad context is defined also as including the adjacent sessions. The broad context also includes concurrent measurements of the psychotherapy sessions with psychological or physiological measures; some of these may be the same as those recorded in the immediate context.

The three most common types of broad background context methods that are illustrated in this book are (a) rating whole sessions, as is illustrated in chapters 3, 4, and 8; (b) analyzing an entire series of whole sessions by means of factor analysis and cluster analysis of the whole sessions (see chap. 7); and (c) analyzing the whole session by means of the Core Conflictual Relationship Theme (CCRT) method (see chap. 15), which is introduced in the next section.

Physiological or Biological Methods

The examination of the context should not be limited to the psychological level; it should also include physiological and biochemical measures, especially those in the probable substrate that can be concurrently sampled. A variety of these are illustrated in chapters 7, 13, and 14 and in the resources listed in the Appendix to this chapter.

RELATED PROCEDURES USED IN THE SYMPTOM-CONTEXT METHOD

The CCRT as a Background Assessment Measure

The CCRT method is an assessment system for inferring the central relationship patterns that emerge from relationship narratives (Luborsky, in press-a). Several studies provide evidence of the method's reliability (Crits-Christoph, Luborsky, Popp, Mellon, & Mark, 1990; Luborsky, in press-a, in press-b; Luborsky & Diguer, 1995; Luborsky & Diguer, in press). Narratives are parts of sessions in which a patient spontaneously tells episodes about relationships, hence they are referred to as relationship episodes or REs. Ten REs is a desirable lower limit to provide a basis for the CCRT.

The steps in the CCRT method were chosen because they represent a common type of formalization of the inference process used by clinicians for formulating the central relationship pattern. From each RE in a session, inferences are made about each of three types of components: types of wishes, responses from other, and responses of self. To arrive at the scores for each narrative, two systems of inference are used. With the tailor-made system, for each CCRT component, the judge describes the component in his or her own preferred language. With the standard category system, so called because all judges use the same categories, for each CCRT component, the judge translates each type of tailor-made component into a standard category. Specifically, the CCRT is the combination of the most frequent types of wishes, responses from other, and responses of self across all the REs. A more complete guide to the CCRT is in chapter 15 and in Luborsky (in press-b) and Luborsky and Crits-Christoph (in press).

Procedures for Symptoms Without a Clear Point of Onset and Cessation

Many symptoms have only a gradual and sometimes even a fuzzy onset and termination. Even such symptoms can be studied by adapting the symptom-context method, as is illustrated in chapter 6. The main necessary procedure is to develop criteria for scoring the beginnings and ends of such symptoms. Three examples of such symptoms are states of boredom of the patient or the therapist, states of anxiety, and states of insecurity of the patient about the degree of contact in the relationship with the therapist (as in the work of Greenberg, Rice, & Elliott, 1993).

Labeling Controls

The points for the onset of symptoms and of control points need to be marked on the transcript. Both the symptoms and the controls should be marked in the same way, for example, "forgetting" or "laugh" so that the judge assumes that they are all actual forgettings or actual laughs, although usually about half of them are actually controls.

Another system might be tried: Instead of naming the symptom, only the word *symptom* is used so that the judge's preconceptions about the preconditions of the particular symptom might play less of a part. A label for the type of symptom or just noting that a symptom appeared can have an effect on judgments. This effect has been shown in the peaks in the ratings of the control material around the onset of the control point. These peaks would probably be obliterated when no designation is given of the point of the symptom or the type of symptom.

Using Transcripts, Videotapes, Audiotapes, and Process Notes

Almost all studies included in this book have relied on transcripts alone; it is not known what might have been added if video- or even audiotape were available as well (with the exception of one patient with absence epilepsy episodes, described in chap. 9, of whom a videotape was made). Clearly more information is provided by the videotape. The question is, does the information add substantially to the reliability and validity of assessments that are based on the transcripts? We need special studies in which transcripts are compared with transcripts plus videotape. Several researchers have had experience using videotapes for assessments (e.g., Thorne & Klohnen, 1993), but comparison of the two approaches has not yet been reported, except by Zander et al. (1995), who suggested no clear difference.

Process notes have been helpful, especially in combination with tape recordings, as is shown in chapter 4 and in Luborsky (1967) and Weiss, Sampson, and the Mount Zion Psychotherapy Research Group (1986). However, using process notes alone creates a greater risk that the data of the session may be distorted, although they often provide a simplified access to understanding the relatively lengthy transcripts. As such they can be especially helpful for the initial method of each symptom-context analysis, that is, clinical review.

STATISTICAL ISSUES

The decisions that have been made about the statistical issues rely heavily on a review following my presentation on the symptom-context method at a meeting of the Harvard Statistical Seminar with Robert Rosenthal, Don Rubin, Douwe Yntema, Alan Zaslavsky, Frank Sullaway, and others on May 4, 1995. Although this group is not responsible for the decisions, their views were decidedly influential. The statistical analyses were also helped along by several people; outstanding among them were long-time collaborator Louis Diguer and recent collaborator James McKay, with the help of Suzanne Johnson and David Seligman and the prior help of Roberta Bailey Harvey, Donald Phoenix, and Shirley Heineman.

Reliance on *t* Tests for Paired Symptom Segments

For each patient, a real symptom value is always paired with a control value. The pairing relies on the point at which the symptom appeared—each symptom point is matched with a control point from a session where no symptom appeared, but its location in the session is the same for the control point as it was in the symptom session. The reason for the time-equated pairing is that the location within a session might influence the appearance of the symptom; the pairing could serve as a control for this.

Using One-Tailed Tests

One-tailed tests were recommended by the statistical advisory group (led by Rosenthal). The bases for the recommendation were that (a) these tests were required for meaningful significance testing in meta-analytic work (Rosenthal, 1991), and (b) all variables that were examined for the significance of differences between symptom segments and controls were based on explicit hypotheses.

Adding to the Number of Controls

This step could be of help because it might increase the significance of differences between symptom segments and controls for some symptoms. However, Rosenthal and his group estimated that the increase in significance of differences would not be very great and not be commensurate with the effort to arrange for the enlarged number of controls.

Using the Most Appropriate Word Unit

My colleagues and I initially used 50-word units and mostly continued with that unit across cases. However, we did also try thought units (see chap. 11), although we do not have a clear comparison about the relative value of the word unit and the thought unit.

Intercorrelating Variables in the Segments Before Real Symptoms

To determine the significant variables before each type of symptom, my colleagues and I performed intercorrelations and mean correlations to see how the variables were related to each other and to learn more about how the underlying variables might be involved in the qualities before each symptom.

Locating Time Trends Within Immediate Onset Conditions

We systematically displayed graphically the level of the variables in the 50-word units in the context around the symptom and control segments over time.

Using Lag Correlations to Examine Temporal Dependencies in Word Units

From a statistical point of view, analyses over time across word units may violate the assumption of independence of units because they may well be correlated with each other (Kenny & Judd, 1986). For some of the cases, we examined the degree of independence of the units by lag correlations pairing each score with the score for the next segment in time. As an example we carried out lag correlations for a case of recurrent crying (see chap. 12) but found minimal auto correlation, which suggested that our analyses were not influenced by auto correlation of the observations over time.

Expanding the Focus of Analysis to After the Symptoms

Most of the analyses that are focused on in this book are based on analyses of antecedents of symptoms versus controls within patients. I do have data on the sequelae after symptoms appear; results of the analyses are summarized in the last chapter.

Examining Presymptom Variables Such as Helplessness, to See What Follows Them

This method is a reverse symptom-context design that has only rarely been tried. The method requires examining the data from the momentary forgetting patient, for example, to see what follows after high levels of rejection—rather than seeing what comes before momentary forgetting. Momentary forgetting would only rarely follow high points of rejection because many other methods of coping are available, not just forgetting.

Keith Alexander and I tried a study of this kind and found it difficult to identify the high points in helplessness (Luborsky & Alexander, 1989). We were able to do this for a few high points in helplessness but found, in fact, that after these there was a considerable variety of coping mechanisms and other behavior but almost never, forgetting. This one-way directionality is consistent with our results. The expectation was first stated by Engel and Schmale (1967), who called it a one-way directionality in symptom formation. That is, if the examination is from the symptom back to the antecedents, then clear antecedents are found. But when the examination is of the sequelae of the antecedents, the occurrence of symptoms is rare.

TWO LIMITATIONS OF THE SYMPTOM-CONTEXT METHOD

Dividing the context into units presents one limitation to the use of the symptom-context method. An arbitrary system for dividing the context into units risks violating the naturally meaningful phases presented by the patient, according to Fonagy and Moran (1993). Such meaningful units occur, for example, in cyclical variations in mood that follow each patient's special time intervals for fluctuations in mood. Yet, as will be seen in later chapters, my colleagues and I have been able to extract some meaningful trends despite the possible distortion based on our possibly arbitrary units of the text. (See, for example, the very lawful-looking curves that appear before momentary forgetting in Figures 1, 2, and 3 in chap. 3.) Such lawfulness implies that something meaningful has been picked up, even though the effect might still have been slightly distorted by the choice of units.

Another limitation to using the method is posed by individual differences in the way patients express themselves. Patients obviously differ in the degree to which their spoken words reveal what is going on in their minds, which affects the ease with which judges can understand them. The variations in understandability can occur because of a patient's lack of ability to communicate, as well as because of some intentional noncommunication. In dealing with this issue, it is good to remember that despite variations, generally patients are not so opaque and so unrevealing that they are unreadable. They are readable enough in most of their psychotherapy sessions so that the clinical judges can agree in inferring what the patients are experiencing. In the chapters that follow, witness the level of agreement of clinical judgments achieved for these symptom contexts as well as the significance of the difference between symptom segments and controls for many of these contexts.

APPENDIX
SYMPTOM-CONTEXT AND RELATED STUDIES[1]

Adler, R., Hermann, J., Schafer, N., Schmidt, T., Schonecke, O., & Uexkull, T. (1976/1977). A context study of psychological conditions prior to shifts in blood pressure. *Psychotherapy and Psychosomatics, 27,* 198–204.

Berman, E. (1975). Acting out as a response to the psychiatrist's pregnancy. *Journal of the American Woman's Association, 30,* 456–458. (Uses a method that is similar to the symptom-context method—the patient's behavior before, during, and after the therapist's pregnancy.)

Blacker, K. H. (1975). Tracing a memory. *Journal of the American Psychoanalytic Association, 23,* 51–68. (An analysis of the context of a recurrent memory during psychoanalysis.)

Brenman, M., Gill, M., & Knight, R. P. (1952). Spontaneous fluctuations in depth of hypnosis and their implication for ego function. *International Journal of Psychoanalysis, 33,* 22–33. (This is the only early example of a study using a similar method.)

Docherty, J. P., Berger, F., Oradei, D., & Leigh, H. (1977). Psychological factors associated with premature ventricular contractions: A controlled study. *Proceedings of the 4th Congress of the International College of Psychosomatic Medicine,* Kyoto, Japan, September 5–9, pp. 375–379.

Docherty, J. P., Leigh, H., & David, T. (1974). The immediate psychological context of premature ventricular contractions. *Psychosomatic Medicine, 36,* 461–462.

Docherty, J. P., Van Kammen, D., Siris, S., & Marder, S. (1978). Stages of onset of schizophrenic psychosis. *American Journal of Psychiatry, 135,* 420–426.

Engel, G., & Schmale, A. (1965). Psychoanalytic theory of somatic disorders: Conversion, specificity and the disease onset situation. *Journal of the American Psychoanalytic Association, 15,* 344–365.

Fisher, C., Byrne, J., Edwards, A., & Kahn, E. (1970). A psychophysiological study of nightmares. *Journal of the American Psychoanalytic Association, 18,* 747–782. (See, especially, pp. 760–761 for the heart rate and other measures before and after the nightmares.)

Fisher, S., & Greenberg, R. (1977). Stomach symptoms and up–down metaphors and gradients. *Psychosomatic Medicine, 39,* 93–101.

Gay, E. (1975). *A study of the treasured objects of early childhood and the contexts in which they are used.* Unpublished doctoral dissertation, Bryn Mawr College, PA.

---

[1]This is complete, so far as I know, for all symptom-context studies. However, it is without first-authored studies by Lester Luborsky, which can be found in the References to this and other chapters.

Gay, E., & Hyson, M. (1977). Blankets, bears, and bunnies: Studies of children's contacts with treasured objects. *Psychoanalysis and Contemporary Science, 5,* 271–316. (The context for contact with loved objects in preschool children.)

Gottschalk, L. A. (1973). The psychoanalytic study of hand–mouth approximations. In L. Goldberger & V. H. Rosen (Eds.), *Psychoanalysis and contemporary science: Vol. 3* (pp. 269–291). New York: International Universities Press.

Gottschalk, L.A. (1985). Hope and other deterrents to illness. *American Journal of Psychotherapy, 39,* 515–524.

Greenberg, L. S., Rice, L. N., & Elliott, R. (1993). *Facilitating emotional change: The moment to moment process.* New York: Guilford Press.

Henry, J. (1984). On triggering mechanisms of vasohagal syncope [Editorial]. *Psychosomatic Medicine, 46,* 91–94.

Holmes, T. S., & Holmes, T. H. (1968, May). *Short-term intrusions into the life style routine.* Paper presented at the annual meeting of the American Psychiatric Association, Boston, MA.

Holzman, P. (1973). Some difficulties in the way of psychoanalytic research: A survey and a critique. In M. Mayman (Ed.), Psychoanalytic research: Three approaches to the experimental study of subliminal processes [Monograph No. 30]. *Psychological Issues, 8*(2), 88–103. (See, especially, pp. 97–99 for a review of the symptom-context method.)

Horne, G., Yank, M., & Ware, W. (1982). Time series analysis for single subject designs. *Psychological Bulletin, 91,* 178–189.

Horowitz, L., Sampson, H., Siegelman, E., Wolfson, A., & Wiess, J. (1975). On the identification of warded-off mental contents: An empirical and methodological contribution. *Journal of Abnormal Psychology, 84,* 545–558. (Focuses on emergence of new—probably previously warded-off—contents that a patient becomes aware of during psychoanalytic treatment. Study #4 in this paper deals with the positive, neutral, or negative therapist response to patient challenges that facilitate the emergence of such warded-off contents.)

Horowitz, M., Marmar, C., & Wilner, N. (1979). Analysis of patient states and state transitions. *Journal of Nervous and Mental Disease, 167,* 91–99.

Kächele, H. (along with Schaumburg, Cornelia, & Thomä, Helmut). (1974). A study of recurrent anxiety. Universität Ulm. (A study in progress of the sessions of an anxiety patient where the authors use a form of the symptom-context methods.)

Kaneko, S. Y. (1972). The role of humour in psychotherapy. (Doctoral dissertation, The Smith College School for Social Work, 1972). *Dissertation Abstracts International.* (Analyzes the context in which humor appears in psychotherapy.)

Klein, G. (1968). *Two theories or one? Perspectives to change in psychoanalytic theory.* Paper presented to conference of Psychoanalysts of the Southwest, Galveston, TX.

Knapp, P., Muchatt, G., Nemetz, S. J., Constantine, H., & Friedman, S. (1970). The context of reported asthma during psychoanalysis. *Psychosomatic Medicine, 32,* 167–188.

Lewis, H. B. (1971). *Shame and guilt in the neuroses*. New York: International Universities Press. (Uses a method derived from the symptom-context method: Each selected segment from psychotherapy begins with an episode of shame and guilt and ends with the development of a symptom.)

Lincoln, K. (1971). An intercorrelational study of some factors relating to therapeutic sensitivity (Doctoral dissertation, New York University, 1971). *Dissertation Abstracts International, 33*(9), 73–5292. (Used the 24 pairs of the pre-stomach pain sentences, got judges to make judgments of which was a symptom segment and which a control, got confidence ratings, and then gave them a clue: "One of these just before stomach pain shows a feeling of helplessness to get something he wants.")

Mahrer, A., & Nadler, W. (1986). Good moments in psychotherapy: A preliminary review, a list, and some promising research avenues. *Journal of Consulting and Clinical Psychology, 54,* 10–15.

Marsden, G. (1971). Content analysis studies of psychotherapy: 1954–1968. In A. E. Bergin & S. L. Garfield (Eds.), *Handbook of psychotherapy and behavior change* (pp. 345–407). New York: Wiley. (See, especially, pp. 353–354.)

Martindale, C. (1974). Syntactic and semantic correlates of verbal tics in Gilles de la Tourette's syndrome: A quantitative case study. *Brain and Language, 4,* 231–247.

Peterson, C., Luborsky, L., & Seligman, M. E. P. (1983). Attributions and depressive mood shifts: A case study using the symptom-context method. *Journal of Abnormal Psychology, 92,* 96–103.

Rice, L., & Greenberg, L. (1974, June). *A method for studying the active ingredients in psychotherapy: Application to client-centered Gestalt therapy.* Paper presented at the meeting of the Society for Psychotherapy Research, Denver, CO. (A related method focusing on "client markers' behaviors.")

Rice, L., & Greenberg, L. (1983). The new research paradigm. In L. Rice & L. Greenberg (Eds.), *Patterns of change: Intensive analysis of psychotherapy process* (pp. 7–26). New York: Guilford Press.

Schors, R., & Grünzig, H. J. (1987). Der einflus der psychotherapiesitzung auf körperliche beschwerden [The influence of the status of psychotherapy on physical condition]. *Sonderdruck Zeitschrift für Klinische Psychologie, 2,* 148–157.

Shevrin, H. (1963). *Shifts or gaps in associations before report of a dream.* Unpublished manuscript.

Spence, D. (1969). Computer measurement of process and content in psychoanalysis. *Transactions of the New York Academy of Sciences, 31,* 828–841.

Spence, D. P. (1970). Human and computer attempts to decode symptom language. *Psychosomatic Medicine, 32,* 615–625.

Spence, D. P. (1973). Tracing a thought stream by computer. In B. Rubinstein (Ed.), *Psychoanalysis and contemporary science, 2,* 188–201. (The varieties of prerecognition indicators in the patient's language of a patient's increasing concern with the possibility that her analyst might be pregnant.)

Spence, D. (1996). *Time sequences in psychoanalysis: A quantitative study of a clinical event.* Manuscript in preparation.

Spence, D. P., & Lugo, M. (1972). The role of verbal clues in clinical listening. In R. Holt & E. Peterfreund (Eds.), *Psychoanalysis and contemporary science* (pp. 109–131). New York: International Universities Press.

Stern, D. (1974). *Symptoms during free association sessions.* Doctoral dissertation, Michigan State University, Lansing.

Vingerhoets, A. (1984). Biochemical changes in two subjects succumbing to syncope. *Psychosomatic Medicine, 46,* 95–103. (Two subjects who fainted during a psychophysiological experience were examined. The onset of fainting appeared to involve the rapid succession of two stress reactions: the fight–flight reaction and the conservation–withdrawal reaction.)

Zabarenko, L. (1972). *The context of reported dreams during psychoanalysis.* Paper presented at the meeting of the Psychoanalytic Institute, Pittsburgh.

REFERENCES

American Psychiatric Association. (1994). *Diagnostic and statistical manual of mental disorders* (4th ed.). Washington, DC: Author.

Benjamin, L. S. (1986). Operational definition and measure of dynamics shown in the stream of free associations. *Psychiatry, 49,* 104–129.

Brenman, M., Gill, M., & Knight, R. P. (1952). Spontaneous fluctuations in depth of hypnosis and their implication for ego function. *International Journal of Psycho-Analysis, 33,* 22–23.

Crits-Christoph, P., Luborsky, L., Popp, C., Mellon, J., & Mark, D. (1990). The reliability of choice of narratives and of the CCRT measure. In L. Luborsky & P. Crits-Christoph (Eds.), *Understanding transference—The CCRT method* (pp. 93–101). New York: Basic Books.

Edelson, M. (1988). *Psychoanalysis: A theory in crisis.* Chicago: University of Chicago Press.

Engel, G., & Schmale, A. (1967). Psychoanalytic theory of somatic disorder: Conversion, specificity, and disease onset situation. *Journal of American Psychoanalytic Association, 15,* 344–365.

Erdelyi, M. L. (1985). *Psychoanalysis: Freud's cognitive psychology.* New York: Freeman.

Fonagy, P., & Moran, G. (1993). Selecting single case research designs for clinicians. In N. E. Miller, L. Luborsky, J. P. Barber, & J. Docherty (Eds.), *Psychodynamic treatment research: A handbook for clinical practice* (chap. 5). New York: Basic Books.

Freud, S., (1953). The interpretation of dreams. In J. Strachey (Ed. and Trans.), *The standard edition of the complete psychological works of Sigmund Freud* (Vols. 4 & 5). London: Hogarth Press. (Original work published 1900)

Freud, S. (1955). Psychotherapy of hysteria. In J. Breuer & S. Freud, *Studies in hysteria* (Vol. 2). In J. Strachey (Ed. and Trans.), *The standard edition of the complete psychological works of Sigmund Freud* (pp. 255–305). London: Hogarth Press. (Original work published 1895)

Freud, S. (1959). Inhibitions, symptoms and anxiety. In J. Strachey (Ed. and Trans.), *The standard edition of the complete psychological works of Sigmund Freud* (Vol. 20, pp. 87–174). London: Hogarth Press. (Original work published 1926)

Gottschalk, L., & Gleser, G. (1969). *The measurement of psychological states through the content analysis of verbal behavior*. Berkeley: University of California.

Greenberg, L. S., Rice, L. N., & Elliott, R. (1993). *Facilitating emotional change: The moment to moment process*. New York: Guilford Press.

Janis, I. (1958). *Psychological stress*. New York: Wiley.

Kächele, H., Thomä, H., & Schaumberg, C. (1975). Veränderungen des sprachinhaltes in einem psychoanalytischen process. *Schweizer Archive für Neurologie, Neurochirurgie und Psychiatrie, 116,* 197–228.

Kenny, D., and Judd, C. (1986). Consequences of violating the independence assumption in an analysis of variance. *Psychological Bulletin, 99,* 422–431.

Luborsky, L. (1967). Momentary forgetting during psychotherapy and psychoanalysis: A theory and research method. In R. R. Holt (Ed.), Motives and thought: Psychoanalytic essays in honor of David Rapaport [Monograph No. 18/19]. *Psychological Issues, 5*(2–3), 177–217.

Luborsky, L. (in press-a). A guide to the CCRT method. In L. Luborsky & P. Crits-Christoph (Eds.), *The CCRT Method for Understanding Transference* (Rev. ed.). Washington, DC: American Psychological Association.

Luborsky, L. (in press-b). Core conflictual relationship themes (CCRT)—A basic case formulation method. In T. Eells (Ed.), *Handbook of psychotherapy case formulation*. New York: Guilford Press.

Luborsky, L., & Alexander, K. (1989). [Depression analyses]. Unpublished raw data.

Luborsky, L., & Crits-Christoph, P. (Eds.). (in press). *The CCRT Method for Understanding Transference* (Rev. ed.). Washington, DC: American Psychological Association.

Luborsky, L., & Diguer, L. (1995). A novel CCRT reliability study: Reply to Zander et al. *Psychotherapy Research, 5,* 237–241.

Luborsky, L., & Diguer, L. (in press). The reliability of the CCRT—A needed update. In L. Luborsky & P. Crits-Christoph, *The CCRT Method for Understanding Transference* (Rev. ed.). Washington, DC: American Psychological Association.

Luborsky, L., Docherty, J. P., & Penick, S. (1973). Onset conditions for psychosomatic symptoms: A comparative review of immediate observation with retrospective research. *Psychosomatic Medicine, 35,* 187–204.

Rosenthal, R. (1991). *Meta-analytical procedures for social research*. Newbury Park: Sage Publications.

Sargent, H. (1961). Intrapsychic change: Methodological problems in psychotherapy research. *Psychiatry, 24*, 93–108.

Thorne, A., & Klohnen, E. (1993). Interpersonal memories as maps for personality consistency. In C. Tomlinson-Keasey, R. Parke, K. Widman, & D. Funder (Eds.), *Studying lives through time: Approaches to personality and development*. Washington, DC: American Psychological Association.

Weiss, J., Sampson, H., & the Mount Zion Psychotherapy Research Group. (1986). *The psychoanalytic process: Theory, clinical observations, and empirical research*. New York: Guilford Press.

Zander, B., Strack, M., Cierpka, M., Reich, G., Staats, H., assisted by Biskey, J., Homburg, H., Krannich, S., Ratzke, K., & Seide, L. (1995). Coder agreement using the German edition of Luborsky's CCRT method in videotaped or transcribed RAP interviews. *Psychotherapy Research, 5*, 231–236.

II

THE ONSET CONDITIONS FOR PSYCHOLOGICAL SYMPTOMS

3

THE CONTEXT FOR MOMENTARY FORGETTING

LESTER LUBORSKY and JIM MINTZ

William James (1890) was struck by the marvel of our well-functioning "intentions to say thus-and-so" that fill a large portion of our waking lives. He observed that we form the intention to say something and launch into speech fulfilling it, although at first we have only a skeleton of an intimation about how the intention will be fleshed out into words; they are "rapid premonitory perspective views of schemes of thought not yet articulate" (p. 253).

One occasional dysfunction of these intentions—momentary forgetting—was not mentioned by James. In this form of forgetting the nascent to-be-said thought abruptly fades, but the awareness of having intended to say something remains. When such forgetting happens during speaking, the loss may become embarrassing. The speaker may try to pass over the hiatus by persistently trying to rekindle the memory of the snuffed-out thought or may give up and start a new train of thought. Although the momentary forgetting experience is only an infrequent aberration of the intention to say "thus-and-so," it is common enough for all of us to have experienced or witnessed it. The experience flits by so quickly, how-

An earlier version of this chapter appeared in Luborsky, L., & Mintz, J. (1974). What sets off momentary forgetting during a psychoanalysis? Investigations of symptom-onset conditions. *Psychoanalysis and Contemporary Science, 3,* 233–268. It has been adapted, revised, and expanded by the author with permission of the publisher.

ever, that few of us have been able to pay close attention to it—any more than any of us have had a good look at a hummingbird feeding.

Different styles of research on remembering and forgetting rarely compete with each other directly because they tend to be fostered by separate research groups. One of the dominant traditions in research on memory is experimental: Situations are created in which forgetting occurs, and a research effort is then made to measure and to manipulate the conditions that influence the forgetting. In contrast, an older and simpler tradition is illustrated by Freud's (1901/1960) collection of incidents of forgetting from everyday life, which he analyzed clinically to discover the conditions for forgetting, and then used these to construct a theory of motivated forgetting. Such reliance on loosely specified data that are comprehended by an unchecked observer—the analyst—has remained the preeminent research style in psychoanalysis.

The study in this chapter returns to Freud's method of collecting and analyzing incidents of forgetting in their natural context, but with a new style and aim. In sharp contrast to many laboratory studies of forgetting, in this study, special methods were enlisted to observe the conditions for such memory disturbances. The old–new combination serves a purpose: Some variables relevant to concepts of motivated forgetting are not easily uncovered in the laboratory, but they may be discernible in so-called natural settings such as psychotherapy sessions. I hope that this new approach will lessen the segregation of research styles by showing ways of coupling the attractions of laboratory work—quantification and manipulation of relevant variables—with the deep penetration achievable by the clinical-quantitative mode.

Except for three pilot studies (Luborsky, 1964, 1967, 1993), both the clinical and the experimental literature contains nothing about this type of forgetting, probably because of its brevity and seeming inconsequence. This forgetting within the context of the patient's speaking occurs in a classic form: A thought appears that one intends to say, then it vanishes before it can be said, and after a brief delay—almost always less than a minute—the thought often reappears and is spoken, along with an explanation of the delay, "Oh, I just had a thought, but I forgot what it was. (pause) Oh! It was . . . ."

But it was not only the fact that momentary forgetting had never been subjected to examination that led to a study of this form of forgetting. It was chosen for study mainly because of these properties: its regularity of form at each appearance, its presence in most people, and its completeness and rapidity of the forgetting–remembering sequence. In summary, momentary forgetting includes not only the loss of a thought but also its retrieval as well. This sequence permits analysis not only of the context of lost thoughts but also of the content of recovered thoughts.

The symptom-context method was used to understand the onset conditions for one patient's recurrent momentary forgettings in the light of information from psychotherapy. The single-case method is likely to uncover relationships that might be obscured by analyses based on averaging across many patients (as in chap. 4). In this chapter, I illustrate controlled methods, applicable to a psychoanalytic treatment, for showing regularities in the easily defined symptomatic phenomenon of momentary forgetting, and I consider which theoretical concepts seem most applicable to explain the momentary forgetting. It was psychotherapy data, after all, from which concepts related to motivated forgetting first arose. It seems natural, therefore, to return to this milieu to examine the suitability of concepts, such as repression, to explain the forgetting.

As I explained in chapter 1, the spark for the idea of the symptom-context method was set off by a fresh hearing of a patient going through a momentary forgetting during a psychotherapy session. Because momentary forgetting had a role in setting off the idea of the method, it is fitting that this book should begin with an expanded version of a case study (from Luborsky & Mintz, 1974) of a patient who was unusually prone to recurrent momentary forgetting.

DESCRIPTION OF THE PATIENT AND THE PROCEDURES

Mintz and I were fortunate to have access to the tape-recorded psychoanalysis of Ms. Rachael Apfel,[1] a patient who had experienced momentary forgetting relatively often. She was a 31-year-old, unmarried professional woman whose main complaint was a recurrent problem with men that prevented her from marrying. She was seen four times a week for about 8 months (103 sessions), at which point her male analyst, Dr. A, became ill and had to stop the treatment. After a delay of several months, she resumed treatment, this time with Dr. B, a female analyst, and continued for 3 more years (363 sessions more). The patient's symptoms and treatment will be detailed later in the chapter.

Choosing the Samples of Momentary Forgettings

Thirteen instances of momentary forgetting were located in recordings of sessions. (The sessions of the entire treatment were lent to us through the generosity of Dr. A, a well-known research analyst.) The 13 instances included all those through session 300 that fit our criteria for

---

[1]All patient names have been changed.

momentary forgetting. Six occurred in the analysis with Dr. A and seven in the analysis with Dr. B.[2]

One problem with relying on a naturalistic method for collecting specimens where one finds them is their variability. A good way to cope with this problem is to define an ideal form and estimate the degree to which each example fits it. Fortunately, momentary forgetting shows much stereotypy, making its ideal form rather easy to define. The goodness-of-fit criteria that must be met before any instance can be accepted as an instance of momentary forgetting are (a) a thought must have *just* been in the patient's mind, (b) it must vanish, and (c) the patient must admit the loss. The more fully the thought was in awareness just before the loss, the better (e.g., "I just had a clear thought in mind, and now it's gone" but not "I had a thought before a session, and I'm trying to think of what it was"). Retrieval of the lost thought is not a criterion of momentary forgetting because no difference between contexts with recovery and contexts without recovery was found in the pilot study (Luborsky, 1964, 1967).

Locating the Onset of the Symptom

An early step in the data analysis is to locate the site of the initiation of the momentary forgetting. Fortunately the exact point of onset is usually clear—the patient stops speaking, pauses, and explains the stoppage, as in session 20: "(pause) I lost the other point that I was about to make." The point of onset is judged to be the beginning of the pause before the explanation. Statements such as the one just quoted or "I forgot what I was going to say just now," represent patients' attempts to explain what happened during the pause and why they cannot go on to say the thought they had intended to say.

Preparing Segments and Units Within Segments for Analysis

Sessions were transcribed from the tapes with special attention to accuracy. Segments around the forgetting point were listened to by another

---

[2]An apparently more complete list of momentary forgettings from the second analysis became available through Dr. Hartvig Dahl, who arranged for the second analyst, Dr. B, to note the presence of momentary forgetting on the basis of abbreviated transcripts of sessions 104–466. She identified 22 more instances. Sixteen of these, however, did not meet our standards. We have not listened to the tape recordings of the six other instances noted by Dr. B, because we did not have them at the time of our study. (Moreover, the frequency appears to have decreased in the later phase of the analysis—Dr. B noted only four after session 300.) It therefore seems reasonable to conclude that our sample of 13 includes most of the momentary forgettings that meet our standards. Incidentally, an efficient way to deal with the laborious job of symptom retrieval from psychotherapy sessions is for the therapist to use a convenient "therapy checksheet" (Graff & Luborsky, 1977; Luborsky, 1996a) that is designed for recording forgetting and other symptomatic behavior immediately after each session, while the memory of the session is still fresh. The alternative of searching through tape recordings of sessions is very time-consuming when there are many sessions.

person independently and were further corrected so that the transcript accurately reflected the patient's actual verbalizations, including each "oh," "ah," slip, pause, mispronunciation, and emphasis. The initial set of segments had consisted of 1,100 words of the patient's discourse—550 words before the momentary forgetting and 550 words after it—the same length as was used in previous research (Luborsky, 1973). These segments were subdivided into eleven 50-word units before the forgetting, and eleven 50-word units after it. But for economy's sake, we focused on an immediate context of six 50-word units before and six 50-word units after. Each set of six units took this patient about 3 to 4 minutes to utter.

Each symptom segment was arbitrarily matched with a control segment taken from a session that was free of momentary forgetting and that had occurred within eight sessions before or eight sessions after the symptom session. Within each control session a control point was designated: This point was as far into the session (in minutes and seconds) as was the matched momentary forgetting. After the control point was established, the 50-word units of the patient's speech were counted off before and after it. This method of selecting control sessions and control points prevented experimenter bias in the choice of the control sessions and controlled for position in the session of the selected word sample.[3]

METHODS FOR UNDERSTANDING THE PATIENT'S MOMENTARY FORGETTINGS

As was described in chapter 2, the four main methods of analysis applied to the symptom and control segments follow a natural progression from more clinical and global to more quantitative and atomistic: (a) clinically reviewing the segments to locate promising categories that appear before the symptom, (b) rating the segments on these categories, (c) scoring or objectively coding content of some of these categories, and (d) evaluating the broad background context.

Method 1: Clinical Review of Contexts

Through reading and rereading the 600 words surrounding each forgetting, the themes of the patient's struggles came more and more into focus. These are a sample of four instances with 50-word units before forgetting during the sessions with the first analyst, Dr. A:

---

[3]For each of the 13 variables, we did a correlation to determine the degree to which the pairs of real and control variables were related. We had assumed that these were generally not related, and, in fact, the correlations were low and not significant.

Brief Excerpts From Momentary-Forgetting Segments, Series 1 (Analyst A for Ms. Apfel)

(The probable point of forgetting is noted by (FORG.); the report of the momentary forgetting is italicized.)

Session 20. |⁵⁰I know I was even thinking [5 s] that maybe you would decide t' have t' tell me - that you had to tell me uh, that we couldn't continue treatment anymore because uh, because it wasn't doing me any good. [4 s] Or that you judge me uh, [3 s] my case not be amenable to-to the treatment [4 s] (FORG.) And I *I lost the other point that I, that I was about to [4 s] make,* after I tried to make, after I tried to explain why I wanted to make sure I didn't seem confused today [14 s] For whatever reason the asso- the associated- the thing that flashed into my mind was a- (hesitates) was again a scene with my mother. This-(hesitates) probably was when I was about twelve or|⁵⁰. . . .

Session 36. |⁵⁰didn't mention. I was going to uh, [4 s] mm, why I feel better - I-I wonder whether it had something to do with -with the fact that I uh, [2 s], the business about uh, 'I present myself to you in such a way that I can't like you,' Whatever reasoning uh, is behind that [7 s] that uh, nonsensical statement, (FORG.) uh *Now I've lost the other thing that I was going to say* [7 s] Oh, (giggles) (sigh) Now it's- it's so s- I mean it's silly, but I suppose (clears throat) it needs to be said, because it came to my mind, that uh, [4 s] that uh, either on Monday or Tuesday, I think - on Monday, probably hah- I I became conscious eh, uh, of this I mean I heard a sound that I heard|⁵⁰. . . .

Session 53. |⁵⁰it (hesitates) just seemed to me to suggest that uh, all was not uh, I mean to - to be further (pause) uh, corroboration of . . . that's not the word I want - I mean - seems to fit into the picture of this uh, of this boy's uh, personality as far as I could gather - in a couple of hours. (FORG.) [3 s] uh, [6 s] *I forgot not what I- -what I had started to say just after that.* [7 s] Oh, well, one this is that I did f- I mean - I did feel a little uh, frightened as I said, partly because of not being able to uh, eh, I - it seemed - the minute I couldn't [2 s] I couldn't understand uh, a reaction of his. I [2 s] I just, I mean - became almost mm frozen with fear|⁵⁰. . . .

Session 66. |⁵⁰made uh, clear, uh, when I left uh, or the way you said, 'we have to stop,' - it was - to indicate that it wasn't because of what I'd been saying, uh, we j- we just had to stop because the time was up. In other words, you - I mean that was kind of you, and uh (FORG.) [15 s] *I -- there was something else that I was leading up to, and I seem to have lost it.* [25 s] Oh, then I --- (T clears throat) --- um, somehow, um, last night I started thinking again about uh, about the summer, [4 s] (clears throat) appearing as if I would uh, I ss- it's partly [4 s] I mean, for what - whatever the analyzable roots of it are, I feel as if, [4 s] as if I want to uh, to do something to uh, bear witness to uh, certain|⁵⁰. . . .

Brief Excerpts From Momentary-Forgetting Segments, Series 2 (Analyst B for Ms. Apfel)

Session 123. |[50]ill uh, the day we moved. And uh, [3 s] and also depressed at moving. It seemed very uh, doleful to me. [4 s] And uh, we had to take a cab, [2 s] and my mother was just angry with me for being ill and being that extra expense, when they didn't have very much money at the time. (FORG.) *There was a--it seemed to me there was another memory that-that I also [2 s] i-it came up at, uh, just that moment, and it--now it slipped out of my mind.* [8 s] I also wonder why I - I have just a few things that I remember, and they come up again and again. [2 s] Nothing that - I mean, nothing new opens up. It's the same five or six things. [21 s] But I'm not - I - part of that i- what I remember at that time|[50]. . . .

Session 136. |[50]just not at all uh - uh, [2 s] real concern or anxious, but just, again, this stray thoughts. And I think it was because of [2 s] that my feelings worrying were that I don't- I'm not sure I have anything to say, but that's all right - it will be all right. I can come anyway. Uh, (FORG.) *Now I don't know--I was going somewhere--I forgot now* [9 s] Oh, that I-that I thought- I was think- feeling positive about th-the analysis in general [3 s] with the idea that [2 s] even if uh, [3 s] that it was - that even if it didn't - it didn't prove to uh, to enable me to [2 s] to get married, which, of course, it can't- I mean not in|[50]. . . .

Session 165. |[50]liked or that [13 s] or that I was a y'know - an awful person. I'm not sure what I, that I mean anything specific by y'know, - that's an excessive phrase, too. [18 s] And I just now thought - about my saying uh - what I said earlier about your hair. And [2 s] - uh [2 s] and your feelings towards me. (FORG.) *And there was another thought, uh, after that and I repressed it.* But anyway, as a--it's a juxtaposi-juxtaposition -uh [9 s] It's like - ihm, you know, like asking or anyway hoping uh [2 s] that you do like me. [5 s] No, the other thought was [2 s] I'm sorry - I thought about that, which probably (hesitates) was ihm s-- had the sense of something like what I just said but then after|[50]. . . .

Session 170. |[50]talked, as if [2 s] as if he or she were alone, while other people sat around. And I guess - I don't remember that anyone else went through this except myself, in the dream, but uh, [3 s] in the dream you [2 s] I'm trying to remember exactly how it was, but I don't really remember. (FORG.) *In fact, I--just slipped out of my mind entirely for a minute,* but uh, [2 s] I guess I was talking about how I hadn't - [2 s] well, I hadn't i-it appeared that i-some time previously I had uh, confided in you or said to you that I really didn't do enough work for school. And you brought this out in front of all these people.|[50]

Summary of Clinical Review Findings

All six forgetting contexts from the first analysis (with Dr. A) were about a relationship with a man; in five of the six, the man was explicitly the therapist. In all six Ms. Apfel saw the man as either rejecting her or managing to avoid rejecting her only out of consideration for her feelings. The man was presented as either liking her or not liking her. In essence, the momentary forgettings concerned a moment of truth in which it was revealed what a man felt for her, or what she felt for a man. It is easy to discern the main theme even in the 50 words before each forgetting.

The examples show a theme. In session 20, the forgetting followed Ms. Apfel's thought that the therapist would say that she was not amenable to the treatment. In session 36, the forgetting followed a slip in which the patient revealed her hostility to the therapist by saying, "I present myself to you in such a way that I can't like you" when she had meant to say ". . . that you can't like me." In session 53, the lost thought followed the patient's mentioning that the boy she had been dating "says he hates his father, . . . and I don't really think it applies to me"—an example scored as a denial of rejection. In session 66, her preceding thought was that now when the therapist said the time was up, she realized he did not mean to reject her. In session 83, the patient was considering how she would feel if the therapist forgot her session. In session 91, there was another near slip: The patient said, "I seem very nicely to have picked on men who get in my way," when she had meant to say ". . . who don't treat me well"; "get in my way" provides more evidence of the intrusion of her hostility toward men.

The seven instances of momentary forgetting during the treatment with Dr. B, a female analyst, occurred in contexts laden with similar ideas. As examples, in session 123, Ms. Apfel recalled her mother's being angry at her at the time they were moving; in session 136, after a nagging thought about "pushing someone off the subway platform" she had nothing to say and reassured herself that "it will be all right; I can come anyway," meaning that the therapist would not put her out of the treatment. In the next four examples, the preceding thoughts dealt directly with the therapist and remained concerned with the theme of the therapist's favorable or unfavorable response to her. Even from this cursory clinical review of the 13 examples, a consistent theme preceding the forgetting is evident. Typically, the preliminary to the forgetting was a version of a thought about rejection, often a concrete example of it in relation to the analyst.

The Recovered Thoughts

The list in Table 1 is designed to help the reader to keep one part of the results clear: This part of the review is restricted to the thoughts specifically designated by the patient as being momentarily forgotten. Examination of the instances of momentary forgetting reveals that in 8 of the 13, the patient clearly or moderately clearly designated the thought as being recovered. In 8 of these 8 recovered thoughts, the theme appears to be rejection: actual, potential, or considered and then avoided or denied.

TABLE 1
Tally of 13 Instances of Ms. Apfel's Momentary Forgettings for Recovery, Rejection, and Associated Qualities

Session number	Thought recovered?	Explicit rejection theme	Explicit reference to therapist?	Description of recovered, prior, and associated thoughts
20	no	—	—	P's associated thought is about rejection from mother and sister.
36	yes	yes	yes	At the previous session, P thought T was not listening to her.
53	yes (partial)	implied	yes (partial)	P was frightened because she could not understand the boy's reaction to her ("He hates his father—I don't think it applied to me.") It was the same fright that she felt about T.
66	no	—	—	Possibly P was leading up to asking T for time off for her summer plans.
83	no	—	—	P could not recall the forgotten thought but had an associated memory about feeling rejected by T a couple of weeks earlier.
91	yes	yes	no (ref. to "men")	P was justified in feeling that men treat her badly—but she chooses them.
123	no	—	—	The immediately prior thought was of "mother being angry at me because I was ill."
136	yes	implied or denied	yes	P was thinking positive thoughts about the analysis—even if it did not prove to enable her to get married.
165	yes	yes or denied	yes	P's thought probably was "like asking or hoping you (T) *do* like me . . . one of the reasons I can speak openly is you never seize upon remarks and make me feel embarrassed."
170	yes	yes	yes	In P's dream, T criticized, betrayed, and reviled P in front of other people.

continues

TABLE 1 (*Continued*)

Session number	Thought recovered?	Explicit rejection theme	Explicit reference to therapist?	Description of recovered, prior, and associated thoughts
174	no	—	—	The immediately prior thought was about feeling offended by what P felt was an unfair comment by T.
178	yes	implied	yes	P thought of how T was dressed, and a comparison with herself left her feeling less sophisticated, very helpless, like a child.
300	yes	yes or denied	yes	P thought, in comparison with T's description of P as being buffeted about as a child, that it was not true; P really was given a lot of attention (that is, she was not rejected).

Note. P = patient; T = therapist.

Also, in 7 of the 8, the patient makes an explicit reference to the therapist. Even in the one remaining instance in session 178, the content may be somewhat similar: a feeling of helplessness based on a comparison with the analyst that may have been experienced as a rejection. In fact, in many of the examples, some element of helplessness is evident in the face of the rejection. In two instances when the thought was not recovered, the patient nevertheless provided what she considered to be an "associated thought" about what might have been forgotten; in both of these rejection is obvious—by the mother and sister in session 20, and by the therapist in session 83. In two other instances when the thought was not recovered (sessions 123 and 174), the immediately preceding thoughts were about rejection.

Clinical reviews such as this one tend not to consider control data in detail, and I will not be entirely atypical. A brief inspection of the controls suggests that the same main themes are also present in them, but they are less frequent. The more exact methods in the next sections were used to extract and measure the essence of the presymptom segments as compared with the essence of the precontrol segments.

Method 2: Rating Variables in Symptom Versus Control Segments

Ratings by clinicians require complex quantified judgments of specific variables. Thirteen variables were defined and then rated on 5-point scales (see the Appendix). Three of the variables—Rejection, Involvement with Therapist, and Reference to Therapist (Explicit)—were chosen for use in Ms. Apfel's case, because in the clinical review they were found to be especially pertinent to momentary forgetting. Other variables were included not only because they seemed relevant for this patient, but also to facilitate comparison with other similarly analyzed symptoms (Katcher, Luborsky, Brightman, & Mijoskovic, 1970; Luborsky, 1970; Luborsky & Auerbach, 1969).

Rejection especially needs an explanation, because it appears to be the central variable that emerges from the clinical review. Rejection is defined as a negative response to the patient by another person. Negative responses include dislike or lack of interest, withholding something, evaluating the patient as inadequate, or revealing an intention to break off with the patient. The Rejection scale ranges from *none* to *very much*. The denial of rejection, that is, when the patient stresses that the person "was *not* rejecting me," is also scored on the same scale. The scale, therefore, is one of preoccupation with the theme of rejection, whether its presence or its absence is emphasized.

To prepare the segments for rating, all references in the context to the momentary forgetting were deleted from the 13 symptom segments (except that the word *forgetting* remains at the actual or designated point of the forgetting for *all* 26 contexts). To make the rating task a more manageable one, the 26 segments were marked off into only twelve 50-word units—six immediately preceding the forgetting (or control point) and six immediately following it—for a total of 156 control units and 154 symptom units (one forgetting occurred late in the session, so that only enough words followed it to allow for four 50-word units).

Agreement of Judges

Two judges independently rated all segments on the 13 variables (one judge had had experience as a rater but no clinical experience). Each segment was consecutively rated, unit by unit, on all categories before another segment was rated. The 26 momentary forgetting contexts were rated in random order.

To evaluate the degree of agreement between the judges, from each of the 26 segments, one 50-word unit was selected at random from the six preceding the forgetting (or the control point) and one from the six following it. Correlations between judges were computed for the 13 variables over these 52 units. Applications of the Spearman-Brown formula to these single judge's reliabilities yielded estimates of the reliabilities of their pooled ratings (see Table 2). Agreement was moderate to good on all the variables except Hopelessness, Anxiety, Hostility to Therapist (Direct), Hostility to Others, and Sex and Affection. But, the low agreement on

TABLE 2
Agreement of Two Judges' Ratings and Scorings of Variables for Ms.
Apfel's Momentary Forgettings

	Estimated reliabilities of ratings	
Variable	Pooled	Per judge
Rated		
Rejection	.76	.61
Helplessness	.75	.60
Hopelessness	.36	.22
Separation Concern	.80	.67
Anxiety	.55	.38
Hostility to Therapist (Inferred)	.79	.65
Hostility to Therapist (Direct)	−.06	−.03
Hostility to Others	.53	.36
Sex and Affection	.54	.37
Guilt	.78	.64
Shame	.75	.60
Involvement with Therapist	.91	.83
Scored		
Reference to Therapist (Explicit)	.95	.90
Cognitive Disturbance	.92	.86[a]
Speech Disturbance	.96	.92[a]

[a] Taken from Session 3 of MS 17.

these exceptional variables was probably due to their infrequent appearance in the segments.

Comparison of Ratings of Symptom Segments Versus Control Segments

A comparison was made of the 50-word units just before momentary forgetting with the 50-word units just before the control points on the 13 variables rated by the two independent judges (one judge was completely blind; the other might have had some information on only one or two of the contexts). However, the results showed that the two judges had somewhat similar results: For the differences between symptom segments versus controls, for one judge, seven variables were significant, for the other only five variables were significant, and for both judges, five variables were significant. The results for each judge were similar enough so that the analyses that follow use the mean of the two judges.

The comparison of results for the 50-word unit before symptom segments versus before control segments (see Table 3) shows, starting with the most significant variable first, these variables to be significant: Involvement with Therapist, Rejection, Separation Concern, Hopelessness, Helplessness, and Hostility to Therapist. The 100-50 word segment tends to

TABLE 3
Rated Variables That Were Significantly Different Before Momentary Forgettings Versus Before Controls for Ms. Apfel

Variable rated (13 symptom versus 12 control segments)	t 100-50 unit	t 50-0 unit	p[a] (one-tailed)
Involvement with Therapist	2.26	4.20	.000
Rejection	2.11	4.04	.001
Separation Concern	1.30	2.13	.022
Hopelessness	1.78	2.04	.027
Helplessness	2.63	1.80	.043
Hostility to Therapist (Inferred)	1.97	1.80	.043

[a]The ps in rank order refer to the 50-0 word unit for the significance of the difference between before symptom versus before control segments.

show the same results, with the addition of Anxiety. We may speculate, partly based on the clinical review, about how these variables operate interactively. This may be the usual sequence: The patient feels Rejection by the therapist and in consequence becomes highly Involved with the Therapist; the patient then feels Separation Concern and Hopelessness about losing the therapist and Hostility to the Therapist for the Rejection as well as for losing the therapist.

A more extensive analysis is provided by an analysis of variance of the judges' ratings on the variables. The ratings were first summed for the 310 units, then a two-factor repeated-measurements analysis of variance was calculated for each variable (Winer, 1962, p. 302). The two factors were (a) symptom versus control and (b) within symptom or within control. These analyses are summarized in Table 4, which shows the statistical significance (F ratios) of the tested effects. The three main findings are:

1. The among-control-units test assessed the significance of moment-to-moment variation within the control data. No significant effects were expected and none were obtained, the F ratios being less than one for every variable. The control mean was therefore a reasonable comparison value for the values from the symptom-segment data for each of the 13 variables studied.

2. The symptom mean versus control mean compared the average symptom-segment ratings with the average control-segment ratings. Variables that showed significant effects were Rejection, Helplessness, Hostility to Therapist (Inferred), and Involvement with Therapist—all rated generally higher in symptom segments than in control segments.

TABLE 4
Analyses of Variance for Rated and Scored Variables on Momentary Forgetting Data

Variable	Among-control units	Symptom M vs. control M	Among-symptom units[c]	Unit preceding symptom
Rated				
Rejection	<1	17.85**[a] (1)	1.74	29.01** (1)
Involvement with Therapist	<1	4.30* (4)	2.84**	22.64** (2)
Helplessness	<1	17.22** (2)	<1[b]	12.99* (3)
Hostility to Therapist (Inferred)	<1	7.28** (3)	<1[b]	6.26* (5)
Separation Concern	<1	2.78[a]	1.10[b]	2.15
Shame	<1	<1	2.40**[b]	<1
Guilt	<1	<1	1.18	<1
Scored				
Reference to Therapist (Explicit)	< 1	1.72	1.06	7.51* (4)
Cognitive Disturbance	1.68	<1	1.02	<1
Speech Disturbance	1.63	<1	1.30	1.99

Note. Rank of the size of the F ratios appears in parentheses.
[a] Variance of segments in symptom data significantly larger than in control data.
[b] Interaction (error) variance significantly larger in symptom data than in control data. Tests for among-symptom units used within-symptom error term ($df = 130$).
[c] Before and after the symptom.
* $p < .05$. ** $p < .01$.

3. The among-symptom-units test assessed the significance of changes preceding and following symptom occurrence. Two variables showed significant unit-to-unit variation within the 600-word segment: Involvement with Therapist tended to peak just before the forgetting (see Figure 1 and Table 4), and Shame was level before the forgetting but rose significantly after it.

Time Trends Before and After Momentary Forgetting

Because it seemed likely that any effects related to the forgetting would be progressively more dramatic immediately before it occurred, the mean rating of the 50-word unit immediately preceding the forgetting (averaged over all segments) was compared with the mean rating of all control data for each variable. This test was significant for all of the variables that were rated generally higher in the symptom data than in the control data (listed earlier under finding #2). In addition, there was a significant difference in Reference to Therapist (Explicit) between the overall control mean and the single 50-word unit immediately preceding the forgetting. This was, however, the only unit in which Reference to Therapist (Explicit)

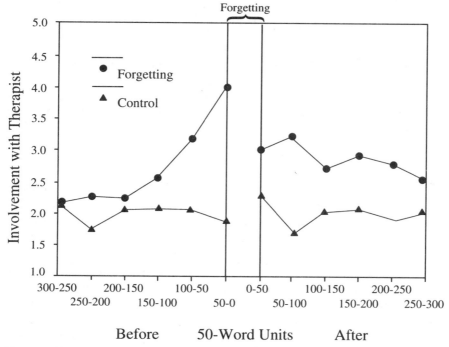

Figure 1. Mean ratings of Involvement with Therapist in six 50-word units before versus six 50-word units after momentary forgetting for Ms. Apfel.

differed from the controls. This variable, in fact, has been found to differentiate symptom from control segments in other cases (see chaps. 10 and 11) and between forgetting and control segments in a sample of 10 patients (Luborsky, 1973; see also chap. 4). For three variables—Reference to Therapist (Explicit), Rejection, and Involvement with Therapist—the size of the difference just before the forgetting was much greater than the overall differences between means.[4] To carry the trend analysis further, the mean ratings of the two judges were plotted for six 50-word units before and six 50-word units after the momentary forgetting.

Trends Before Forgetting

This graphic way of displaying the results showed clear time trends. Before the momentary forgetting, the significant variables (those with significant differences between symptom and control segments) tended to

---

[4] To further examine possible bias, we did the analyses of variance separately for the two judges. Although the ratings of the entirely blind judge alone have lower reliability than the pooled ratings (as would be expected for a single judge), the analyses of the entirely blind judge's ratings alone confirmed all of the major findings. In short, the pooled data appeared to be appropriate for both judges and were not much affected by possible bias.

show gradually increasing ratings and increasing *ts* before the momentary forgetting. Examples are shown in Figures 1, 2, and 3. In Figure 1, Involvement with Therapist in the symptom segments showed an increase starting about 200 words before the momentary forgetting. In Figure 2, for Rejection, the 150-word point was the beginning of a rise in the ratings before the momentary forgetting. The Helplessness curve (see Figure 3) showed the beginning of a rise for the symptom segments beginning at about 200 words before the momentary forgetting.

Trends After Forgetting

There was a tendency for the variables with the largest significant differences between real and control variables to show a gradual decrease in the units after the forgetting. There were two exceptions to the trend toward decline in the variables after the forgetting. These exceptions were Rejection and Hostility to the Therapist (Inferred), which continued to show significant differences between real and control variables throughout the six units after the forgetting. The level of significance of these differences remained high in the immediate contexts both distally and proximally, so it appears to be true that the patient holds on to feeling rejected

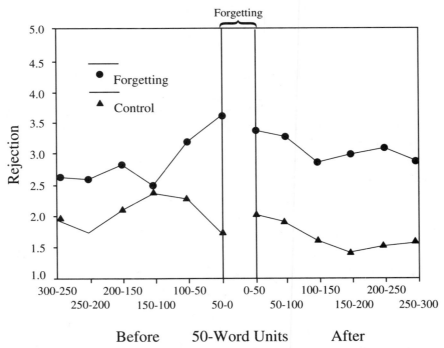

Figure 2. Mean ratings of Rejection in six 50-word units before versus six 50-word units after momentary forgetting for Ms. Apfel.

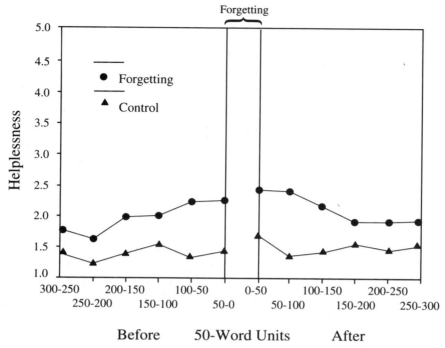

Figure 3. Mean ratings of Helplessness in six 50-word units before versus six 50-word units after momentary forgetting for Ms. Apfel.

and angry at the therapist through most of the period of the immediate context. In summary, these graphs of the ratings of 50-word units before and after the forgetting reveal that for most of these variables there is an area of special activity extending from three or four 50-word units before the forgetting to three or four 50-word units after the forgetting.

Intercorrelations of Rated Variables

How much overlap was there among these discriminating variables? Might they really be highly similar variables hiding under different labels? To find out, intercorrelations were computed among the rated variables using the mean ratings of the two judges for the 50-word unit before the forgetting. (Because of the possibility that one judge's ratings were contaminated in one or two instances, these correlations were first computed separately for each judge. However, the resulting pattern of intercorrelations was similar for each judge; therefore, the corresponding values were averaged.) The seven significantly discriminating rated variables were low to moderately correlated with each other within the symptom segments. The highest mean correlation was .45 between Helplessness and the other variables; the lowest mean correlation was .22 for Anxiety.

Another type of intercorrelation method was also used. Intercorrelations were computed among the rated variables using the mean ratings of the two judges *only for the 100 words before the forgetting*. These two units of 50 words each were pooled and the intercorrelations computed, because we know from the trend analysis that in these two units, the main differentiating variables between real and control are most evident. The matrix of 7 × 7 variables is shown in Table 5.

Several of these variables were moderately correlated with each other. The highest was, as usual, Helplessness and Hopelessness (.75). A moderate relationship appeared between Involvement with Therapist and Rejection. This was no surprise because an involvement, as was shown, occurs around the expectation of Rejection (.57). The involvement also occurs around Hostility (.51). Otherwise, most of the correlations with each other were low.

One of the correlations involving a scored variable was high and should be noted here: Involvement with Therapist and Reference to Therapist were highly correlated with each other (.81). Our conclusion, therefore, is that, with these exceptions, the main variables are only moderately but not highly correlated with each other.

Method 3: Scoring Variables

The task of developing or finding a scoring system with counts of specified contents for each rated variable was aimed at improving reliability and validity of measurement. The scored version might also uncover more of the details of the content related to each variable. So far, this time-consuming development of scoring procedures has been achieved for only a few of the rated variables. These results are as follows.

TABLE 5
Intercorrelations of Rated Variables for 100 Words Before Momentary
Forgetting in Symptom Segments

Variable	1	2	3	4	5	6	7	M^a
1. Hostility (Inferred)	—	−.08	.41	.27	.51	.48	.20	.30
2. Anxiety		—	.35	.21	.27	.34	.21	.22
3. Helplessness			—	.75	.39	.45	.37	.45
4. Hopelessness				—	.22	.31	.22	.33
5. Involvement with Therapist					—	.56	.36	.38
6. Rejection						—	.43	.43
7. Separation Concern							—	.30

[a]Mean of the correlations for that variable.

Reference to Therapist

Because Involvement with Therapist showed such promise from a rating before momentary forgetting versus before controls (see Table 3), scored measures of it were examined. It was clear that the Involvement with Therapist was associated with an easy-to-score measure of Reference to Therapist; there, references to therapists were merely counted. The 50-word unit before the forgetting compared with the 50-word unit before the controls was inconsistent. With one judge it was ($p < .025$), and with another it was nonsignificant.

Helplessness Manual

Because Helplessness was rated with significant differences between before momentary forgetting versus before controls, a Helplessness manual was tried for scoring Helplessness. A description of the manual and its scale appear in chapter 5, which presents its first use in a depression case. This manual did not achieve significant differences between symptom segments and controls.

Cognitive Disturbance

Attention difficulties (estimated by a global rating) were thought in the pilot study (Luborsky, 1964, 1967) to be a crucial aspect of the state that builds up before momentary forgetting. Because these attention and related cognitive difficulties were suitable for exact scoring, 26 types, each with examples, were listed in a manual with the encompassing label *Cognitive Disturbance* (Luborsky, 1966, 1966). The 26 types fall into three categories of disturbance: memory dysfunction, uncertainty about one's knowledge, and unclarity of expression. A score of 1 is given for each occurrence in the patient's speech. Because the method leaves little to the scorer's judgment, agreement of judges was high. The Cognitive Disturbance measure had first been cross-validated for 10 patients, each of whom had produced two or three instances of momentary forgetting (Luborsky, 1973). It worked well in the sense that it revealed more disturbance in the symptom contexts than in the control contexts. Most examples scored were of uncertainty, a few were of unclarity, and fewer still were of memory dysfunction. We tried the Cognitive Disturbance measure on Ms. Apfel's 13 symptom segments versus 13 control segments (twelve 50-word units for each), but the analysis of variance showed no significant differences on any of the comparisons (see Table 4), perhaps because her usual level of cognitive disturbance tended to be consistently very high relative to other patients.

Speech Disturbance

Mahl's (1956) Speech Disturbance measure was another objectively scored and conveniently ready-made measure to be tried, because it is supposed to estimate anxiety from the patient's speech. However, if a repressive defense is involved in the instigation of the forgetting, only "signal anxiety" may be present, and that may be too little to be easily measured. Yet it still seemed worth trying to measure the anxiety on the chance that some would register on the Mahl measure.

There were some significant effects: Speech disturbance was significantly less (.03 level) in the 50-word unit before the forgetting and significantly greater in the 50-word unit just after the forgetting (.01 level). Otherwise, the curve over the rest of the 12-unit segments was mainly flat.

Gottschalk-Gleser Variables

These are well-known and well-validated scoring systems for variables with great clinical utility (Gottschalk & Gleser, 1969). Gottschalk kindly scored his set of variables with his computer system, although the set includes many more variables than those for which we had hypotheses. Of the 22 variables scored by the computer on the total 300-word unit, 4 were significant at the .05 level or better by one-tailed tests. These 4 were (low) Hostility-Outward, overt (.03); Hostility-Outward, covert (.05); (low) Hope (.005); and Guilt Depression (.03). Of all of these, the most differentiating was low Hope, which was greater in the symptom segments than in the control segments. Low Hope appears to be in a continuum with Hopelessness.

Method 4: Evaluating the Broad Background Context With Whole Sessions

Computer Scoring With Word Categories

Our aim here was to see whether the whole sessions that contain momentary forgetting differ from sessions that do not. Objective scoring of more than a few whole sessions would have been prohibitively time-consuming, except for our luck in obtaining the aid of a computer program designed for this purpose by Dahl (1972). The system consists of 53 categories, many suggested by psychoanalytic concepts, which Dr. B, the second analyst, had scored from the *abbreviated* transcripts for all sessions. Dahl's factor analysis of 363 sessions of the second analysis yielded six factors: He interpreted two as "resistance" factors (sum of resistance Factors 1 and 6) and four as "content-conflict" factors (sum of Factors 2, 3, 4, and 5—i.e., family, sex, dreams, and anxiety).

The mean scores on these factors were similar in the 13 symptom sessions and the 13 control sessions, that is, the session analysis by the Dahl method revealed no significant differences between the sessions with momentary forgetting and those without. In contrast, differences between symptom sessions and control *sessions* have been found in patients with other symptoms, including stomach pain (see chap. 7) and migraine head-ache (Luborsky & Auerbach, 1969; see also chap. 8), although other meth-ods of analysis were used.

Comparison of the CCRT and the Symptom-Context Theme

We gradually began to be aware that the main differentiating variables in the segments before forgetting versus before control points can be seen as a symptom-context theme that has an impressive parallel with the CCRT of this patient. We carried through on checking this initial obser-vation by carefully comparing these two themes. The results of this com-parison for this patient and for three other patients are in chapter 4.

External Factors That Might Trigger Forgettings

We should at least look at the possibility that momentary forgettings could have been triggered by noises or other distractions in the room or from the therapist's responses or silences. But when we looked, we saw that such distractions were not obvious, either to the therapist or to other lis-teners to the tape recordings. Furthermore, the forgettings almost always occurred in the midst of the patient's speech, implying that the relevant factors were not in the spoken therapist's interventions but rather in the stream of the patient's thoughts.

Furthermore, if external factors rather than internal factors played a big part, we might also have expected that the sex of the therapist would have had some effect on the frequency of the forgettings or on the context in which the forgettings occurred. But again there were no such obvious effects—the frequency of forgetting and their context were not markedly different for Analyst A, a man, and for Analyst B, a woman.

IMPLICATIONS OF THE SYMPTOM CONTEXT FOR THE PATIENT'S TREATMENT

In essence, our study was the first to show systematically that mo-mentary forgetting, a will-o'-the-wisp recurrent memory dysfunction, is closely associated with a recurrent conflict-laden set of variables. When this memory dysfunction appears, it tends to be preceded by a set of vari-ables including Involvement with Therapist, Rejection, Helplessness, Hopelessness, and Hostility to Therapist. I will now reembed these findings in the clinical matrix to show where they fit with the patient's other symp-toms and to show their possible role in the course of the treatment. It will then be possible to see which concepts fit best in explaining these findings.

The symptoms that led Ms. Apfel to treatment involved a series of attachments to unsuitable men, all much younger than she, by whom she felt unfairly treated (rejected?), which led to her decision to terminate each relationship. In the first session she described her reasons for entering analysis as follows: "I'm 31 years old and I'm not married, although I'd like to be, and have had various unsuccessful sexual relationships. . . . The thing which made me seek therapy was that I was in an unusually emotional state, with crying, depression . . . and an encounter with a young man touched or culminated the whole thing." As part of the pattern, she described choosing men younger than she was and taking a maternal role in relation to them. In the fourth session, the patient mentioned that in a previous contact with a therapist (whom she had been seeing once a week for a year, just before the first analyst), "He pointed out I always set up the relationship with men, or I always choose one which I could feel terrible anger against, and that I would be forbearing and accept the conditions as laid down by them, meekly on the surface, but meanwhile would be feeling very resentful and ill-treated."

The patient was also afraid that she was "homosexual," although the only such contact she had had, when she was 12 or 13, was with her younger sister, and it consisted of asking her sister to masturbate her. She also had a fear, perhaps contributed to by her own self-blame for her request to her sister, that she would harm children.

In the second session, Ms. Apfel brought up her difficulty with graduate work. She stated that, after coming back from Europe in the spring semester in 1963, "I wrote a prospectus for the dissertation. . . . I got very tense, just felt on the brink of falling apart at certain moments, and then I had the feeling one morning, after I finished typing this prospectus—I'd been up all night—I was afraid I was going to have an hallucination that I was going to see a man that didn't really exist." (At the start of her analysis, the patient had been in graduate school for 8 years and still had not started a thesis.)

Of all the presenting problems—unsuccessful relationships with men, work inhibition, depression, "fear of going crazy," "homosexual fear," fear of harming children—her failure with men seemed to her the most pressing and led to the most depression and anger. Her symptoms fit with a diagnosis of personality disorder, with borderline and dependent features, but her symptoms did not completely satisfy the criteria for either. Therefore, the most suitable diagnosis according to the DSM-IV (American Psychiatric Association, 1994) is personality disorder, not otherwise specified (301.4).

As would be expected, the patient did not list momentary forgetting among her symptoms. It must have seemed to her, as it does to most people, to be a minor, occasional, accidental loss of a thought that she had intended to say. However, this patient experienced momentary forgetting more frequently than did any other patient my colleagues and I have studied. Furthermore, the momentary forgetting was part of a pervasive disturbance in her flow of speech—she had more cognitive disturbances of all kinds than any other patient we have studied. Her momentary forgetting can be designated as a symptom in the sense that it implies a dysfunction of a usual memory function for thoughts that one has intended to say.

It is impressive that a brief review of her presenting symptoms suggests a correspondence between her outstanding symptom—difficulties with men—and the recurrent expectation of rejection, which was found more often in the momentary forgetting contexts than in the control contexts. The high rate of cognitive disturbance may even reflect her habitual caution about communicating her thoughts directly and clearly.

The events and course of treatment, as was briefly summarized by Dahl (1972), trace her experiences of rejection during the treatment:

> At the time she began her analysis with Dr. A, two of her expressed hopes were that she would be able to change her relationships with men in such a way that she could get married, and that she would be able to have children. During the early months of the analysis with Dr. A, it seemed quite clear that she was developing a positive transference—perhaps it might even be called a working alliance. Then, suddenly and unexpectedly, Dr. A became ill. The patient was given little or no information about the circumstances, and was finally told that he would not be able to return. (pp. 250–251)

After several months, she entered treatment with Dr. B, who was 5 months pregnant. The first major interruption of 38 days in the second analysis came after 18 weeks, when the analyst left to have her baby. This event coincided with decreased productivity—Factors 2, 3, 4, 5—and increased resistance—Factors 1 and 6—of Dahl's measures of the content of the patient's speech.

> Shortly after the 40th week, during the summer when there were several holidays, the patient met a married man with whom she quickly began an affair. She promptly got pregnant, and then during the 53rd week (of analysis) had an abortion, with the approval of her lover. Following this, with the single exception of some events between the 70th and 80th week, our measure shows a steady decline (i.e., Factors 2, 3, 4, 5, decreased and Factors 1, 6 increased).
>
> ... It is evident from an independent summary of the case (by another analyst) that the patient took the fact that the man readily agreed to the abortion and was very supportive during it as a sign that nothing could come of her relationship with him. The abortion occurred just before the peak of ... productivity in the 53rd week); the course from there on was downhill with a single exception.
>
> ... The independent summary of the analysis during this period (80th to 108th week) is replete with comments about the stalemate, the stagnation, the difficult resistance, and the analyst's nearly futile efforts to do something successful about it. (Dahl, 1972, pp. 251–252)

It is easy to see from Dahl's account that the events of the treatment provided a heavy dose of just the kind of aversive conditions that the initial symptoms and the main theme of the forgetting show that the patient was least able to tolerate—the illness of the first analyst, her abortion and its meanings, and so forth. It is of special interest here that a consultant to the second analyst offered the opinion, after having been involved in the treatment for several years, that it was crucial to try to analyze the patient's expectation of rejection from her analyst and to note the way in which the patient's interpretation of the research aspect of her treatment also played into her negative expectation. Clearly, therefore, the patient's expectation of rejection was not just another important theme, but was crucial to the outcome of the treatment.

THE BEST-FITTING THEORETICAL CONCEPTS

Having presented a clinical matrix of symptoms and treatment, I can now offer a theoretical account of the context in which momentary forgetting appeared for this patient. The concepts that seem to fit best with our findings are clinical psychoanalytical ones that do what clinical psychoanalytical theory is best at doing—the "reading of intentionality" from the standpoint of the patient (Klein, 1973). The imminent emergence of Ms. Apfel's intention to communicate something to her analyst (high Involvement with Therapist) led her to feel that she was approaching a dangerous situation; she was in danger of experiencing rejection and telling a person she depended on about her feeling rejected and her consequent anger to the therapist. Thus, she experienced a thought about expecting rejection from him, and telling him that could have increased the risk of actually losing him. She might also have felt that her hostility toward the analyst, probably originating from her expectation of rejection, would provoke rejection from him, which would in turn lead her to feel even more helpless and hopeless and to feel separation concern and anxiety. (The archaic models for her thoughts about the relationship with the therapist may be either her mother, as was mentioned in reference to Session 36, or her father, who had a heart condition. With the father, her recurrent situation as a young child was feeling a similar combination of rejection from him and hostility toward him, followed by helplessness and hopelessness in handling these feelings, because any expression of them to him might exacerbate his heart condition.)

Instead of developing high anxiety when she thought of expressing her expectation of rejection, she may have called on a variety of defensive operations—of which momentary forgetting may be one. In this sense, the forgetting or near-forgetting may have been triggered by a repressive defense into momentarily concealing, and therefore directing attention away from, the threatening theme. In view of the evidence that a conflict-laden theme recurs at the time of the momentary forgetting, the concept of repression may be a more fitting explanation than, for example, externally caused diversions of attention.

Given that repression is an applicable explanatory concept, Schlesinger's (1970) idea of repression may be helpful here: repression can be thought of not only as a facilitator of forgetting but also, paradoxically, as "the enemy of forgetting." It serves to preserve the memory of an idea. Ms. Apfel had retained an easily aroused, conflict-laden idea that she will be rejected (which probably is linked with a similar idea in her early relationship with her parents). When this idea is revived within the interaction with the analyst, the patient has two opposing impulses simultaneously: to know and say it, versus a version of the idea involving rejection that is sometimes momentarily forgotten.

Why, then, is the lost thought often subsequently recovered and expressed? Possibly because the delay permits some cooling off (an isolation defense?) or some substitution during the momentary delay, of a less threatening derivative of the originally forgotten thought. Why was the rejection theme occasionally followed by forgetting? Probably because it was so threatening and omnipresent that it overshadowed other themes. Consistent with this, we found that the rejection theme was also frequent in the control segments, but it was significantly less frequent than in the momentary forgetting segments.

Finally, is our main finding a usual one? Is it typical to find around recurrent forgetting a central-to-the-treatment main theme? It probably is, even though Ms. Apfel is the only patient for whom this has been demonstrated for a relatively long series of forgettings. Although we found no other patient with such a large number of momentary forgettings recorded on tape, a clinical analysis of other patients suggests a similar conclusion. In the pilot sample of 15 patients (Luborsky, 1964, 1967) 4 showed a repeated sexual theme, 4 a hostility theme, and the remaining 7 an anxiety about maintaining control or competence. For example, for Mr. Herman, the main recurrent central theme was concern about sex or affection toward a girl. Whenever forgetting occurred, this theme was evident (Luborsky, 1970; Luborsky & Auerbach, 1969). In all of these patients, a recurrent main theme seems to be invariably present, but patients do differ in the choice of theme and its pervasiveness.

CONCLUSIONS

Ms. Apfel's recurrent memory dysfunction, momentary forgetting, was examined by clinical–quantitative methods that demonstrate the value of using a progression of methods—from a clinical review, to ratings, to scoring systems. The three methods were applied to the patient's words both immediately before and after the symptom (the immediate context) as well as to the entire session in which symptoms appeared (the background context), with the following results:

- The recurrence of the central content theme of Rejection, first discerned by a clinical review, was corroborated by ratings of brief segments of the immediately surrounding context. Independent raters were able to discriminate significantly between segments of sessions before the momentary forgetting symptom and segments before the control points.
- Forgetting was also found to be associated with high Involvement with Therapist, in which there was a significant mean difference between the symptom and the control segments, and which peaked just before the forgetting. But the patient often talked about rejection without subsequent momentary forgetting or any other signs of defense-related activity. More must happen than the appearance of the theme—it must be activated in the relationship with the therapist. High Involvement with Therapist, therefore, seems to increase the probability of momentary forgetting. A scoring system for Involvement with Therapist, Reference to Therapist, was highly correlated with it (.81) and for the unit before the forgetting was significantly different from the controls.
- There may also be some concomitant current revival of thoughts associated with archaic relationships. Many of the patient's comments around the time of forgetting seem consistent with a transference activation. For example, in session 20, after feeling that the analyst was rejecting her at the moment, Ms. Apfel shifted to an early memory of her mother and sister poking fun at her.
- A highly significant difference in mean Helplessness and Hopelessness was found between the symptom segments and the control segments. Freud (1926/1959) and others (e.g., Engel & Schmale, 1965) considered Helplessness and Hopelessness to be of central importance in the genesis of neurotic symptoms.
- Mean Hostility to Therapist (Inferred) also discriminated the symptom segments from the control segments and peaked significantly in the two or three 50-word units preceding the symptom. The hostility was probably related to Ms. Apfel's expectation of receiving hostility from others (i.e., rejection).
- Separation concern was significantly greater before the forgetting than before the controls.

- A common hypothesis about the function of a psychological symptom is that it averts the continued buildup of anxiety. The mean ratings showed that some anxiety was discernible, but we were not able to show an increase in anxiety before forgetting in this patient, either by ratings of anxiety or by scorings on Mahl's (1956) speech disturbance scale.

- The entire-session context appeared to be less related to the symptom than was the immediate context in some respects. The categorization of abbreviated sessions according to Dahl's (1972) factor scores did not discriminate between symptom and control sessions. In contrast, in studies of other symptoms, the entire session has usually been found to contain content similar to that of the immediate context (Luborsky & Auerbach, 1969).

- Only one of the patient's thoughts about rejection or denial of rejection was forgotten, usually *a concrete example of what she experienced as the analyst's rejection.* For example, in Session 36, Ms. Apfel remembered that in an earlier session she had heard a sound as though the analyst were brushing a spot off of his trousers, and she had thought this meant he was not listening to her. The surrounding context of the forgetting tended to be replete with other content concerned with rejection.

- The main content theme associated with the forgetting—expectation of rejection—turned out to be not just another important theme but the crucial theme of the treatment. It was the difficulty of resolving it that was responsible for the limited success of the entire treatment effort; the patient was not able to work out or to master her expectation of rejection from the analyst or from others. From our data and from data on other patients, I suggest a generalization: *An individually specific recurrent theme preceding a symptom that appears during the treatment sessions may be crucial for the fate of the treatment.*

APPENDIX
SYMPTOM-CONTEXT RATING SCALES FOR VARIABLES APPLIED TO MOMENTARY FORGETTING

Instructions: Put a mark on each 1 to 5 scale to show your rating. Do this for each 50-word unit of the immediate context of each forgetting. The context consists of 300 words (in six 50-word segments) before the instance and 300 words (in six 50-word segments) after its occurrence.

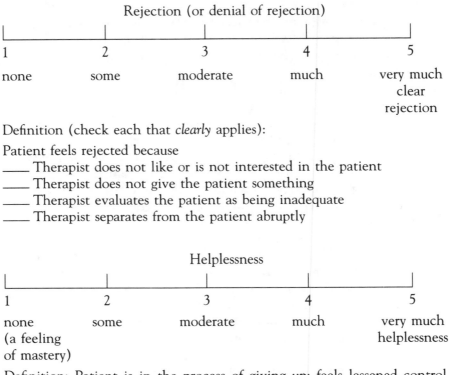

Rejection (or denial of rejection)

1	2	3	4	5
none	some	moderate	much	very much
				clear
				rejection

Definition (check each that *clearly* applies):

Patient feels rejected because
____ Therapist does not like or is not interested in the patient
____ Therapist does not give the patient something
____ Therapist evaluates the patient as being inadequate
____ Therapist separates from the patient abruptly

Helplessness

1	2	3	4	5
none	some	moderate	much	very much
(a feeling				helplessness
of mastery)				

Definition: Patient is in the process of giving up; feels lessened control, weak, inadequate, abnormal, or squeezed; feels he or she is not handling situations well; is afraid of being (or has been) beaten, overpowered, or over-influenced.

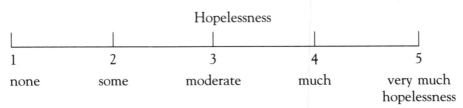

Hopelessness

1	2	3	4	5
none	some	moderate	much	very much
				hopelessness

Definition: Patient has given up, is no longer trying: "It's no use."

Separation Concern

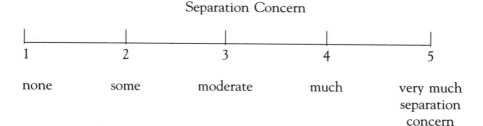

Definition: Patient is concerned about having less time with the therapist or losing the therapist altogether; talks about changing sessions, vacations, or other interruptions; talks of separations from others. References to desertion, abandonment, ostracism, loss of support, loss of love or love object, or threat of such as experienced by the patient; talks about interruptions for vacations and holidays by therapist or patient or talks about changing frequency of sessions.

Anxiety

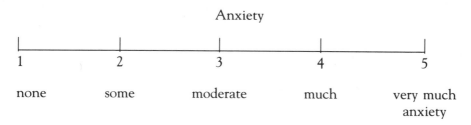

Definition: The amount of manifest anxiety that is obvious to an observer. It is usually, but not always experienced by the patient (e.g., worry, fear, or concern).

Hostility to Therapist (Inferred)

Hostility to Therapist (Direct)

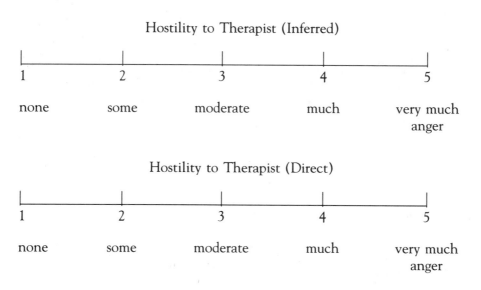

Hostility to Others

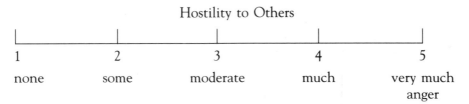

1	2	3	4	5
none	some	moderate	much	very much anger

Note whether direct or inferred.

Sex and Affection

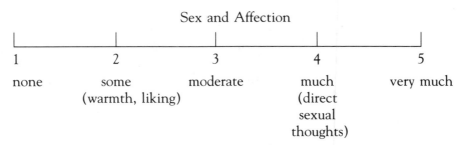

1	2	3	4	5
none	some (warmth, liking)	moderate	much (direct sexual thoughts)	very much

Definition: The amount of emphasis on sexual content. (Direct reference gets a higher rating than indirect.)

Examples: wanting sexual contact (5)
wanting to receive affection (5)
wanting to give affection (3)

Guilt

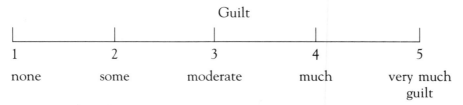

1	2	3	4	5
none	some	moderate	much	very much guilt

Definition: Expected or experienced self-criticism, abuse, condemnation, or moral disapproval of self, with guilt resulting. (Examples: "should," "ought," "must," "right and wrong," "good and bad.") With reference to a particular transgression, failure to do something that one should have done (and that one is able to do) or desire to make amends to the injured other.

Shame

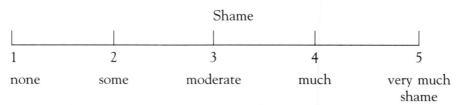

1	2	3	4	5
none	some	moderate	much	very much shame

Definition: References to receiving from others derision or ridicule; feelings of worthlessness, inferiority, inadequacy, or embarrassment; desire to run away, disappear, or hide because of feelings of shame; humiliation, over-exposure of shameful deficiencies, or threat of such experienced by the patient.

Reference to Therapist

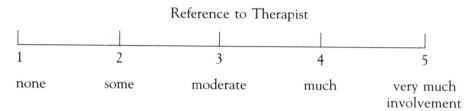

Definition: Degree to which reference to therapist is explicit.

Involvement with Therapist

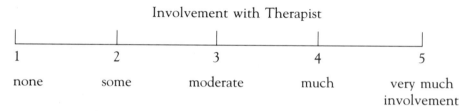

Definition: Degree to which high involvement with the therapist is shown in the segment.

REFERENCES

American Psychiatric Association. (1994). *Diagnostic and statistical manual of mental disorders* (4th ed.). Washington, DC: Author.

Dahl, H. (1972). A quantitative study of a psychoanalysis. *Psychoanalysis and Contemporary Science, 1,* 237–257.

Engel, G. L., & Schmale, A. H. (1965). Psychoanalytic theory of somatic disorders: Conversion, specificity, and the disease onset situation. *Journal of the American Psychoanalytic Association, 15,* 344–365.

Freud, S. (1959). Inhibitions, symptoms, and anxiety. In J. Strachey (Ed. and Trans.), *The standard edition of the complete psychological works of Sigmund Freud* (Vol. 20, pp. 87–172). London: Hogarth Press. (Original work published 1926)

Freud, S. (1960). The psychopathology of everyday life. In J. Strachey (Ed. and Trans.), *The standard edition of the complete psychological works of Sigmund Freud* (Vol. 6, pp. 1–310). London: Hogarth Press. (Original work published 1901)

Gottschalk, L., & Gleser, G. (1969). *The measurement of psychological states through the content analysis of verbal behavior.* Berkeley: University of California.

Graff, H., & Luborsky, L. (1977). Long-term trends in transference and resistance: A quantitative analytic method applied to four psychoanalyses. *Journal of the American Psychoanalytic Association, 25,* 471–490.

James, W. (1890). *The principles of psychology* (Vol. 1). New York: Dover.

Katcher, A. H., Luborsky, L., Brightman, V., & Mijoskovic, M. (1970). Comparison of four predictors of physical illness [Abstract]. *Psychosomatic Medicine, 32,* 554.

Klein, G. S. (1973). Is psychoanalysis relevant? In B. B. Rubinstein (Ed.), *Psychoanalysis and contemporary science: An annual of negative and interdisciplinary studies.* New York: Macmillan.

Luborsky, L. (1964). A psychoanalytic research on momentary forgetting during free association. *Bulletin of the Philadelphia Association for Psychoanalysis, 14,* 119–137.

Luborsky, L. (1966). *A cognitive disturbance scale.* Unpublished manuscript.

Luborsky, L. (1967). Momentary forgetting during psychotherapy and psychoanalysis: A theory and research method. In R. R. Holt (Ed.), Motives and thought: Psychoanalytic essays in honor of David Rapaport [Monograph No. 18/19]. *Psychological Issues, 5*(2–3), 177–217.

Luborsky, L. (1970). New directions in research on neurotic and psychosomatic symptoms. *American Scientist, 58,* 661–668.

Luborsky, L. (1973). Forgetting and remembering (momentary forgetting) during psychotherapy: A new sample. In M. Mayman (Ed.), Psychoanalytic research: Three approaches to the experimental study of subliminal processes [Monograph No. 30]. *Psychological Issues, 8*(2), 29–55.

Luborsky, L. (1993). Documenting symptom formation during psychotherapy: The conditions for momentary forgetting. In N. Miller, L. Luborsky, J. Barber, & J. Docherty (Eds.), *Psychodynamic treatment research: A handbook for clinical practice* (pp. 3–13). New York: Basic Books.

Luborsky, L. (1996). *The therapy session checksheet: A method for maximizing psychotherapists' research capacity.* Manuscript in preparation.

Luborsky, L., & Auerbach, A. H. (1969). The symptom-context method: Quantitative studies of symptom formation in psychotherapy. *Journal of the American Psychoanalytic Association, 17,* 68–99.

Luborsky, L., & Mintz, J. (1974). What sets off momentary forgetting during a psychoanalysis? Methods of investigating symptom-onset conditions. In L. Goldberger & V. Rosen (Eds.), *Psychoanalysis and contemporary science* (Vol. 3, pp. 233–268). New York: International Universities Press.

Mahl, G. (1956). Disturbance and silences in a patient's speech in psychotherapy. *Journal of Abnormal Social Psychology, 53,* 1–15.

Schlesinger, H. J. (1970). The place of forgetting in memory functioning. *Journal of the American Psychoanalytic Association, 18,* 358–371.

Winer, B. J. (1962). *Statistical principles in experimental design.* New York: McGraw-Hill.

4

THE CONTEXT FOR MOMENTARY FORGETTING: STUDIES OF GROUPS OF PATIENTS

LESTER LUBORSKY, HAROLD SACKEIM, and
PAUL CRITS-CHRISTOPH

This chapter further examines, using the symptom-context method, the phenomenon of momentary forgetting. Its vantage point is very different, however. It looks across a group of patients, not as in the usual symptom-context method within a patient over time. With this new view, one can answer new questions, such as, "How many patients experience momentary forgetting?" or "Which of the conditions discovered in the individual within-patient approach appear by this aggregate of a group of cases approach?" These analyses of data in this chapter come from and build on mainly three sources: Luborsky (1973, 1988) and Luborsky, Sackeim, and Crits-Christoph (1979).

Before launching on these results, it will be helpful to provide a brief orienting sketch of what to expect in this chapter: First will be a brief description of the samples of patients and the frequency of their momentary forgetting, then the results will be presented in terms of four methods.

Earlier versions of this chapter appeared in Luborsky, L. (1973). Forgetting and remembering (momentary forgetting) during psychotherapy. In M. Mayman (Ed.), *Psychoanalytic research: Three approaches to the experimental study of subliminal processes* [Monograph 30]. *Psychological Issues, 8*(2), 29–55; in Luborsky, L. (1988). Recurrent momentary forgetting: Its content and context. In M. Horowitz (Ed.), *Psychodynamics and cognition* (pp. 217–245). Chicago: University of Chicago Press; and in Luborsky, L., Sackeim, H., & Crits-Christoph, P. (1979). The state conducive to momentary forgetting. In J. Kihlstrom & F. Evans (Eds.), *Functional disorders of memory* (pp. 325–353). Hillsdale, NJ: Erlbaum. They have been adapted, revised, and expanded by the author with permission of the three publishers.

Method 1 offers a variety of discoveries providing an expanded description of typical qualities of momentary forgetting. Method 2 yields results of *ratings* of variables in the immediate context, and method 3 yields results of *scorings* of variables in the immediate context. Method 4 provides a view of the broad background qualities of momentary forgetting: where forget-tings occur in the session, the results of ratings of the whole session, and an in-depth comparison of the two grand themes found in psychotherapy sessions—the CCRT and the symptom-context theme. Parallels of these two themes are illustrated in three cases. The chapter ends with two kinds of conclusions: those about the specific conditions preceding momentary forgetting, and those about the general conditions for momentary forget-ting.

DESCRIPTION OF THE PATIENTS AND THE PROCEDURES

Three samples are discussed in this chapter: the pilot sample ($N = 19$), the new sample ($N = 10$), and the new enlarged sample ($N = 17$). The pilot sample was derived from my preliminary work on momentary forgetting (Luborsky, 1964, 1967), which was based on the near-verbatim process notes that I made while examining a record number of 67 instances of momentary forgetting, together with the contexts of the patients' words before and after each forgetting, during 2,085 psychotherapy sessions with 19 patients.

The more controlled studies of momentary forgetting that followed the pilot studies were based on the 10 patients' transcripts of tape record-ings of psychotherapy. One of the 10 patients in this new sample is Ms. Apfel, whose case was the focus of chapter 3 (Luborsky & Mintz, 1974). One or more instances of momentary forgetting occurred for each of the 10 patients (Luborsky, 1973), and, as was revealed in chapter 3, 13 in-stances of momentary forgetting were found for Ms. Apfel.

The enlarged new sample consists of the 10 patients in the new sam-ple, plus 7 additional patients (Luborsky, 1973). One to four instances of momentary forgetting were found for each patient (except for Ms. Apfel with 13), for a total of 46 instances (see Table 1). The patients were mainly young adults (age range 20–39, $M = 27$). Almost all had a diagnosis in the neurotic range and were in long-term psychotherapy or psychoanalysis in private practice settings. Consistent with their diagnoses, their global ratings on the Health-Sickness Rating Scale (HSRS) (Luborsky, 1962, 1975) ranged from 50 to 75 ($M = 64$).

I treated 9 of the 17 patients; the others were treated by psychother-apists who lent me tape recordings of their sessions. These two subgroups showed no obvious differences in health-sickness ratings or momentary forgetting-related conditions. As examples, there were no significant differences in the rate of forgetting per session (.02 vs. .03) or in the percentage of recoveries of these forgettings per patient (67% vs. 70%). Because there were no significant differences in any area related to the conclusions, I do not separate the two subgroups for discussion in this chapter.

To prepare the data, my colleagues and I first matched each forgetting point with a comparable point in another session with the same patient that did not contain momentary forgetting (a control session). For each of the control sessions, a control point was marked off that was as far along in time as the matched instance of momentary forgetting was in the real session. The contexts for the momentary forgetting, as well as for the control point, were marked off into 50-word units. The onset of the momentary forgetting was taken as the beginning of the pause before the usual indication of the onset of the forgetting (e.g., [pause] "I forgot what I was going to say"). We counted 1,100 words—550 before and 550 after the momentary forgetting point—and selected similar units before and after the control point. We also marked off eleven 50-word units before and after the real (momentary forgetting) and control (nonforgetting) points. The time interval for 550 words was approximately 6 minutes. The decision to choose approximately 12 minutes of time to investigate the factors associated with momentary forgetting was arbitrary. Because we could not be sure where "the action" was, we felt it necessary to sample what appeared to be a rather large section of the immediate context of instances of momentary forgetting.

The tape recordings of therapy sessions were transcribed with great care. Two people independently listened to each 1,100-word segment. The final transcripts were an accurate record of what the patients had said, exactly as they said it, including all the slips, pauses, mispronunciations, and all nonword expressions. Because our procedures and results are easier to follow when verbatim examples are examined, we have included as specimens three extensive examples from sessions with Mr. John Dannon in the Appendix to this chapter.

METHODS FOR UNDERSTANDING THE PATIENTS' MOMENTARY FORGETTING

Method 1: Observing the Context Naturalistically

Evaluating the Fit of Each Instance of Forgetting to an Ideal Form

Naturalistic observation yields a sample of instances that vary in form. It is necessary to pick out those that fit most closely to the definition of the phenomenon to be studied. Fortunately, the task is eased because momentary forgetting tends to occur in stereotypic form: The patient typically pauses at the moment of forgetting and explains, "I just had a thought which I was about to tell but I lost it." For such an instance to be included in the sample, two criteria had to be met. First, there must have been evidence that the thought was in awareness before it was forgotten; the more fully the thought was in awareness before the forgetting, the better the fit between the instance and the concept of momentary forgetting. The second criterion concerns the suddenness of the loss of the thought; the more sudden the loss, the more likely the speaker had been fully and faithfully reporting the thoughts before the forgetting, and, therefore, the better the fit between the instance and the concept.

For the new sample, I and three other judges selected instances of momentary forgetting. Each judge then independently rated on 5-point scales how well each instance met each of the two criteria for momentary forgetting. Similarly, the judges rated other variables that might be related to the goodness of fit: the degree to which the forgotten thoughts were subsequently recovered, the amount of cognitive disturbance associated with the forgetting, the amount of external distraction present during the forgetting episode, and the degree to which the therapist promoted recall. The judges showed high levels of agreement for goodness of fit; the range of correlations among the judges' ratings was .63 to .87. As expected, ratings of the two components of the definition of goodness of fit that were included as criteria in its definition (clarity of thought prior to forgetting and suddenness of the forgetting) correlated well with ratings of overall goodness of fit (.59). Although recovery of the thought was not one of the criteria for momentary forgetting, the ratings of degree of recovery turned out to be substantially correlated with goodness of fit (.64, $p < .001$).

Frequency of Symptom Occurrence

The majority of the patients in the pilot sample experienced momentary forgetting during the course of psychotherapy (Luborsky, 1964, 1967). Of 19 patients studied, 15 produced one or more instances of momentary forgetting.

The enlarged new sample of 17 patients consisted only of patients who had one or more forgettings tape-recorded. In this sample we observed 2,826 sessions and found 46 instances of forgetting, a mean rate of .027, which is more than 2 per 100 sessions.

Momentary forgetting happens to most people during therapy, even though it is an infrequent phenomenon. In different samples the incidence of momentary forgetting differs; the differences in incidence may be due to differences in therapist or patient variables. We do not know what factors distinguish the minority who do not produce momentary forgetting from the majority who do. We do know that the rate of forgetting within our sample was not related to health-sickness ratings (see Table 1).

TABLE 1
A Summary of Momentary Forgettings in the Enlarged New Sample

Patient	Age	# of sessions observed	Instances of forgetting observed	# of recovered thoughts	HSRS score	Rate (instances /session)
1 Mr. PG	20	15	2	1	60	.13
2 Mr. Berger[a]	29	193	4	0	55	.02
3 Ms. CG	23	230	2	2	70	.01
4 Ms. Francis	39	176	3	3	60	.02
5 Ms. GH	27	146	2	0	65	.01
6 Mr. MH	26	117	2	2	65	.02
7 Ms. JP	23	205	2	1	68	.01
8 Mr. JC	26	194	2	2	50	.01
9 Ms. SE	19	68	2	1	55	.03
10 Ms. RJM	29	66	2	1	75	.03
11 Mr. AB	26	179	2	1	64	.01
12 Ms. MS	30	61	1	1	70	.02
13 Mr. Q	24	225	1	1	65	.00
14 Mr. TRK	35	31	1	1	75	.03
15 Mr. Dannon	28	259	3	3	70	.01
16 Mr. WS	24	365	2	1	68	.01
17 Ms. Apfel	31	296	13	8	58	.04
Total	—	2,826	46	29	1093	.47
Mean	27	166.2	—	—	64.3	.027

Note. HSRS = Health-Sickness Rating Scale judged after the initial point when the patient began treatment.
[a]The names spelled out are those of the only patients described in the text.

Frequency of Recovery of Forgotten Thoughts

Two judges rated the degree to which patients recovered their for-gotten thoughts. Typically, the judges relied directly on what the patients said about their thoughts. For example, patients usually remarked when they successfully recovered their thoughts and made comments about the extent to which the recoveries were complete and exact. The reliability of the pooled ratings of the two judges was .94. The forgotten thoughts were observed to be recovered in 63% of the instances (29 out of 46) in the enlarged new sample; this figure compares well with the 74% frequency of recovery obtained in the pilot sample.

Certainty and Abstraction in Recovering Thoughts

Inspection of patients' transcripts in the pilot sample had revealed that there was a considerable range of certainty that the recovered thoughts matched the momentarily forgotten thoughts. Sometimes the patient was uncertain about the match of the lost and recovered thoughts, but sometimes the patient claimed with certainty that the exact forgotten thought had been recovered. At times, the uncertainty about the recovered thought was so great that neither the patient nor the therapist could discern whether, in fact, a particular thought was actually the forgotten one. These uncertainties resemble the range of uncertainties expressed in recalling dreams.

Some of the recovered thoughts appeared to be high-level abstractions from the presumably more specific thoughts that had been forgotten. This abstract quality of some recovered thoughts suggested that they were often not exactly the thoughts that had been forgotten but were derivatives of them. The variations in certainty about the exactness of the recovery and occasional abstractness of recovered thoughts might reflect the operation of a defensive process or the fact that the thoughts were difficult to catch due to attentional overload.

Time Intervals Between Forgotten and Recovered Thoughts

In the pilot sample, the therapist routinely made an estimate of the elapsed time between the onset of momentary forgetting and the recovery of forgotten thoughts. The range of recovery times was estimated to vary from 5 to 70 seconds, with a mean estimated interval of about 20 seconds.

For the enlarged new sample, the intervals between the onset of the forgetting and the recovery of the forgotten thoughts were timed from the tape recordings of the therapy sessions. The range of recovery intervals varied from 7 to 210 seconds, with a mean of 57 seconds and a median of 26.5 seconds. Thus, the majority of recoveries of momentarily forgotten thoughts occurred within one half of a minute after the forgetting. After this short period, explicitly labeled recoveries of forgotten thoughts were very unlikely.

External Distraction and the Genuineness of the Symptom

There is little support for the idea that momentary forgetting is due to the disruptive effects of external distraction; very few of the instances studied showed evident external distraction before the momentary forgetting. The paucity of evidence for the role of external distraction in producing momentary forgetting reinforces our view that the determining processes are largely internal to the patient. The evidence for this conclusion came from these observations: Two judges read the transcripts and rated on a 5-point scale the extent to which any external distraction occurred during the real and control segments. The reliability of their pooled ratings was .77. External distraction was correlated neither with the overall goodness-of-fit rating of the forgetting (.25), nor with the degree of recovery of the forgotten thoughts (.17). The average rating of external distraction for all instances was quite low ($M = 1.8$). In only 7 of the 31 instances was there any evidence for the presence of external distraction, and these 7 instances received only moderate ratings.

Does momentary forgetting really occur, or is the patient telling an untruth—is it really a conscious experience in which the patient says that a thought is forgotten, and acts as though it is forgotten, but in fact remains aware continuously of the forgotten thought? Even such a far-out alternative hypothesis as this needs to be entertained by any properly relentless researcher in this area. But there is no evidence to support this hypothesis; in fact, there is strong circumstantial evidence against it. Among the many patients with instances of reported forgetting who have been studied over the last 25 years, not one has ever intimated in any way that a forgetting experience was voluntary and not a true account of the forgetting. Nor has there ever been an instance in which a patient, thinking back over the phenomenon immediately after it occurred or later, has recanted and confessed that it was anything other than the experience of an intrusive gap in recalling the thoughts that had just occurred. On this issue, the patient's own experience is unquestionably uniform.

Method 2: Rating Variables in Symptom Versus Control Contexts

In the pilot sample, the most discriminating variables for reals versus controls (from most to least according to size of the t value) were new attitude or behavior, difficulty with attention, guilt, lack of control and competence, and oedipal conflict (Luborsky, 1967). These findings were based on the two- or three-sentence contexts immediately adjacent to the momentary forgetting or matched control contexts. A similar analysis was performed for recovered thoughts versus control thoughts. The discriminating variables were approximately the same, with the addition of a high level of abstraction, observation about oneself, references to an important relationship, and elated mood.

In the new sample of 10 patients, the most discriminating rated variables (Luborsky, 1973) were Involvement with Therapist and Helplessness.

Because forgetting occurs in the presence of the therapist, the forgetting may indicate a patient's compunction about saying or thinking something in his or her presence. As the involvement in the relationship with the therapist changes, so also may the frequency of forgetting change. Therefore, we had two judges rate the variable Involvement with Therapist for six 50-word units before momentary forgetting. The reliability of these ratings had been shown to be high in chapter 3. As is seen in Figure 1, there is a steep increase in ratings of Involvement with Therapist around 150 words before instances of forgetting.

We showed this effect in a striking way in the intensive single-case analysis (Luborsky & Mintz, 1974; see also chap. 3) of Ms. Apfel. For

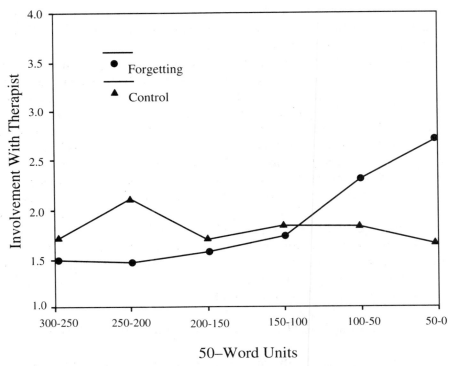

Figure 1. Ratings of Involvement with Therapist before momentary forgetting in 50-word units of patients' speech (means for 10 patients in the new sample).

example, the patient revealed in Session 36 that her forgotten thought was, "it struck me that you weren't really listening." This thought reflects a high degree of involvement in the relationship with the therapist around the idea that the therapist would reject her and show it by inattention.

Momentary forgetting is also temporally associated with increased explicit References to Therapist (as measured by counting such references) before the forgetting occurs (see Figure 2). Furthermore, these results imply that it is not just the content of what is being talked about but also the heightened involvement in the relationship at the moment that may set off momentary forgetting. Therefore, what has been noted for some psychophysiological functions may also be true for this memory phenomenon: It is not only the psychological content itself that is an important determinant of a psychophysiological change (such as in diastolic blood pressure; see Williams, Kimball, & Williard, 1972), but also the direction of attention and the amount of interpersonal interaction during an interview (Hardyck, Singer, & Harris, 1962; Singer, 1967, 1974).

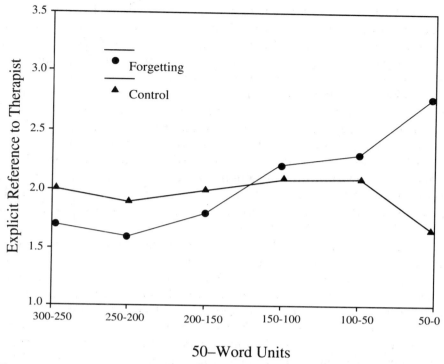

Figure 2. Explicit Reference to Therapist before momentary forgetting in 50-word units of patients' speech (means for 10 patients in the new sample).

Method 3: Scoring Variables

Cognitive Disturbance

Because momentary forgetting is just one of many types of cognitive disturbances, we decided to examine whether the onset of momentary forgetting was associated with other types of disturbances. A scale was constructed (Luborsky, 1966) to measure the frequency of occurrence of three main types of dysfunctions: disturbances in the recall of memories, disturbances in the certainty of thoughts, and disturbances in the ability to express thoughts clearly. Because difficulties in recall are far less common than the other two types of disturbances, the scores on the scale are primarily composed of the second and third types of cognitive disturbance. The scoring manual lists 26 subtypes of such disturbances, as was noted in chapter 3. Each 50-word unit of the symptom and control segments was scored for degree of cognitive disturbances by two judges independently. The reliability of these judgments was high, ranging from 71% to 84% agreement, with an overall figure of 78%. Almost all of the disagreement occurred when one judge noted an item and the other judge missed it. Cognitive disturbance scores for real and control instances, taken from the eleven 50-word units before and after the momentary forgetting points, were compared in a repeated-measures analysis of variance. The main effect of groups (real vs. control) was not significant.

Because the effects on cognitive disturbances might be more proximal to the forgetting, the three 50-word units before and after real and control instances of forgetting were explored more intensively. An analysis of variance, for Real Versus Control × Before Versus After × Units with repeated measures on the last factor, revealed no significant main effects. Importantly, however, the interaction between real and control groups and before versus after forgetting approached significance, $F(1, 60) = 3.14$, $p < .08$; and the interaction between groups and units was clearly significant, $F(2, 120) = 3.88$, $p < .025$.

Our main expectation was that the immediate onset conditions were crucial and that cognitive disturbance would increase just before forgetting. In fact, the interaction between groups and the factor of before versus after forgetting appeared primarily to be due to differences between the groups *before* instances of momentary forgetting (see Figure 3). This impression was supported by the results of a repeated-measures analysis of variance for the scores of real and control groups for the three units before forgetting. The effects of groups closely approached significance, $F(1, 60) = 3.80$, $p < .06$, and the interaction between groups and units was clearly significant, $F(2, 120) = 3.38$, $p < .05$.

Of the three types of cognitive disturbance in the scale, only scores for certainty and clarity were examined in these analyses, and these two subscales of cognitive disturbances were found to be uncorrelated. But both types of disturbance tended to increase before real instances of forgetting, as was shown by comparisons of real and control instances of momentary forgetting for scores on the two subscales.

Thus, momentary forgetting is temporally associated with other cognitive disturbances, particularly in the 150-word unit prior to the forgetting (about one to 2 min) and especially in the 50 words before momentary forgetting. Prior to forgetting, patients demonstrated greater uncertainty about their thoughts and greater disturbance in clearly expressing their thoughts. This indicates, of course, that the designation *momentary* for this type of forgetting is not entirely apt, because some of the process clearly begins more than momentarily before the forgetting.

The Relation Between Goodness of Fit and Cognitive Disturbance

It might be expected that those instances that were judged to best fit the concept of momentary forgetting should most clearly show the relation between momentary forgetting and other types of cognitive disturbance. However, our working definition of ideal instances of momentary forgetting

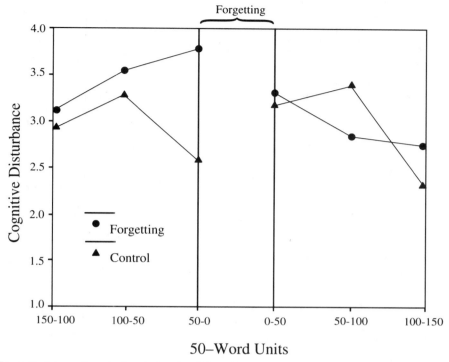

Figure 3. Interactions between levels of Cognitive Disturbance before and after momentary forgetting versus in control instances (means for 10 patients in the new sample).

posits that the clearer the person has the to-be-forgotten thought in mind, the better the instance is as an example of the phenomenon. Thus, there is some tension between our definition and the empirical findings: We found that momentary forgetting is associated in general with more unclarity of expression of the thoughts prior to the forgetting, as measured by the cognitive disturbance scale.

Instances of momentary forgetting were divided into two groups—those above ($n = 15$) and those below ($n = 15$) the median of mean ratings of overall goodness of fit to the ideal form. A repeated-measures analysis of variance on cognitive disturbance scores for the three 50-word units before and after forgetting (Good Vs. Poor Fit × Before Vs. After Forgetting × Units) revealed that instances judged to have poor fit with the ideal form concept of momentary forgetting showed increased cognitive disturbance scores as forgetting approached, whereas instances judged to have good fit did not change in cognitive disturbance scores.

Thus, differences in the rated quality of goodness of fit of each instance of momentary forgetting among those accepted into the sample had a negative predictive power in relation to levels of cognitive disturbance prior to forgetting. The poorer-quality instances showed greater levels of cognitive disturbance before forgetting. Two points should be made in reference to this result. First, the ratings of goodness of fit were only distinctions among instances of the phenomenon, all of which were considered to be acceptable examples. Second, our working definition of an ideal instance of momentary forgetting was arbitrary. In fact, from these findings we might think of the lack of clarity of the thought as another impact of the high cognitive disturbance that our previous findings indicated was associated with the forgetting. In essence, the assumption may be inappropriate that the clarity of the thought that is to be forgotten would be or should be a criterion of an ideal instance of momentary forgetting.

The Relation Between Recovered Thoughts and Cognitive Disturbance

Ratings of the degree to which momentarily forgotten thoughts were recovered were bimodally distributed in the enlarged new sample, permitting instances of momentary forgetting to be divided into recovered and nonrecovered groups. The nonrecovery group ($n = 10$) comprised instances of forgetting that received mean ratings of 2 or below on a 5-point scale, and the recovery group ($n = 21$) comprised instances of forgetting that received mean ratings of 4 or above (that is, 31 of the 46 instances met these cutoffs).

A repeated-measures analysis of variance (Recovered Vs. Nonrecovered Groups × Before Vs. After Forgetting × Units) on cognitive disturbance scores for the three units before and after forgetting showed a significant main effect for recovery groups ($F (1, 29) = 4.51$, $p < .05$). As is seen in Figure 4, the cognitive disturbance scores for the group that was judged not to have recovered momentarily forgotten thoughts were higher before and after forgetting. This suggests that greater cognitive disturbance is associated with the nonrecovery of momentarily forgotten thoughts.

This finding indicates that levels of cognitive disturbance are associated not only with the occurrence of momentary forgetting but also with the recovery or nonrecovery of momentarily forgotten thoughts. The implication is that where there is a high level of cognitive disturbance, there will be interference in the underlying process involved in retaining thoughts.

Speech Disturbance

Mahl (1956) presented as a measure of anxiety a scale for measuring the frequency of disruptions in speech. The scale is composed of seven types of speech disruptions: sentence correction, incomplete sentences, word repetition, stuttering, intruding incoherent sounds, slips of the tongue, and omission of words or parts of words. Each 50-word unit of real and control segments was scored for the amount of speech disturbance in

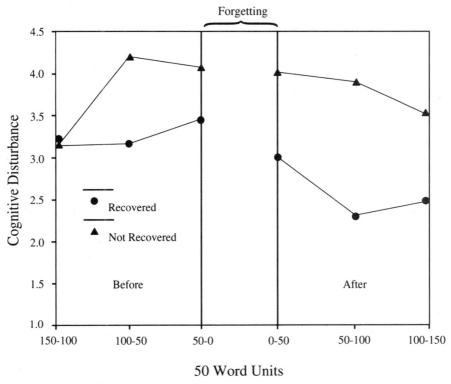

Figure 4. Interactions between recovered versus nonrecovered momentary forgetting and before versus after forgetting, on cognitive disturbance (means for 17 patients in the new enlarged sample).

the new enlarged sample by only one judge (because of the high reliability of the scale as reported by Mahl).

Although none of the seven categories of the speech disturbance scale overlaps in content with the categories of the cognitive disturbance scale, moderate correlations were expected between the two scales because of similarities in concept. But in the enlarged new sample the correlation of mean scores on the speech disturbance with those on the cognitive disturbance scales for the eleven 50-word units *prior to forgetting* for the total sample of real and control instances was only .17 ($p > .05$, n.s.); however, the correlation for scores *after forgetting* was $r = .40$, $p < .01$.

In order to examine the relationships among cognitive disturbance, speech disturbance, and momentary forgetting, the analyses already reported on cognitive disturbance scores were repeated for speech disturbance scores. Repeated-measures analyses of variance showed no significant main effects or interactions for real versus control instances of forgetting on speech disturbance scores (either 11 or 3 units before and after forgetting).

When real instances of forgetting were grouped by ratings of goodness of fit or by ratings of recovery of forgotten thoughts, no significant main effects of group and no significant interactions with the factor of group were found. It appeared that momentary forgetting and speech disturbance scores were not related. Thus, the Mahl (1956) speech disturbances scale that was reported to measure anxiety did not show any significant relation to momentary forgetting. If the scale actually measures anxiety, we could conclude that variations in levels of anxiety are not related to the occurrence of momentary forgetting.

In the pilot sample, the number of references to important relationships was rated for the recovered thoughts after sessions with momentary forgetting and for comparison sentences in control sessions. It was found that references to important relationships were more prevalent in the recovered thoughts than in comparison sentences. The important relationships generally included father, mother, spouse, and male or female friend.

Time Intervals Between Symptom and Variables

A note needs to be added now about the time intervals for the buildup and decline of the immediate context conditions for momentary forgetting. My colleagues and I had examined an immediate context of 5 or 6 min both before and after the forgetting, which turned out to be more than enough time to catch some of the action of the associated conditions. In fact, the shape of the time curves is a peak that gets launched only about 200 words before (about 2 min) for Cognitive Disturbance and 150 words before for Involvement with Therapist. The curves achieve their maximum height at the moment of forgetting, and they decline afterward in about the same time to about their original level—the increase accelerates as it nears the symptom onset, and after that point it begins to subside in reciprocal symmetry to its ascending phase. For those qualities that built up before momentary forgetting, the increase tended to be greater the nearer it came to the onset.

The interval for the most related variables (for example, Cognitive Disturbance, Involvement with Therapist, and Reference to Therapist) was 1 to 2 min before the momentary forgetting. Those qualities that built up before the momentary forgetting tended to decline within 1 to 2 min after the episode (Luborsky, 1973; Luborsky & Mintz, 1974). As was mentioned earlier, the process underlying momentary forgetting is not really momentary—it requires a minute or two to build up and a comparable time to decline.

The Recurrent Content of Recovered Thoughts

If a specific content is recurrently forgotten, it is then likely that the content has a specific meaning for the patient. It would also suggest that the meaning of the topic to the patient rather than an external distraction was involved in the forgetting.

An analysis of the consistency of recovered forgettings has never been done in a properly controlled fashion. When it was first tried (Luborsky, 1967) on a pilot sample of patients, the data were the therapist's notes, not recordings. In that study, the comparison was between the recovered thoughts and control thoughts, with the main discriminating variables noted earlier (see p. 69).

About 1978, I began studies of the temporal consistency of the content of the recovered forgotten thoughts within the cases in the new sample of 17 patients. To study consistency requires a series of instances; I settled on a minimum of three or more instances of momentary forgetting per patient. Only 4 of the 17 cases in the new sample qualified, and 1 of these had a severe limitation: There were no recoveries of the forgotten thoughts. The four patients (with the number of forgettings in parentheses) are as follows: Ms. Apfel (13), Mr. Dannon (3), Mr. Berger (4, but no recoveries), and Ms. Francis (3). Table 2 describes the content and rate of occurrence for their recovered thoughts.

For the sake of brevity, Mr. Dannon's three momentary forgettings are excerpted in the Appendix to this chapter. The instances in which Mr. Dannon recovered his thoughts, which are summarized in Table 3, suggest as a recurrent theme the imminence of the outbreak of anger at the therapist. This theme is absent from the segments from three control sessions with the same patient, that is, sessions with no forgettings (see Table 4). Another independent judge was given these six segments, in no special order, to rate a set of variables. His ratings on a 5-point scale clearly confirmed the presence of this core content of anger (mean 3.5) and clearly indicated that the control sessions from the same patient did not have it (M = 1).

TABLE 2
Recurrence of Content in the Recovered Thoughts of Four Patients in the New Enlarged Sample

Patient	Content of recovered thought	Rate of recurrence
Ms. Apfel	Fear of being rejected	high
Mr. Dannon	Fear of expressing anger	high
Mr. Berger	Fear of expressing anger[a]	high
Ms. Francis	Fear of expressing indulgence in forbidden gratification	moderate

[a]Because the forgetting was not recovered, this is an inference based on the immediate context.

TABLE 3
Mr. Dannon: Excerpts of Three Recovered Forgettings

Session 12	Session 68	Session 137
Oh! I began having—resentment towards you [2 s] (wheezes) having resentment, feeling resentment [3 s] and I had the feeling although there a—I didn't have, [2 s] I was very much aware at the time that there were, there was no-nothing you had done. [2.5 s] but I had the feeling [3 s] again that if I let loose [4 s] whatever there is inside me, here we go again, [2 s] I could almost kill you with my words, [2 s] that you couldn't stand the onslaught. [6 s]	It had something to do with letting go, that if I lower my guard [4 s] you will penetrate me, [2 s] rip me to pieces, tear me apart. [13 s] You're a nice guy. You wouldn't do that. [10 s] Again I have thought of—biting your genitals off.—It's a—terrible thought—being on guard here. [4 s] It's almost as if my mind becomes a sphincter and I've got to—tightly control that (hesitates) so that—you can't get in and all this shit can't come out. [2 s] It was that thought. [7.5 s]	Oh! And, and, what investments can you possibly have in my getting better. No, that isn't what I was g- [7.5 s]: If you don't want me to get better I'm pissed off and if you do I'm pissed off. [2 s] I if you don't, you don't care and if you do, you want something from me. [15 s]

My conclusion is that there is a patient-specific content in the recovered momentary forgettings for Mr. Dannon, which appears to be the fear of expressing anger toward the therapist and receiving anger from the therapist. The anger may well be about feeling dominated by the therapist. The fact that this content is evident in all three of the recovered forgettings suggests that it may play a part in instigating the forgetting. The associated conditions that are discovered in the context of the forgetting, which are analyzed in the next section, should reveal how much of a part it plays.

Method 4: Evaluating the Broad Background Context in Whole Sessions

Location of Symptom Occurrences

Across entire treatments, the sessions were divided into units of 10% of the sessions (from the new sample $N = 10$ patients with 25 instances). More momentary forgettings occurred at the beginning of treatment, with a decrease in frequency as treatment proceeded and an increase again in

TABLE 4
Mr. Dannon: Excerpts of Three Controls Segments With No Forgetting

Session 13	Session 70	Session 129
I want to smoke again. (hesitates) I'm getting anxious. I have another thought. Oh h- (something bangs) [10 s] I can't. I just can't. I'm sorry. [18 s] I also had the f-the fantasy last night—of being in bed with Phyllis, this girl that—I'm taking out this Friday. [7 s] In a way last night it was just good being in bed with somebody; I didn't care who. There was another person in bed with me. (hesitates)	Something has to happen. [4.5 s] And again usually my-my fantasies are homosexual I don't consciously try to control them [2 s] and all I could think of was screwing the girl I'm taking out tomorrow night. [2 s] Of entering her fully erect pushing her lips—aside—and I suppose there's a reason for my-using that word. [3 s] And the thought came along now she's gonna suck me with her vagina [2 s] but that I wouldn't lose it—and that I would be erect and be able to take my time and really—get her so hot—and she could have such a glorious orgasm and it would be so great—it was a nice fantasy. [6 s]	I have a, the analysis is like coming off-filling the—I don't even know what I'm saying. [T: It's like what?] Coming off. Like ejaculating [3 s] I don't know why I said that. I have no idea why. [3 s] but the fantasy was that it's really ejaculating. — Whole room, boy that's pretty grandiose.—This whole room—filled with semen. (Sharp intake of breath) Oh! (breathes out) [15.5 s]

the latter part of treatment. The distribution of momentary forgetting within sessions was observed in 10 units of 5 minutes each across the 50-minute therapy sessions. Forgettings were most likely to occur in the first 20 minutes or last 15 minutes of the session.

Thus, this distribution of forgetting both across the treatments and within sessions suggests that the symptom's appearance is a function of the patient's sense of security about the relationship with the therapist. At the beginning and ending of the treatment and of the session, there may be higher levels of insecurity about the relationship. If this supposition is correct, the same pattern of increased symptom appearance should be found around other kinds of interruptions of the treatment. It is of interest that other types of recurrent symptoms show a similar distribution during psychotherapy—for example, the report of stomach pain in a stomach ulcer patient (see chap. 7), the appearance of cluster headaches (Luborsky &

Auerbach, 1969), and absence epilepsy (petit mal) attacks (Luborsky et al., 1975).

Similarly, the distribution of occurrences of momentary forgetting follows a pattern that is familiar for certain psychophysiological measurements; that is, there is a decline during sessions and across the series of sessions. For example, decline effects for almost all patients have been reported for repeated measures of blood pressure (Luborsky, Crits-Christoph, et al., 1982), and such a decline is typically attributed to initially greater insecurity followed by habituation to the situation.

Ratings of Whole Sessions

Some of the factors conducive to momentary forgetting may also be evident in the larger context of the complete therapy session rather than just in the context immediate to the momentary forgetting that we have taken in some studies to be 6 minutes before and 6 minutes after the forgetting. When the partial-session context was first studied systematically with Ms. Apfel (Luborsky & Mintz, 1974), by means of Dahl's (1972) factor scores of word categories, these scores did not discriminate between symptom versus control sessions. However, in studies of symptoms other than momentary forgetting, the entire session usually contained content similar to that of the immediate context (Luborsky & Auerbach, 1969).

At the end of every session, I completed a form containing forty 5-point scales that described aspects of the whole session for the nine patients in the new enlarged sample that I treated. The variables included those from the pilot study as well as from the study of ratings of tape-recorded sessions (Auerbach & Luborsky, 1968). The principal limit of this method is that of estimating the single therapist-as-judge's reliability. However, on many of these same variables, this judge showed high agreement with other judges (e.g., Auerbach & Luborsky, 1968). Because all the sessions were tape-recorded, I hope that the results will yield leads to be tested further by independent judges who will use the same tapes and transcripts on which to base their judgments. One other limit may influence the results: All the momentary forgetting sessions were included on the basis of a notation by the therapist of the presence of momentary forgetting, but the *quality* (that is, the degree of fit to an ideal form) of each instance of momentary forgetting was not rechecked by relistening to the tape recording.

Each real momentary forgetting session was paired with two to four control nonforgetting sessions. For each variable, the significance of differences between mean ratings for the real versus the control sessions was tested. This was done for both the group of nine patients as a whole and each individual patient. The across-patient analyses yielded findings similar to those of the pilot study (Luborsky, 1964, 1967). Those variables that significantly discriminated the forgetting from the control sessions were Attention Difficulties ($p < .001$), Elation ($p < .005$), and New Attitude or Behavior ($p < .05$).

The analyses were also repeated for each patient separately. New Attitude or Behavior was significantly discriminating for three patients. Several other variables discriminated for no more than two patients each: Elation, Separation, Anxiety, Receptiveness, Shame (less shame with the reals for two patients), Helplessness, Therapist's Warmth, and Therapist Responds Effectively. Several other variables were discriminating for only one patient. The variables that discriminated within each patient usually made instant clinical sense for that patient. As was reported before (Luborsky, 1967, 1970; Luborsky & Auerbach, 1969), the main themes of the momentary forgetting are recurrent for a particular patient and coincide with an important memory system for that patient. For one patient, the discriminating variables were Guilt and Shame. The points in the treatment at which he had been most upset were those in which he experienced guilt and shame, directly or indirectly, in relation to his father. Recurrently from the beginning to the end of the treatment, this theme was the most difficult for him to deal with and yet the most necessary to change. For another patient, Separation Anxiety and Helplessness were tremendously prominent; Separation Anxiety, which precipitated her into feelings of Helplessness, might be thought of as her presenting problem and as part of her core conflict. For still another patient, fears about homosexuality were part of the presenting problem and remained central throughout the treatment. Similar central theme statements can be made about some of the other patients.

The whole-sessions analyses turned up two main leads toward understanding the larger context in which momentary forgetting occurs. It was found that greater feelings of Elation and the expression of a New Attitude or Behavior characterized sessions in which momentary forgetting occurred. The presence of Elation further supports the concept that a changed state of consciousness is associated with the occurrence of momentary forgetting. The presence of increased cognitive disturbance also provides evidence for a changed state of consciousness. Possibly the expression of a New Attitude or Behavior is increased by the elated state, and this elated state may help the patient to venture a New Attitude or Behavior. In any case, the concept that a New Attitude or Behavior suggests is that the person is able to express a content that has been previously withheld. Furthermore, one might expect compensatory defensive processes, including momentary forgetting, to occur in sessions showing greater Elation and New Attitude or Behavior because of the greater venturing of new thoughts and a consequent concern about going too far. The concept of the emergence of previously withheld ideas or behavior is central to the thinking of the psychoanalytic research group of the Mount Zion Hospital, San Francisco (Horowitz, Sampson, Seigelman, Wolfson, & Weiss, 1975, as reviewed by Luborsky & Spence, 1978; Sampson, Weiss, Mlodnosky, & Hause, 1972).

Further work must be done using these two concepts in the studies of the immediate context of momentary forgetting. They were found to be present in the pilot sample but not studied further because the concept of a new attitude or behavior is a difficult one to apply—it requires a judge who is familiar with the entire treatment so the judge can decide whether a particular attitude or behavior is new or not.

Comparison of Two Grand Themes: The CCRT and the Symptom-Context Theme

A compelling observation drew our attention to the potential insights to be derived from comparing the content of the forgetting with the content of the CCRT (Luborsky, in press). We observed that the patient's Involvement with Therapist increased markedly during the period surrounding the momentary forgetting, as was shown most dramatically in the rise in the number of explicit References to Therapist. Furthermore, these references tended to occur during the telling, and sometimes even the enactment, of relationship episodes with the therapist, which often include the instances of forgetting.

The four patients listed earlier can serve as the basis for comparing the content of the forgetting with the CCRT because they had the highest frequency of forgetting in the new enlarged sample (See Table 1).

The first research step, as was reported earlier, was to have a judgment made of the content of the momentary forgettings, because the main themes of the momentary forgetting were recurrent for each patient and these main themes may be related to a central conflictual memory system for that patient. To explore this possibility, the next step was to compare the core content of each patient's forgetting with the CCRT formulation made by independent judges. The narratives that are commonly told during sessions are the primary data for the judgments because these narratives about relationship episodes (REs), are an especially fine source of information about relationship patterns. Each narrative contains a major other person (O) with whom the patient is interacting. The main other person most often is one of these: the patient's parents, siblings, friends and lovers, bosses, or the therapist.

The CCRT scoring procedure begins with a judge going through the sessions and locating reasonably complete narratives. The judge then reads the transcript of the session and identifies in each narrative the patient's wishes, needs, and intentions toward the main other person (W), the responses from the main other person (RO), and the responses of self (RS).

The combination of the most frequent of each of these components constitutes the CCRT.

The steps in the method are like the informal inference sequence used by many clinicians in formulating the transference pattern (Luborsky, Crits-Christoph, & Mellon, 1986). The judge follows these two precise steps:

Step 1. Score wishes (W) and responses (RO, RS) in each relationship episode (RE).

Step 2. Count these, review, and state in a CCRT format.

Then the operation is repeated, and the judge recounts and reformulates (Steps 1′ and 2′).

For the present study, the CCRT judges also scored the session after omitting the RE containing the forgetting. The yield from this comparison of the forgetting theme and CCRT will be illustrated for Ms. Apfel and Mr. Dannon.

Ms. Rachael Apfel. The ratings for Ms. Apfel show that the recovered forgotten thoughts contain a highly recurrent content: various versions of the idea of being rejected (as was detailed in chap. 3). The rejection was often experienced as coming from the therapist, sometimes as coming from mother, sister, or friends. In 9 of the 13 instances, the forgotten thoughts were recovered; all of them contained the idea of being rejected by someone.

Because this patient had two different analysts in succession, another very special data analysis was tried: a comparison of the four recovered forgettings for analyst A with the five recovered forgettings for analyst B. The fact that the two analysts were very different people and one was a man and the other a woman, could have made an important difference in the content of the recovered forgettings, but it did not. Differences between the analysts were not sufficient to alter the major recurrent contents of the patient's momentary forgetting; obviously some of patient's characteristics remained unchanged by differences in the therapist's personality or therapeutic style.

It should be noted that the scale used for measuring rejection included a variety of evidence of the patient's experience of being rejected or of not being rejected. The common element in the rejection scale is the presence of the idea of being rejected, whether it is negative (rejection) or positive (avoiding rejection). Two of the instances were about the avoidance of rejection, and both of these occurred with analyst B, which suggests that the relationship with her was somewhat more positive than the one with analyst A.

Ms. Apfel's thoughts in all three time segments reflect a progression of closely associated thoughts rather than an obvious disjunction, even including the thoughts that comprise the forgetting: rejection content is in the thoughts before forgetting, in the forgetting thought, and in the thoughts after forgetting. There are some differences in quantity of some kinds of thoughts, but the core qualities of the content remain similar. Perhaps in some instances, however, the forgotten thought that is recovered might not have been exactly the thought was forgotten, but rather a more abstract version of it.

Each of the sessions in which the forgetting occurred was analyzed for the CCRT by two independent judges. To help make more clear how the CCRT is derived, Figure 5 depicts an abbreviated list of the REs in Session 36 in the order they were told in the session. The CCRT in the

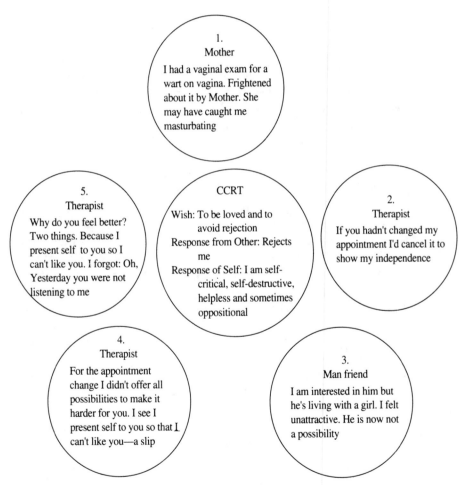

Figure 5. CCRT and relationship episodes from Ms. Apfel, Session 36.

center circle reflects the most repeated wishes, responses from others, and responses of the self in the five episodes in the session (and the CCRT is much the same in the other two sessions). The following is the CCRT as judged by two judges:

W: I wish to be loved and positively responded to and to avoid rejection

RO: Rejects and dominates me

RS: I am self-critical, self-destructive, helpless, and sometimes oppositional (e.g., "I'd cancel. . . .")

Inspection of the core content of what has been forgotten alongside of the CCRT indicates that what is forgotten is the most frequent version of the RO: "rejects me."

Mr. John Dannon. Mr. Dannon started psychoanalysis at age 28, while he was in training as a graduate student in one of the mental health professions. He was bi-sexual, and his goal was to be able to remain consistently heterosexual. He was treated by an experienced analyst who, after the treatment, lent us a sample of sessions in which we found the three instances reported in Table 3. All three contain a fear of expressing anger toward the therapist. In Session 12, it is, "Oh, I began having resentment toward you. If I let loose I could almost kill you with my words." In Session 68, it is, "Oh, it had something to do with letting go. I've got to control so you can't get in and this shit can't come out." In Session 137: "Oh, I'm pissed if you do and pissed if you don't"; that is, show interest in my getting better. The three control (nonforgetting) segments (see Table 4) do not contain this content; instead the content happens to be mainly sexual.

The CCRT formulation made by two independent judges from the three sessions (see the abbreviated REs in Figures 6 and 7) is as follows:

W_1: I wish to not be dominated

W_2: I wish to be close with someone

RO: Dominates and rejects

RS: Submissive, impotent, manipulated, frightened, angry

The core content of the forgotten thoughts, the imminence of anger at the therapist, is contained in the responses of self in the CCRT. This similarity may be based partly on the patient's anger and partly on the high degree of fearfulness the patient has about responding with anger to the therapist.

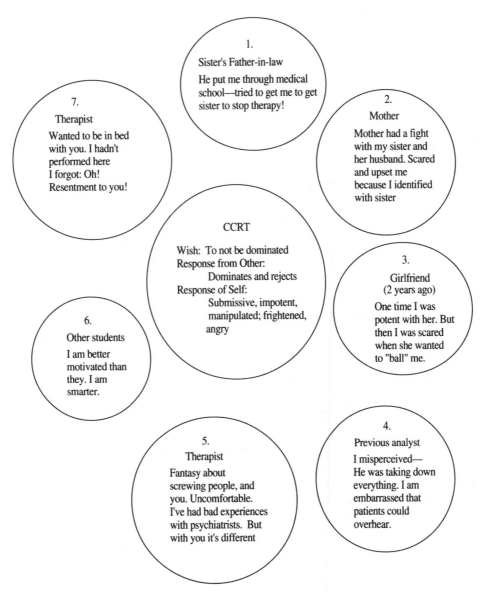

Figure 6. CCRT and relationship episodes from Mr. Dannon, Session 12.

CONDITIONS THAT PRECEDE MOMENTARY FORGETTING

Which Factors Precede Momentary Forgetting?

After all of the naturalistic observation based on old and new research, which significant factors were found to be related to the momentary

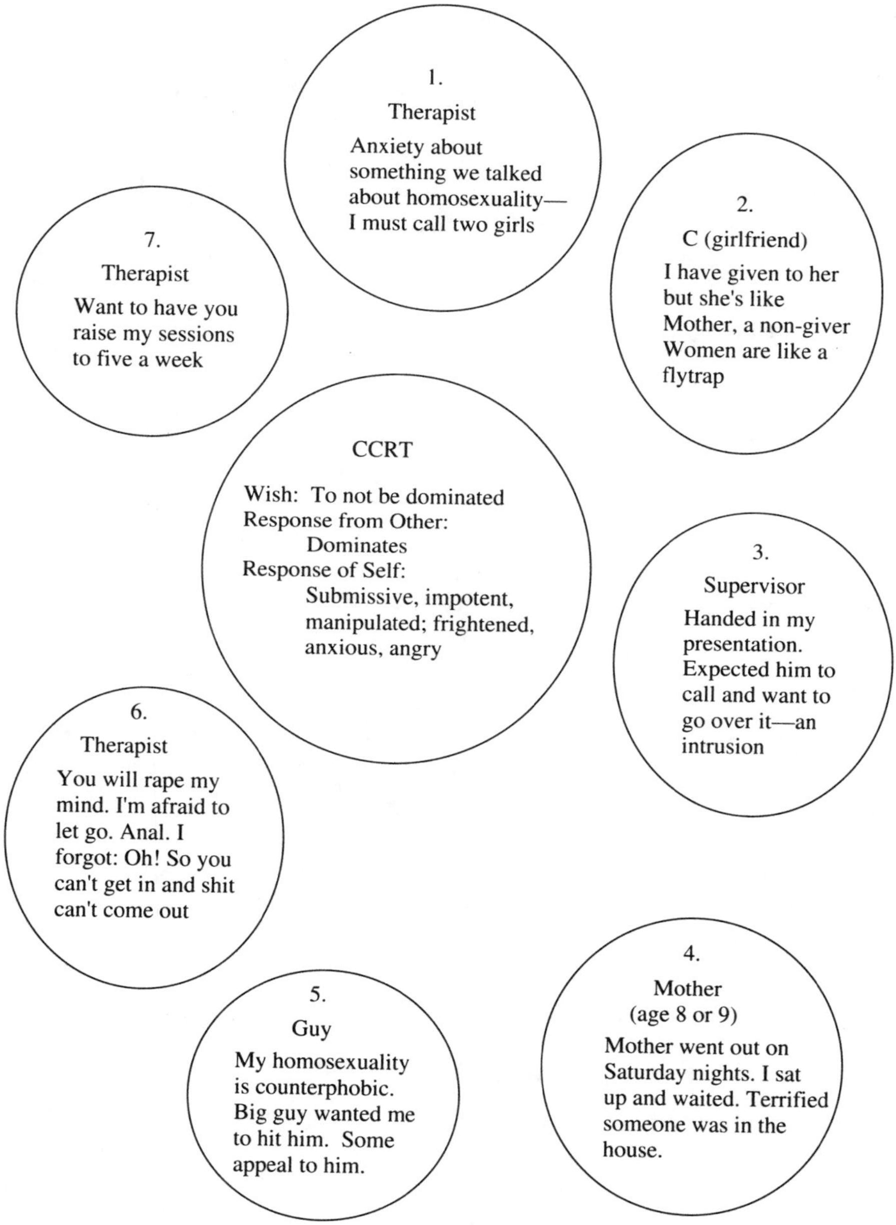
1.
Therapist
Anxiety about something we talked about homosexuality—I must call two girls
2.
C (girlfriend)
I have given to her but she's like Mother, a non-giver Women are like a flytrap
3.
Supervisor
Handed in my presentation. Expected him to call and want to go over it—an intrusion
4.
Mother
(age 8 or 9)
Mother went out on Saturday nights. I sat up and waited. Terrified someone was in the house.
5.
Guy
My homosexuality is counterphobic. Big guy wanted me to hit him. Some appeal to him.
6.
Therapist
You will rape my mind. I'm afraid to let go. Anal. I forgot: Oh! So you can't get in and shit can't come out
7.
Therapist
Want to have you raise my sessions to five a week
CCRT
Wish: To not be dominated
Response from Other:
Dominates
Response of Self:
Submissive, impotent, manipulated; frightened, anxious, angry

Figure 7. CCRT and relationship episodes from Mr. Dannon, Session 68.

forgetting? The varied observations we have made revealed three main classes of factors.

Factor 1: A Cognitively Disturbed State

Just before a momentary forgetting, there is an increase in cognitive disturbance. The types of cognitive disturbance that increase before forgetting involve uncertainty about thoughts and unclarity of expression. Individuals become more unclear in communicating their thoughts, and they make more qualifications about the content of their thinking before instances of momentary forgetting. Then, greater disturbances of this type are associated with reduced recovery of forgotten thoughts. But the level of anxiety, as measured by speech disturbance scores (Mahl, 1956), does not predict either forgetting or recovery of forgotten thoughts.

Factor 2: A Heightened Insecure Involvement With Therapist

Just before momentary forgetting, patients show a heightened insecure Involvement with Therapist as shown by ratings and by the fact that they make more explicit references to the therapist before instances of forgetting. The heightened Involvement with Therapist generally reflects feelings of insecurity about the relationship and possibly feelings of helplessness. For example, for the momentary forgetting in Session 36, Ms. Apfel explained that she had had the thought, "It struck me you weren't really listening."

Further evidence for the significance of this factor is given by data related to the temporal patterning of instances of momentary forgetting both within sessions and over the treatment. One might expect greater intensity of feelings of insecurity about the relationship with the therapist when the relationship is resumed or is temporarily broken off, that is, at the beginning and ending of sessions. It is at these points that the incidence of momentary forgetting is greatest. Over the course of the treatment, one might expect greater intensity of feelings of insecurity in the beginning phase. In fact, it is in the earlier stages of treatment that frequency of momentary forgetting is highest.

Factor 3: An Activated, Individually Specific CCRT

Around the moment of the forgetting, a specific CCRT is activated that reverberates in the relationship with the therapist. This theme differs among patients. For example, for Ms. Apfel, the expectation of rejection was associated with instances of momentary forgetting (see chap. 3); for Mr. Dannon, the theme was anger at the therapist or expectation of anger in return from the therapist. Content analysis indicates that, although the themes differ among patients, they are relatively consistent within patients.

In presenting these three factors, I am not claiming that they provide an exhaustive list of the conditions necessary and sufficient for the onset of momentary forgetting. It is quite conceivable, for instance, that all three factors may be present at a point in therapy, after which a symptom other than momentary forgetting may occur, or even no symptom at all. Examination of the conditions preceding other symptoms as well suggests that this is often the case (Luborsky & Auerbach, 1969; Luborsky et al., 1975; Luborsky et al., 1979). The list of factors explaining momentary forgetting was essentially derived from the variables that discriminated between momentary forgetting and control segments. The decisions to examine particular variables were determined by previous findings about the onset of symptoms and clinical intuitions about the nature of momentary forgetting. It is quite possible that other variables that have not yet been tested would reveal additional factors. Furthermore, our results so far do not include information about the independence of the factors that have been established. The factors may operate together. For example, a cognitively disturbed state (Factor 1) may result from a patient's heightened insecure involvement with a therapist (Factor 2) and may not independently contribute to momentary forgetting. In the next few sections, I will discuss how alternative methodologies may be valuable in exploring the independence of the factors as well as the question of whether momentary forgetting is motivated forgetting.

Why Is a Particular Thought Selected to Be Forgotten?

A theory about why a specific thought is selected to be forgotten may help in understanding the factors that influence forgetting. The particular thought that is forgotten is a derivative of a specific core relationship theme, as Factor 3 indicates. The themes or conflicts that patients present during momentary forgetting differ among patients but are consistent within patients. Over the course of treatment, patients show remarkable consistency in the themes or conflicts that emerge when they interact with other people (Luborsky, 1977; Luborsky & Crits-Christoph, 1990). Comparisons of the themes related to momentary forgetting with the CCRT yield striking congruence. It appears at the moment that patients generally demonstrate momentary forgetting of thoughts that are central to the core conflicts they have in their interpersonal relationships.

A related issue is whether the forgotten thought is a deviant version of the core theme or whether there is continuity in thought content before and during the forgetting. Inspection of the contexts of forgetting suggests that there is continuity in the stream of associations between what is said before the forgetting and what is recovered. There is no marked break or shift in topic. The lost thought appears to be a specification of the immediately prior-to-forgetting thought. It may have been selected for forgetting because it was experienced as a little more dangerous to think or express at the moment in the current relationship with the therapist than the prior thought.

Why Is a Particular Symptom Selected?

The conditions that precede the onset of momentary forgetting appear to have much in common with the conditions before the onset of other symptoms. Evidence for this view is derived from applying the symptom-context method in single case studies of patients. But unlike the across-group results for patients in the enlarged new sample, the common variable before symptom onset for single-case patients was the intensity of the patient's feelings of helplessness and hopelessness.

Given the premise that there is some uniformity in the factors that relate to the onset of diverse symptoms, what additional factors might determine a patient's selection of a symptom? I can only add some speculations. One, it is well known that people have different "preferred" symptoms. Two, with some somatic symptoms, such as petit mal attacks, genetic and constitutional factors may underlie the individual differences in choice of system. And, three, situational variables may also play a role in symptom choice.

The topic that is to be forgotten differs for each person. But there are common limits. It is doubtful that patients will forget their own names or even the names of their therapists—thoughts or concepts that are overlearned are naturally more difficult to forget (Neisser, 1967). Forgotten thoughts are more flimsy and fresher than thoughts that are overlearned, which may contribute to their susceptibility to momentary forgetting. Conversely, the thoughts that are momentarily forgotten during the course of therapy are threatening because they appear to be derivatives of, or are examples of, the patient's core interpersonal conflicts that are being reenacted at the moment with the therapist.

Why Is a Lost Thought Recovered?

To understand momentary forgetting, it may help to consider a related issue: the reason for recovery of momentarily forgotten thoughts. Because one of our assumptions is that the forgotten thoughts are potentially threatening, why should these thoughts not stay lost?

In tackling this issue, it should be kept in mind that not all lost thoughts are recovered. Nonrecovery is more likely to occur the higher the pre-forgetting level of cognitive disturbance. It may be that the interval between forgetting and recovery is a cooling off period and that the conditions that generate the forgetting began to subside in intensity, thereby promoting conditions that allow the recovery of the memories. In fact, following the forgetting, patients appear to become less acutely involved with the therapist. Not only may the conditions that have contributed to forgetting change, but the recovered thought may become more uncertain or less concrete than the original version and, therefore, less threatening.

What Are the Roles of Laboratory Versus Naturalistic Studies in Examining Momentary Forgetting?

The findings reported here help explain the factors that instigate momentary forgetting, but they do not fully confirm the conclusion that momentary forgetting is motivated forgetting. For instance, it could be that the activation in the relationship with the therapist (Factor 2) of a patient's specific hot theme (Factor 3), rather than instigating forgetting directly, establishes a distracted state or introduces attentional overload (Factor 1), and that this condition facilitates momentary forgetting. By this alternative view, the conditions prior to the forgetting increase the likelihood of forgetting, but not with the purpose of avoiding the hot theme.

In order to demonstrate that momentary forgetting is motivated, it is necessary to show that under the same conditions, individuals prefer the consequences of forgetting to those that would occur if forgetting did not take place and, furthermore, that the forgetting helps achieve those consequences (Irwin, 1971). Indeed, in order to firmly establish a motivational basis for momentary forgetting, it must be shown that when the contingencies between the gains (positive consequences of forgetting) and the forgetting behavior, and the contingencies between the negative consequences and nonforgetting behavior are reversed, the frequencies of both behaviors alter appropriately. The method of controlled naturalistic observation that we have employed has not settled some questions concerning the purposeful basis of forgetting.

Possibly, an experimental investigation of momentary forgetting might have added more knowledge on this issue. The huge literature on experimental studies on motivated forgetting has been reviewed elsewhere (Erdelyi, 1990; Holmes, 1974; Kline, 1972; Madison, 1961; Sears, 1943a, 1943b) and appears to continue to be pertinent. Its general conclusion was that the evidence in favor of the existence of motivated forgetting as derived from laboratory studies is equivocal at best, and mostly negative: "There is no consistent research evidence to support the hypothesis derived from the theory of repression" (Holmes, 1974, p. 649).

But against this conclusion it can be argued that laboratory investigators who have attempted to demonstrate the existence of motivated forgetting have used methodologies that were inherently inadequate for that purpose. Freud (1915/1957) had claimed that contents of consciousness that are repressed are highly individual and that repression itself is mobile, varying with the motivational concerns of the individual. In fact, the findings presented in this book indicate that the thoughts that are forgotten during the course of therapy refer to each patient's specific core relationship theme. With a few major exceptions (e.g., Sackeim & Gur, 1978; Shevrin et al., 1992; Shevrin et al., in press), experimental researchers on defensive phenomena have not attempted to relate manipulations of motivational circumstances to individual dynamics. The failure to establish suitable experimental analogies of clinical phenomena may have contributed to the failure to confirm predictions derived from theories based on such phenomena. Typically, researchers concerned with motivational control of behavior attempt to demonstrate behavior and outcome independently. In order to show that behavior is emitted in order to achieve a goal, researchers try to manipulate the contingencies between behaviors and outcomes (cf. Irwin, 1971). But the consequences of forgetting are presumably intrapsychic and may pertain to the warding off of threatening thoughts and to the avoidance of anxiety. It is difficult to see how the contingencies between forgetting and not forgetting, in relation to these types of outcomes, might be manipulated experimentally.

In essence, although it requires a conceptual leap to use our research findings to claim that momentary forgetting is motivated forgetting, our results certainly do not contradict, and seem to support such a claim. Failure to find differences in the conditions that precede instances of forgetting and of control points might have suggested that momentary forgetting was influenced by random factors. Our finding that the contents of forgotten thoughts are related to each individual's specific conflicts, although subject to several interpretations, is supportive of motivational bases for momentary forgetting.

Disruptions in the flow of cognition, such as in the tip of the tongue phenomenon, have proven to be valuable preparations for coming to understand normal cognitive functioning (e.g., Brown & McNeill, 1966). Similarly, a greater understanding of the state conducive to momentary forgetting can also aid us in clarifying these processes. Based on clinical observation and theory, Freud (1930) claimed that the investigation of the psychopathology of everyday life provides an access road into the "psychic apparatus." We have shown that one way to travel this road is to return to the clinical setting and to the recurrent behaviors of everyday life, from which Freud generated concepts such as motivated forgetting, but then to be guided in testing them by controlled observational methods.

CONCLUSIONS

- *People have their own specific recurrent content before momentary forgetting and in their recovered thoughts.* One main recurrent forgetting content is especially prominent in the series of each patient's recovered momentary forgettings. The type of recurrent content and the degree of recurrence of the forgetting are summarized in Table 2 for the 4 patients with three or more forgettings in the new enlarged sample of 17 patients. For three of the four, the uniformity in the recurrent content is clear. For the other one, Ms. Francis, the uniformity is only moderately evident.

The type of recurrent forgetting content tends to be specific for each patient. As was noted in Table 2, for Ms. Apfel the content was fear of rejection; for Mr. Dannon, it was fear of expressing anger; for Mr. Berger, it was a similar fear of expressing anger; and for Ms. Francis, it was a wish to indulge and a fear of indulging in and having to reveal forbidden sexual and oral gratifications.

- *The topic tends to have consistency throughout the forgetting experience.* The type of recurrent thought content tends to maintain considerable temporal consistency through the adjacent segments: from before the forgetting, to the forgetting itself, to after the forgetting.

- *It takes more than the content of the theme to set off forgetting.* The presence of the main recurrent forgetting content is a necessary but not sufficient condition for the occurrence of momentary forgetting. The shift in the threatening content from before forgetting to the forgetting itself can be only slight, and the thought can be present without triggering the forgetting. Both of these observations imply that what sets off the forgetting is not just the fear of expressing the threatening thought, but also the concomitant increased presence of other conditions, such as increases in cognitive disturbance, involvement with therapist, and the experience of the CCRT. However, even a slight shift on the course toward a more specific version of the core content may be perceived as more dangerous, and that perception may play a part in the recourse to forgetting.

- *The core content of the symptom-context forgetting theme has much in common with the CCRT.* The core content of each person's forgetting is similar to one of the three components of the person's CCRT. This is very clear for three of the four patients previously discussed and somewhat evident for the fourth as well. For the three clearest cases, the CCRT component is either the response from other or the response of self.

Why should the recurrent core content of forgetting be similar to a component of the CCRT? As was noted at the outset, the similarity may be partly understandable because the forgetting tends to occur during the REs with the therapist. That relationship, as Freud (1912/1958) observed, is the hardest one for the patient to deal with, because it involves expressing proscribed thoughts to the very person to whom the thoughts relate. Furthermore, the REs with the therapist have been shown to be similar in their content to the larger pattern of other relationships in the CCRT (Fried, Crits-Christoph, & Luborsky, 1990; Luborsky et al., 1986).

- *Awareness of the forgetting content varies for each patient.* The patient's awareness of the forgetting content tends to be low, but it tends to vary from patient to patient and, within patients, from occasion to occasion.

- *The conditions for forgetting are much like the conditions for other symptoms.* The three main symptom-context conditions for momentary forgetting in the 17-case sample (cognitive disturbance, involvement with therapist, and CCRT activation) have some applicability to the other types of psychological and psychosomatic symptoms, when the conditions for these are analyzed intra-individually with the symptom-context method (for summary, see Tables 1, 2, and 3 in chap. 10).

One of these cases (Mr. Berger, see chap. 7) even provided a comparison of two different symptoms within the same case: momentary forgetting and headaches. The three conditions, and helplessness as well, were evident for each of these symptoms, but the content differed for each symptom. The context for momentary forgetting included the imminence of the possible expression of anger. The context for the headaches was the build-up of a feeling of tension and pressure in the relationship along with the helpless and hopeless feeling that nothing could be done about it; this is the quality that is so central in Freud (1926/1959).

WHERE THE FIELD IS NOW AND IS GOING

My initial intention in this research was to examine the conscious and unconscious bases of recurrent momentary forgetting and to see how well my words would fulfill my intention. To try to expand knowledge in this area of the gradient of conscious to unconscious processes is an awesome challenge—in the original sense of awesome as creating awe—because of deficiencies of research methods and of language. Much of what I have to say is consistent with "Freud's cognitive psychology," as Erdelyi (1985) labeled it. What I have added comes from observations aided by the CCRT and symptom-context methods. What I have subtracted comes from my preferred style to stay clear of certain words, even including *the conscious* and *the unconscious* used as mental locations, in order to stay closer to the descriptive level. Rather than speak of *the* conscious and the unconscious, I refer to degrees of awareness. I am trying to heed Freud's (1937/1964) self-admonition about the snares he suffered from getting too involved with "metapsychology," that is, with a set of abstract concepts that are distant from clinical observations. Although I listen to his caution, I am tempted recurrently into momentary romps with the ensnarer. For a measure of safety, I resolve at least to hold on to the rule of starting speculations from a solid platform of well-established observations.

So much for preliminaries. I am ready now to review the list of factors that combine to produce the advent of a momentary forgetting, because these factors can serve as stepping stones to seeing the location of gaps in awareness:

- A particular type of thought, unique for each person, comes increasingly into the person's awareness.
- The person perceives the thought but also experiences a danger signal about thinking or saying it.
- The thought is typically experienced as a danger in interpersonal terms, usually having to do with the relationship with the therapist and, therefore, the involvement with the therapist increases.
- The involvement with the therapist is an aspect of involvement in a larger core conflictual relationship pattern (as measured by the CCRT).
- Various signs of cognitive disturbance appear, showing the person's difficulty in thinking or expressing the thought or related thoughts (and, therefore, cognitive disturbance increases). One of these signs is the momentary forgetting itself.

To make further progress in the search for a deeper psychological understanding of the basis for the consistency in the content of recurrent forgetting and its place in the CCRT, studies with these research goals might be beneficial:

- To investigate other symptoms analyzed in the same fashion as the momentary forgetting in relation to the CCRT, as I do in this book.
- To learn even more about the degree to which the content and context of momentary forgetting are different from the content and context of other recurrent symptoms within the same patient. As was noted earlier, this could be tried for patients with two recurrent symptoms, such as Mr. Berger for

momentary forgetting and headaches and Mr. Quinn for momentary forgetting and precipitous depressions. My impression, so far, is that the themes for each symptom appear to be distinguishable.

- To determine whether laboratory research approaches would indicate thematic contents similar to those from forgetting studies, it could be helpful to try Baars's (1992) method of inducing slips of the tongue.
- To determine whether the thematic contents of momentary forgetting for a patient would show up as an indicator of an associative "complex" in the word associations, selected words from the CCRT could be added to the word association test.
- To see even broader extra-therapy effects in each subject's conscious thought stream, one could sample each subject by Singer's (1984) methods of recurrent sampling of the thought stream.
- To learn more about the conscious-unconscious dimension, researchers should build on this chapter by making further systematic observations about the vicissitudes of awareness of the contents of the momentary forgettings.
- To move to an even deeper level—now defining deeper as physical—it would also be illuminating to examine the concurrent psychophysiological substrate of momentary forgetting. For patients who have provided instances of recurrent momentary forgetting, it would be valuable to have Shevrin et al.'s (in press) evaluation of cortical-evoked potentials (CEP). This procedure might show that words from the recurrent forgettings of each patient have a distinctive CEP.
- To further expand the range of the assessment, other measures of brain function could also be included along with Shevrin's, such as those used by Gur et al. (1983) of cortical blood flow or nuclear magnetic resonance during various psychological states. However, because recurrent momentary forgetting is infrequent, instead of using measures concurrent with the forgetting, it might be convenient to try a tachistoscopic presentation of content related to the forgetting.

Carrying out these eight types of studies should help to bring closer together the two research styles represented in the chapters of this text, the naturalistic-clinical and the laboratory-experimental, because they have complementary assets and liabilities. I will end with reflections about the relative virtues of the two research styles in offering suitable preparations for the investigation of factors influencing forgetting and recall: the systematic-naturalistic style, as reflected in the work conducted by my colleagues and me on momentary forgetting, versus the laboratory style, which I have consorted with from time to time.

What may emerge from the tempting tango of this twosome? The two may bump up against the realities of their own limits. For the laboratory methods, the limits are that the to-be-compared clinical data and related clinical concepts are especially difficult to make sense of in relation to laboratory data. This is a significant limit because it is clinical data that has provided the source of most of the significant constructs about unconscious processes. Even my version of the systematic-naturalistic methods of utilizing clinical data has limits; for example, conditions cannot be varied at will, and the patients do not always reveal their thoughts fully. Yet the attraction that warrants putting up with each other's blemishes is that the systematic-naturalistic method offers for analysis a phenomenon involving both forgetting and remembering, while patients are revealing many of their thoughts and while objective methods are being applied. A fitting resolution is just to marry the two methods, as is illustrated in the proposed studies, and see how their offspring develop.

APPENDIX
THREE INSTANCES OF MOMENTARY FORGETTING FOR MR. JOHN DANNON

The text that follows contains three excerpts from the momentary forgetting protocols of Mr. Dannon, a patient in psychoanalysis. In Session 12 the patient had just said, "And I felt that you just, uh, just hated me." At that point, he forgot what he was going to say. What he was going to say was, "I began having resentment toward you." In Session 68 he had just said when he lost his thought, "I'll shit all over this place." He did not recover it precisely but said, "It had something to do with letting go, that if I lowered my guard you will penetrate me, rip me to pieces." The next instance occurred in Session 137. The patient was obsessing about getting better for himself or for the therapist when he forgot the thought, and what he recovered was, "If you don't want me to get better I'm pissed off, and if you do I'm pissed off." In all three instances, therefore, the recurrent theme clearly deals with anger. The anger is either directed at the therapist or is an expectation of receiving anger from the therapist. (The theme for this patient is, therefore, very much like that found for Mr. P. Berger. The fear of rejection could be seen as a related content. Even for Ms. M. Francis, the danger in revealing sexual or oral thoughts was that the therapist would hurt the patient when this was revealed.)

Because of space limitations, only 200 words before and after Mr. Dannon's forgetting are included here.

Session 12

P: . . . boy in high school--was brighter than I and it always used to bother me that my mother compared us--and now when I actually feel in this group of students that I am--the brightest (hesitates) that I am number one, it bothers me (hesitates). Maude (?) is the name of a homosexual magazine (pause) [7.5 s]. Just had a thought (wheezes) you know, I've got to preface things by "I've just had the thought"--I'm picking it up myself--that this is a way of leading into--something which is embarrassing for me. (hesitates) I don't know why it sort of displaces the thought but it does, or lessens its impact. But I wanted to be in bed with you. Crikes. (pause) [4 s].

T: That little remark has another meaning, too, and it means that rather than saying things as you think them, you're thinking about them first and then saying them.

P: Yes, that's what I was trying to say (pause) [8.5 s]. I'm still not free associating well. (pause) [3 s] That gives me some element of control. (pause) [3 s] I was thinking--the other day that (hesitates) when I--the day that I--I walked out of here I felt so shitty that I hadn't performed or that--nothing had come out (hesitates) (slight wheeze?) God I--everything's coming out in anal terms: shitty, hadn't performed, nothing had come out. (pause) [2.5 s] And I felt (pause) [2 s] that you just--eh--just--hated me (pause) (FORG.) [4 s] (wheeze?) (bangs table) *I forgot what I was gonna say. I just forgot what I was gonna say again* (pause) [4.5 s]. Oh (pause) [2 s] um (pause) [2 s] I began having--resentment towards you (pause) [2 s] (wheezes) having resentment feeling resentment (pause) [3 s] and I had the feeling although there a--I didn't have (pause) [2 s] I was very much aware at the time that there were--there was nothing you had done (pause) [2.5 s]. But I had the feeling (pause) [3 s] again that if I let loose (pause) [4 s] whatever there is inside me here we go again (pause) [2 s] I could almost kill you with my words (pause) [2 s] that you couldn't stand the onslaught. (pause) [6 s] (wheezes). And I don't want to do that to you. (pause) [2.5 s] I'm not talking about anything in specific that I'm hiding, I'm not (pause) [3 s] but particularly this I--I'm in a way I think I'm afraid of the time that I know is going to come when I am gonna resent you. (pause) [4 s] It's much harder for me to dislike you (hesitates) than anybody--much harder. (pause) [2 s] 'Cause you're such a darn decent guy. (pause) [7 s] In a way, that's gonna make the analysis more difficult because I know about you from the County. And I know that you're a decent guy; this isn't fantasy (hesitates). And also in this situation already. You haven't kicked me out yet. (pause) [6 s]. You know I. . . .

Session 68

P: . . . wish for immediate gratification I want that other car. I don't want to have to worry about starting this car in the winter-time again (hesitates). I have too many--other things--to be concerned about--which is a rationalization. I just want the other car (pause) [3 s]. Like a child. (pause) [2 s] I actually can't afford it I suppose but (pause) [27 s]. It has been bucking an awful lot though (pause) [22.5 s]. I'm gonna be honest with you. I'm getting off soft--all these subjects that--

T: Why?

P: Why?

T: Yeah. (hesitates) What are your thoughts about that? (pause) [11 s]

P: I'm through with it that's all. Well probably (slight laugh) it bothers me too much to talk about it or I just sorta feel--wrung--dry on the subject (pause) [3 s] as if I've been dried (pause) [9 s]. You know, I must think of you--in some way in these terms too, what you're going to do to me (pause) [8 s]. You know, are you gonna rape my mind (pause) [14.5 s]. Maybe that's one of the reasons why I have trouble l-letting go completely on the couch. "Letting go" sounds to me just like crapping--I mean, like becoming incontinent--. And I think that's perhaps the way I conceive of it, that if I let go I'll shit all over this place (FORG.) (pause) [5 s]. *I've just (snaps fingers) lost a thought.* [4.5 s] I just lost that thought (pause) [14.5 s], you will penetrate me (pause) [2 s], rip me to pieces, tear me apart. (pause) [13 s]. You're a nice guy, you wouldn't do that (pause) [10 s]. Again I have a thought of--biting your genitals off--. It's a terrible thought.

T: Was that the thought you'd lost? No.

P: No (hesitates). The thought I'd lost (pause) [4 s] it had to do with with uh being on guard here (pause) [4.5 s]. It's almost as if my mind becomes a sphincter and I've got to--tightly control that (hesitates) so that--you can't get in and all this shit can't come out. (pause) [2 s] It was that thought (pause) [7.5 s]. You know, I just have the--the image of--letting myself go, and this whole room literally being--filled to the ceiling--and it's a big room--with with all kinds of horrible internal products, vomit and shit and piss. (pause) [6.5 s] That whatever's inside is filthy. (pause) [16 s] You know, I'm in a period now where I'm not resisting the analysis so much, just in the last 2 days, and I don't understand why but it's been different the last 2 days than it has been (hesitates) in the last couple of . . . .

Session 137

P: . . . around and Sue--was riding by on a bicycle (hesitates). And she stopped and ish she was so tense she was ready to hit the ceiling (hesitates). And she--I--and she sort of--took me aside and asked me whether this was serious with Nancy et cetera (pause) [6.5 s] If Nancy is a castrater the way most of the women whom I've taken out have turned out to be she's a hell of a lot more subtle about it (pause) [5 s].

T: Doesn't seem to me that you're responding to her being a castrater. You're responding to her being a manipulator (hesitates) and, uh, now wanting things from you and placing demands upon you and pretending she's not (pause) [3 s].

P: And this Friday we meet her father and stepmother. (pause) [6.5 s] (sighs) (pause) [7 s] It's like sleep over if you want to sleep over, I'm not placing any demands on you and that's a lot of crap. She wants to sleep with me.

T: (overlapping with above) Of course it's crap. (pause) [4 s] I'm struggling to put into words--my sense that some of that same interaction goes on between you and me. (pause) [3 s] And that I think--I the--I really think that some of the time maybe a lot of the time maybe a little perhaps none--but that some of the time--

P: (laughing) Boy, you've got yourself covered there.

T: Yeah. Well (P still laughing) I'll st-- (T laughs) I'll crawl out on a limb. I think that some of the time--you have to be deliberately --naughty in here (pause) [2.5 s], uncooperative, silent, not free associating, abusive (pause) [3.5 s] i-i-i-in order to assure yourself that I don't need anything from you. (pause) [2.5 s]. That--that thing that Dr. S said to you last week uh that you couldn't make any sense of. I think--rang bells on other levels about--the therapist needing nothing from the patient and, uh, taking no pleasure other than (hesitates) whatever pleasure she said was, was kosher to take.

P: She said no pleasure was kosher.

T: No pleasure. Pleasure of seeing him get well? (hesitates) Not even that.

P: Just the money.

T: Just, oh that's right, just the money. The pleasure of taking the money.

P: Getting well was the last that she said you should look for.

T: (sniffs) Yeah. (pause) [2 s] I--I do think she's speaking to you as a patient (pause) [2 s] that you are terrifically concerned--unconsciously--with what I get out of this. With the question of you being used. (hesitates) And it's so terribly hard for you not to feel used. (pause) [4 s] And that sometimes, well, d--I just now going back to home base--that sometimes you have to be deliberately a crummy patient (hesitates) in order to see what it is I need from you (pause) [10.5 s]. But of course you can feel--then manipulated if I don't respond to that (pause) [2 s] can feel I'm just then treating you like a little boy and humoring you along. I--it's a vicious cycle--in which the essential reassurance is awfully hard to get (sniffs). (pause) [5 s].

P: It's such a paradox. I--I mean (hesitates) you're--if you do want me to get better (pause) [3 s] it's for me but I can only conceive of it in terms of for you.

T: That's right. (pause) [6 s].

P: And you're right. I'm just sort of rephrasing this to understand it myself--the other side of that is (FORG.) (hesitates). Oh, shit, now I lost that thought. (pause) [6 s] Oh (pause) [2 s] n--and, and what investment can you possibly have in my getting better. No, that isn't what I was g-- (pause) [7.5 s]. If you don't want me to get better I'm pissed off and if you do I'm pissed off. (pause) [2 s] If you don't, you don't care, and if you do, you want something from me. (pause) [15 s] I just had a thought I'm gonna get sick this weekend--. Not really--I'm just not gonna take her out. (pause) [9 s] She sure spends my money easily. (pause) [3 s] It's funny 'cause I just had a thought as I came up here this morning (pause) [4.5 s]. As I looked at your house, I kinda walked away from it (hesitates) and (pause) [2.5 s] I was thinking to myself either, you know, I'm sure you don't the way I would do in my obsessive way well this patient's money is for this, this is for that and this is for that-- what do you do with the money I give you? (pause) [4.5 s]. What's it for? (pause) [20.5 s] She does use me. That bitch. (pause) [14.5 s] And I'm damn good to her and it bothers me. I'm always a very solicitous date. (pause) [2 s] Are you too hot? Are . . .

REFERENCES

Auerbach, A. H., & Luborsky, L. (1968). Accuracy of judgments of psychotherapy and the nature of the "good hour." In J. Shlien, H. F. Hunt, J. P. Matarazzo, & C. Savage (Eds.), *Research in psychotherapy* (Vol. 3, pp. 155–168). Washington, DC: American Psychological Association.

Baars, B. J. (1992). *Experimental slips and human error: Exploring the architecture of volition.* New York: Plenum Press.

Brown, R., & McNeill, D. (1966). The "tip of the tongue" phenomenon. *Journal of Verbal Learning and Verbal Behavior, 5,* 325–337.

Dahl, H. (1972). A quantitative study of psychoanalysis. In R. Holt & E. Peterfreund (Eds.), *Psychoanalysis and contemporary science* (Vol. 1, pp. 237–257). New York: Macmillan.

Erdelyi, M. L. (1985). *Psychoanalysis: Freud's cognitive psychology.* New York: Freeman.

Erdelyi, M. (1990). Repression, reconstruction and defense: History and integration of the psychoanalytic and experimental frameworks. In J. Singer (Ed.), *Repression and dissociation* (pp. 1–32). Chicago: University of Chicago Press.

Freud, S. (1930). *Psychopathology of everyday life.* London: E. Benn.

Freud, S. (1957). Repression. In J. Strachey (Ed.), *The standard edition of the complete psychological works of Sigmund Freud* (Vol. 14). London: Hogarth Press. (Original work published 1915)

Freud, S. (1958). The dynamics of the transference. In J. Strachey (Ed. and Trans.), *The standard edition of the complete psychological works of Sigmund Freud* (Vol. 12, pp. 99–108). London: Hogarth Press. (Original work published 1912)

Freud, S. (1959). Inhibitions, symptoms, and anxiety. In J. Strachey (Ed. and Trans.), *The standard edition of the complete psychological works of Sigmund Freud* (Vol. 20, pp. 87–174). London Hogarth Press. (Original work published 1926)

Freud, S. (1964). Analysis terminable and interminable. In J. Strachey (Ed. and Trans.), *The standard edition of the complete psychological works of Sigmund Freud* (Vol. 23, pp. 216–253). London: Hogarth Press. (Original work published 1937)

Fried, D., Crits-Christoph, P., & Luborsky, L. (1990). The parallel of narratives about the therapist with the CCRT for other people. In L. Luborsky & P. Crits-Christoph (Eds.), *Understanding transference—the CCRT method* (pp. 147–157). New York: Basic Books.

Gur, R. E., Brott, E., Skolnick, R. C., Caroff, S., Rieger, W., Obrist, W., Younkin, D., & Reivich, M. (1983). Brain function in psychiatric disorders: I. Regional cerebral blood flow in medicated schizophrenics. *Archives of General Psychiatry, 40*, 1250–1254.

Hardyck, G., Singer, M. T., & Harris, R. E. (1962). Transient changes in affect and blood pressure. *Archives of General Psychiatry, 7* 15–20.

Holmes, D. S. (1974). Investigations of repression: Differential recall of material experimentally or naturally associated with ego threat. *Psychological Bulletin, 81*, 632–653.

Horowitz, L. M., Sampson, H., Siegelman, E. Y., Wolfson, A. W., & Weiss, J. (1975). On the identification of warded-off mental contents. *Journal of Abnormal Psychology, 84*, 545–558.

Irwin, F. W. (1971). *International behavior and motivation: A cognitive theory.* Philadelphia: Lippincott.

Kline, P. (1972). *Fact and fantasy in Freudian theory.* London: Methuen.

Luborsky, L. (with Rubinstein, B., Aronson, G., Bergman, P., Fabian, M., Holt, R., Kaiser, H., Murphy, G., & Watterson, D.) (1962). *The health-sickness rating scale (and sample cases).* Topeka, KS: The Menninger Foundation.

Luborsky, L. (1964). A psychoanalytic research on momentary forgetting during free association. *Bulletin of the Philadelphia Association for Psychoanalysis, 14*, 119–137.

Luborsky, L. (1966). *A cognitive disturbance scale.* Unpublished manuscript.

Luborsky, L. (1967). Momentary forgetting during psychotherapy and psychoanalysis: A theory and research method. In R. R. Holt (Ed.), Motives and thought: Psychoanalytic essays in honor of David Rapaport [Monograph No. 18/19]. *Psychological Issues, 5*(2–3), 177–217.

Luborsky, L. (1970). New directions in research on neurotic and psychosomatic symptoms. *American Scientist, 58*, 661–668.

Luborsky, L. (1973). Forgetting and remembering (momentary forgetting) during psychotherapy: A new sample. In M. Mayman (Ed.), Psychoanalytic research: Three approaches to the experimental study of subliminal processes [Monograph No. 30]. *Psychological Issues, 8*(2), 29–55.

Luborsky, L. (1975). Clinicians' judgments of mental health: Specimen case descriptions and forms for the Health-Sickness Rating Scale. *Bulletin of the Menninger Clinic, 35*, 448–480.

Luborsky, L. (1977). Measuring a pervasive psychic structure in psychotherapy: The core conflictual relationship theme. In N. Freedman & S. Grand (Eds.), *Communicative structures and psychic structures* (pp. 367–395). New York: Plenum Press.

Luborsky, L. (1988). Recurrent momentary forgetting: Its content and context. In M. Horowitz (Ed.), *Psychodynamics and cognition* (pp. 217–245). Chicago: University of Chicago Press.

Luborsky, L. (in press). Core conflictual relationship themes (CCRT)—A basic case formulation method. In T. Eells (Ed.), *Handbook of psychotherapy case formulation*. New York: Guilford Press.

Luborsky, L., & Auerbach, A. H. (1969). The symptom-context method: Quantitative studies of symptom formation in psychotherapy. *Journal of the American Psychoanalytic Association, 17*, 68–99.

Luborsky, L., & Crits-Christoph, P. (1990). *Understanding transference: The CCRT (The Core Conflictual Relationship Theme) Method*. New York: Basic Books.

Luborsky, L., Crits-Christoph, P., Brady, J. P., Kron, R., Weiss, T., Cohen, M., & Levy, L. (1982). Behavioral versus pharmacological treatments for essential hypertension: A needed comparison. *Psychosomatic Medicine, 44*, 203–213.

Luborsky, L., Crits-Christoph, P., & Mellon, J. (1986). The advent of objective measures of the transference concept. *Journal of Consulting and Clinical Psychology, 54*, 39–47.

Luborsky, L., Docherty, J., Todd, T., Knapp, P., Mirsky, A., & Gottschalk, L. (1975). A context analysis of psychological states prior to petit-mal seizures. *Journal of Nervous and Mental Disease, 160*, 282–298.

Luborsky, L., & Mintz, J. (1974). What sets off momentary forgetting during a psychoanalysis? Methods of investigating symptom-onset conditions. In L. Goldberger & V. Rosen (Eds.), *Psychoanalysis and contemporary science* (Vol. 3, pp. 233–268). New York: International Universities Press.

Luborsky, L., Sackeim, H., & Christoph, P. (1979). The state conducive to momentary forgetting. In J. Kihlstrom & F. Evans (Eds.), *Functional disorders of memory* (pp. 325–353). Hillsdale, NJ: Erlbaum.

Luborsky, L., & Spence, D. (1978). Quantitative research on psychoanalytic therapy. In S. L. Garfield & A. E. Bergin (Eds.), *Handbook of psychotherapy and behavior change* (pp. 331–368). New York: Wiley.

Madison, P. (1961). *Freud's concept of repression and defense*. Minneapolis: University of Minnesota Press.

Mahl, G. F. (1956). Disturbances and silences in patient's speech in psychotherapy. *Journal of Abnormal and Social Psychology, 53*, 1–15.

Neisser, U. (1967). *Cognitive psychology*. Englewood Cliffs, NJ: Prentice-Hall.

Sackeim, H., & Gur, R. (1978). Self-deception, self-confrontation and consciousness. In G. E. Schwartz & D. Shapiro (Eds.), *Consciousness and self-regulation: Advances in research* (Vol. 2). New York: Plenum Press.

Sampson, H., Weiss, J., Mlodnosky, L., & Hause, E. (1972). Defense analysis and the emergence of warded-off mental contents: An empirical study. *Archives of General Psychiatry*, *26*, 524–532.

Sears, R. R. (1943a). Experimental analyses of psychoanalytic phenomena. In J. McV. Hunt (Ed.), *Personality and behavior disorders* (pp. 306–322). New York: Ronald Press.

Sears, R. R. (1943b). *Survey of objective studies of psychoanalytic concepts*. New York: Social Science Research Council.

Shevrin, H., Bond, J. A., Brakel, L., Hertel, R., & Williams, W. (in press). *Conscious and unconscious processes: An experimental investigation based on convergent psychodynamic, cognitive and neuropsychological methods*. New York: Guilford Press.

Shevrin, H., Williams, W., Marshall, R., Hertel, R., Bond, J., & Brakel, L. (1992). Event-related potential indicators of the dynamic unconscious. *Consciousness and Cognition*, *1*, 340–366.

Singer, J. I. (1984). *The human personality*. San Diego, CA: Harcourt Brace Jovanovich.

Singer, M. T. (1967). Enduring personality styles and responses to stress. *Transactions of the Association of Life Insurance Medical Directors of America, 51*, 150–166.

Singer, M. T. (1974). Engagement-involvement: A central phenomenon in psychophysiological research. *Psychosomatic Medicine*, *36*, 1–17.

Williams, R. B., Jr., Kimball, C. P., & Williard, H. N. (1972). The influence of interpersonal interaction on diastolic blood pressure. *Psychosomatic Medicine*, *34*, 194–198.

5

THE CONTEXT FOR SUDDEN DEPRESSIVE MOOD SHIFTS

LESTER LUBORSKY, BARTON SINGER, JOHN HARTKE, LOUIS
DIGUER, PAUL CRITS-CHRISTOPH, and CHRISTOPHER PETERSON

Depressions, like momentary forgettings, sometimes start suddenly while one is talking with another person; they also may occur in a context that can be regularly recorded, such as in psychotherapy. When I realized that both of these unlikely conditions could occur at the same moment, that became the donné for a study of concepts about the context of shifts in depressive states. Would the qualities that appeared before momentary forgetting again be fitting ones for understanding these sudden depressions?

It has been hard to achieve consensus on basic concepts about the sequence of states leading to depression. For example, George Engel, at an American Psychoanalytic Association symposium on symptom formation, described a state preceding depression and other symptoms as "the giving-up, given-up complex" because of the underlying affects of helplessness and hopelessness (Engel & Schmale, 1967). The discussant of the paper, Max Schur, expressed the contrary opinion that the helplessness state might be indistinguishable from depression rather than an antecedent to it.

Earlier versions of this chapter appeared in Peterson, C., Luborsky, L., & Seligman, M. (1983). Attributions and depressive mood shifts: A case study using the symptom-context method. *Journal of Abnormal Psychology, 92,* 96–103; and in Luborsky, L., Singer, B., Hartke, J., Crits-Christoph, P., & Cohen, M. (1984). Shifts in depressive state during psychotherapy: Which concepts of depression fit the context of Mr. Q's shifts? In L. N. Rice & L. S. Greenberg (Eds.), *Patterns of change: Intensive analysis of psychotherapy process* (pp. 157–193). New York: Guilford. They have been adapted, revised, and expanded by the author with permission of the two publishers.

A similar idea on helplessness as an antecedent was given a similar reception when Martin Seligman presented his work on learned helplessness in dogs to a conference of the Department of Psychiatry at the University of Pennsylvania (Seligman, Maier, & Geer, 1968). He suggested that learned helplessness was an antecedent to depression-like behavior in certain dogs who had been taught helplessness by being subjected to inescapable shock. Several discussants again questioned the possibility of distinguishing the two affects, helplessness and depression.

One straightforward way of seeing the relationship of the two stages—if they are truly two separate states or mainly overlapping states—is to look at what happens just before and after the onset of a depression, as I do in this chapter. By continuously observing patients who have shifts into or out of depression, one can examine the sequence of states around a shift to increased depression or around a lifting of depression. Psychotherapy is a good medium for this type of study, because the patient is under continuous observation and often tries to say much of what is being experienced. If sessions are tape recorded, then not just the therapist but also independent observers can estimate the temporal course of the affects to determine whether helplessness tends to precede shifts to increased depression, is concurrent with it, or cannot be distinguished from it.

Other control conditions can also be imposed. After having located the instances of the target symptom—increases in depression—the data can then be divided into three parts: the words and other behaviors before the symptom, the selected event of the symptom itself, and the words and other behaviors after the symptom. These three divisions can then be compared with similarly divided material from the same patient around selected control points that do not contain the symptom. The segments around the control points provide a baseline for comparison with the segments containing the nodal symptom. This method may sound somewhat like the same old clinical approach, and it is, but only in part, because there are crucial added ingredients, such as the use of the types of controls just described, which were developed into the symptom-context methods described in chapters 1 and 2.

This chapter expands on research conducted by me and four colleagues (Luborsky et al., 1984). My goal is to show how this research contributes to knowledge about depression. To that end, I examine which concepts of depression fit the contexts for shifts in depressive mood, and I evaluate the applicability of the symptom-context method to understanding mood shifts. Before discussing this research, however, I present a brief history of research on shifts in depression.

No studies like the one I report in this chapter have been done. Most research on depression is conducted with patients who are already depressed or already out of depression. Transient episodes of depression have been commonly noted, as Whybrow, Akiskal, and McKinney (1984) have discussed, but the shifts in and out of these episodes have not been studied. There are, however, studies of individual patients who have changed in their level of depression (e.g., Beck, 1967; Mendels, 1970; Mendelson, 1974).

A study by Leff, Roatch, and Bunney (1970) is a closely related study, because they looked at environmental factors on the basis of patients' reports that might have come just before severe depression. They classified these factors for the most common events that triggered the onset. Muran et al. (1995) actually measured shifts in depression during a session, but they related frequency of such shifts only to the outcome of the treatment. The study by Bunney, Murphy, Goodwin, and Borge (1972) was closer to our own (Luborsky et al., 1984) in design. They investigated shifts in manic–depressive patients from mania to depression and from depression to mania in terms of shifts in daily measures of psycho-endocrine functioning. But they did not look at the shifts in terms of a psychological description of the patient at the time of the shift. Engel and Reichsman (1956) used their method to demonstrate that a child with a gastric fistula abruptly went into a withdrawal state, very much like a depressive state, whenever a stranger entered her room.

DESCRIPTION OF THE PATIENT AND THE PROCEDURES

Preparation of the Data

Singer, Hartke, Crits-Christoph, Cohen, and I (Luborsky et al., 1984) examined the psychological context in which a depressed patient, Mr. James Quinn, experienced sudden shifts in depressive mood during psychotherapy sessions. Using the symptom-context method, we compared those instances of a shift in which depression increased versus those of a shift in which depression decreased. I will describe the methods of analysis that were developed for these data, so that they can serve as a model for further research on the depressions of similar patients.

We obtained the tape recordings of the psychotherapy sessions for this patient, who rapidly shifted his mood either toward increased depression or toward decreased depression. Of the 244 sessions, all but the first 41 were recorded, and brief process notes were available for those 41. It was not necessary to search through all of these sessions because, conveniently, the therapist had completed a brief postsession checksheet (Luborsky, 1971), which provided space to note mood shifts and to rate a set of variables for each session. We needed only to cull from the checksheets the sessions in which mood shifts occurred; only these sessions, a total of 10, were then transcribed.

The postsession checksheet also contained a space for brief process notes that summarized each session. Review of these notes suggested hypotheses for a clinical review of the nature of the context for each mood shift. The hypotheses were then checked by the more precise symptom-context analyses based on the transcripts.

Locating the Onset of the Symptom

The primary criterion for selecting a shift in depression was the patient's spontaneous report of a shift in mood, for example, "My mood just went down." The suddenness of some shifts in this patient's mood was convenient for our method because it helped us to locate the moment of the shift on the transcript of the session. Whenever patient-reported mood shifts occurred, they were also noted by the therapist on the postsession checksheet. (The shifts were one of the 45 qualities of the session to be rated by the therapist on the postsession checksheet.)

To further objectify the selection of the instances to be examined, two independent judges read the transcripts. For an instance to be usable three conditions had to be met. One, both judges had to agree that the patient was, in fact, saying that a mood shift had *just* occurred. Two, the shift had to be more than slight, that is, more than 1.0 on a 5-point depressive mood scale. The majority of the shifts were around 2.0 on the scale, which identified them as of moderate size. And, three, to provide a context containing at least 400 words before and 400 words after the shift, shifts had to appear within a reasonably long sample of the patient's speech. (For this patient, 800 words typically took about 15 minutes.) Therefore, when shifts occurred in close proximity to each other—as they sometimes did—usually the first of the shifts was selected or, occasionally, the one that was in the longer uninterrupted context of the patient's speech.

In the 10 sessions studied, 14 shifts were located, 8 in which depression increased and 6 in which depression decreased. After excluding some instances on the basis of overlap, only 9 of the original 14 remained as the final selections, 4 in which increases in depression occurred and 5 in which decreases occurred. I will briefly note here and expand later on the three ways in which we determined that the shifts in the nine selected segments of transcripts really involved depression.

First, two independent judges rated the affective quality of the voice on the tape recording in terms of the degree of depressive mood that was conveyed in it. Their judgments tended to be consistent with increased depressive affect when the patient was becoming increasingly depressed and somewhat consistent with decreased depressive affect when the reverse was true (Luborsky et al., 1984, p. 182). Second, other independent judges rated the text's degree of depression before and after the shift. Again, the ratings were consistent with the patient's and the judges' classification of the direction of the shift (Luborsky et al., 1984, p. 171). Third, other independent judges applied the depression component of the Gottschalk-Gleser (1969) Hostility-Inward scale to each segment. Again, their scorings were consistent with the direction of the shift (Luborsky et al., 1984, p. 181).

Theoretical Bases for Selecting Variables

Much thought went into deciding which variables would be measured before and after the mood shifts. The variables came from three main sources. Most of the variables were derived from other symptom-context studies[1] because of their relevance to theories of symptom formation. The psychological theories of depression reviewed by Beck (1967) and by Mendelson (1974) provided another source. One additional variable was derived from our reading and rereading of the process notes and transcripts of the sessions: Oedipal Conflict. Table 1 lists the 16 variables that were rated. To examine the context for the patient's shifts in mood toward increased or toward decreased depression, we rated the variables in each 100-word unit of the patient's words. The differences in ratings before and after shifts in depression are depicted in Table 2. It should be noted that although two of the variables are rated singly, they encompass two dimensions: Concern about Supplies includes concern about getting or losing supplies, and Loss of Self-Esteem includes wounded self-esteem. Helplessness and depression were in fact rated for this patient, but not for these segments, which is why only 14 variables are listed in Table 2.

Theorists agree that the state of depression is multifaceted, and they even tend to agree about many of its facets, but they differ about which are central. Four theories of depression for which measures were derived are as follows (see Table 1):

Theory 1: Anger Turned Into Self

This theory is the Freudian theory of depression as stated in "Mourning and Melancholia" (1917/1957), which has as its core concept aggression turned inward in the form of anger at oneself, guilt, and self-blame. Measures derived from the theory include judges' ratings and the Gottschalk-Gleser (1969) Hostility-Inward scale.

---

[1]The following variables were not used: lack of control, because it was so similar to helplessness; new attitude, because it would be so difficult for a judge to know which attitudes are new unless the judge knew much more about the treatment; tired, because it appears so rarely; and attention difficulty, because there was relatively little strong evidence of it.

TABLE 1
Agreement of Two Judges' Ratings and Scorings of Variables for Mr. Quinn's Depressive Shifts

Variable	Correlations	
	Per judge	Pooled
Rated		
Concern about Supplies	.77	.86
Anxiety	.44	.61
Separation Anxiety	.26	.27
Helplessness	.81	.91
Hopelessness	.73	.84
Blocked	.70	.82
Blocked by Therapist	.54	.67
Guilt	.43	.53
Hostility	.69	.82
Hostility to Therapist	.67	.80
Depression	.87	.93
Relective	.47	.64
Involvement with Therapist	.63	.74
Hostility to Self	.52	.56
Loss of Self-Esteem	.51	.66
Oedipal Conflict	.50	.66
Scored		
Reference to Therapist	.69	.72
Helplessness manual score	.86	—
Hostility-Inward (total)[a]	.94	—
Hostility-Inward (a + b)	—	—
Hostility-Inward (c)	—	—
Explanatory style[b]	.83	—

Note. See p. 127 for explanations of Hostility scores. Adapted from Luborsky et al. (1984, p. 173) with permission.
[a]Gottschalk & Gleser (1969) reliability from Viney (1983)
[b]Peterson, Luborsky, & Seligman (1983)

Theory 2: Helplessness

This is the general Freudian (1926/1959) theory of the onset of psychological symptoms. According to this theory, the patient evaluates his or her strength to deal with a potential danger situation defined in terms of expected or remembered situations of helplessness. It is the anticipation of becoming helpless that triggers the symptoms, including phobia and depression. A number of theorists, including Horney (1957) and Goldstein (1939), have developed similar formulations. As I mentioned at the outset, there is some controversy over whether helplessness actually precedes depression or is coincident with it. Beck's cognitive theory (1972; Beck et al., 1979) emphasizes helplessness (Theory 2) but also involves loss of self-esteem (Theory 3) as well as other facets, such as loss of supplies. Each of these involves a negative view of the self and of the future which, in turn,

TABLE 2

Significance of the Differences Between Two Judges' Mean Ratings of Variables Before and After Depressive Shifts for Mr. Quinn

Differences by word unit before depressive shifts

Variable	400–300		300–200		200–100		100–0	
	t	p	t	p	t	p	t	p
1. Concern about Supplies	−1.33	.114	−1.68	.069	−.57	.292	.10	.460
2. Anxiety	.55	.300	.59	.288	1.15	.145	1.63	.074
3. Separation Anxiety	.05	.480	.69	.258	1.14	.146	1.69	.068
4. Hopelessness	−2.83	.013	−3.21	.008	−3.19	.008	−2.70	.016
5. Blocked	−2.31	.027	−4.18	.002	−6.64	.000	−3.02	.010
6. Blocked by Therapist	−.74	.243	−1.77	.060	−2.91	.012	−3.25	.007
7. Guilt	−.97	.184	−1.18	.138	−1.21	.134	.59	.286
8. Hostility	.06	.476	−.21	.420	.06	.478	−.14	.448
9. Hostility to Therapist	−1.13	.149	−1.89	.051	−1.74	.063	−2.18	.033
10. Reflective	1.29	.120	1.73	.067	.99	.179	1.64	.073
11. Involvement with Therapist	−.20	.426	−2.10	.037	−2.05	.040	−3.00	.010
12. Hostility to Self	−1.22	.132	−1.83	.056	−1.04	.167	1.14	.147
13. Loss of Self-Esteem	−1.84	.056	−2.19	.032	−.57	.292	−.11	.457
14. Oedipal Conflict	1.00	.176	1.15	.144	1.69	.068	2.13	.036

Differences by word unit after depressive shifts

Variable	0–100		100–200		200–300		300–400	
	t	p	t	p	t	p	t	p
1. Concern about Supplies	1.99	.044	2.85	.013	2.67	.016	1.42	.100
2. Anxiety	2.43	.023	2.65	.017	2.79	.014	3.27	.007
3. Separation Concern	.61	.282	.00	.500	−.88	.204	−.88	.204
4. Hopelessness	2.85	.013	4.27	.002	5.22	.0005	7.20	.000
5. Blocked	2.41	.024	12.64	.000	11.61	.000	11.64	.000
6. Blocked by Therapist	−.02	.492	1.09	.156	2.17	.033	2.64	.017
7. Guilt	4.15	.002	4.16	.002	2.78	.014	3.63	.004
8. Hostility	.34	.371	−.46	.329	−.82	.219	−.65	.269
9. Hostility to Therapist	−.65	.268	−.63	.274	2.19	.033	2.16	.034
10. Reflective	−.15	.442	−.35	.369	−.61	.282	1.04	.167
11. Involvement with Therapist	−1.88	.051	.32	.379	.89	.203	2.35	.029
12. Hostility to Self	2.97	.011	8.01	.000	3.67	.004	3.66	.004
13. Loss of Self-Esteem	3.33	.007	8.61	.000	8.01	.000	6.09	.000
14. Oedipal Conflict	1.90	.050	−.74	.241	−1.01	.173	−.12	.453

Note. Depressive shifts were derived from nine sessions with Mr. Quinn, five in which decreases occurred (Sessions 60; 77; 144, p. 17; 172; 175—used as controls in *t* tests) and four in which increases occurred (Sessions 135, p. 5; 135, p. 11; 138; 144, p. 22). All *df*s are 7, with the exception at 6.

is related to feeling blocked (Beck, 1967, 1972, refers to this as "feeling thwarted," implying both an affective and cognitive component). Measures derived from the theory include judges' ratings and the scale for scoring helplessness.

Theory 3: Loss of Self-Esteem

This theory holds that loss of self-esteem (as well as helplessness) may be the main precursor of depression. Bibring's (1968) theory, which is representative of this view, stresses that "depression can be defined as the emotional expression (indication) of a state of helplessness and powerlessness of the ego" (p. 163) and that "depression can be defined as the emotional correlate of a partial or complete collapse of the self-esteem of the ego since it feels unable to live up to its aspirations (ego ideal, superego) while they are strongly maintained" (p. 164). The measures derived from this theory are included in the judges' ratings.

Theory 4: Pessimistic Explanations for Negative Events

This theory, based on learned helplessness, has a large array of research to support it (Seligman, 1975, 1990). In brief, the theory holds that when helplessness is experienced, the patient's causal explanation for the state determines both the generality and chronicity of the helplessness deficits as well as the level of self-esteem and possible depression. The relation of this theory to the data presented in this chapter will be discussed briefly; a fuller report is offered elsewhere (Peterson, Luborsky, & Seligman, 1983).

Determining Congruence Between Variables and Theories

The purpose of examining the congruence of the data from Mr. Quinn's contexts of depressive shifts with the four theories of depression is not to generally test the theories of depression; rather, it is to determine whether the shifts in this patient's depression are consistent with what the theories would claim. For example, if as Theory 1 states, inverted hostility is an important precursor for depression, then hostility should gradually increase at the moment of the shift and rise concurrently with the rise in depression. When the patient becomes less depressed, inverted hostility should begin to decrease at the shift point and continue to decrease as depression decreases. Consistency with Theory 2, the general theory of symptom formation, would require helplessness to be associated in time with the shift point for increased depression. When depression decreases, helplessness should decrease. The prediction for Theory 3 would be expressed similarly. For Theory 4, the data should be consistent with shifts in explanatory style. It is even possible that none of these theory-related variables would be associated with shifts in depression, and, therefore, we added a number of variables derived from other symptom-context studies.

History of the Patient's Depression and Treatment

The treatment began just after Mr. Quinn, a bright, 22-year-old man, started veterinary school in a large midwestern city. An experienced psychotherapist provided supportive–expressive dynamic psychotherapy (Luborsky, 1984), as adapted for the psychotherapy of depression (Luborsky et al., 1995). In view of the precariousness of his functioning, especially in the first year of the treatment, he did not seem a suitable candidate for psychoanalysis. In the first 3 years of treatment, there were two sessions per week and in the 4th year only one session per week.

During the year prior to starting veterinary school, his senior year at a university, he had become severely depressed, so severely that at times he found it difficult to function. He said that it started with the preoccupying thought that his girlfriend was not going to give him what he wanted—either as a friend or as a sex partner. In that period he had several months of psychotherapy; in that treatment, according to the patient, there was no change in the general level of his depression. For about the first 2 years of the present treatment, severe ups and downs of depression persisted, along with sleep disturbance, interferences with ability to concentrate, and frequent self-castigations. He seemed, to himself, to have no way of controlling the onset or termination of the depressions; nor at the beginning of the present treatment was he even able to identify the nature of his affect as depression.

Toward the end of the first 2 years of the treatment, he began to label his state more clearly as depression and to recognize its onset and termination. In the last 2 years of treatment, he showed only relatively mild and brief depressions and more equanimity in the face of severe external difficulties—such as the necessity of dealing with the depression of the woman he had married during the last 6 months of his treatment. He was functioning better in school and planning his future training with a relatively high degree of anticipatory confidence and satisfaction.

Diagnostically, the patient would be considered as fitting a longstanding pattern of recurring depression, a DSM-IV (American Psychiatric Association, 1994) dysthymic disorder (300.40). The symptom picture, even at its most severe, does not warrant a diagnosis of major depressive episode. These diagnostic criteria were present.

1. During the past 2 years he had been bothered most of the time by symptoms characteristic of the depressive syndrome.
2. The syndrome had been separated by periods of normal mood lasting a few days to a few weeks, but no more than a few months at a time.
3. During the depressive periods, there was prominent depressed mood with marked loss of interest in almost all of the usual activities.
4. During the depressed periods, these symptoms were present: insomnia; low energy level; feelings of inadequacy; decreased effectiveness in schoolwork; decreased attention, concentra-

tion, or ability to think clearly; social withdrawal; loss of interest in or enjoyment of pleasurable activities; inability to respond with pleasure to praise; less active or talkative than usual; and pessimistic attitude toward the future, brooding about past events, and feeling sorry for himself.

5. Finally, psychotic features were absent.

METHODS FOR UNDERSTANDING THE PATIENT'S SHIFTS IN DEPRESSION

To understand the context of the patient's repeated mood shifts, my colleagues and I used four methods of data analysis successively, each with special assets. We began with a clinical review and reinspection of the contexts (Method 1). Then we derived categories for rating the contexts and added some from other symptom-context research (Method 2). We fashioned or selected scoring systems for some of the categories to be rated (Method 3). Finally, we examined the broader background conditions of the session as a whole (Method 4).

Method 1: Clinical Review of Contexts

Before discussing the themes uncovered in the clinical review, I present excerpts from Mr. Quinn's transcripts to illustrate the contexts in which each of the nine depressive shifts occurred and the main themes across the nine instances.

Excerpts Illustrating Shifts Toward Decreased Depression

Session 60 (p. 7). The therapist interpreted the reason for the patient's depression as wanting the therapist to shove him out of the depression. The patient agreed and then snapped out of his depression.

Session 77 (p. 14). The therapist made a long interpretation about the patient's relationship with him: "When you want to get closer and you're not getting the response you want, then you fall into depression." The patient agreed and then snapped out of his depression, but explained his decreased depression on the basis of having just looked at a note in his hand, which he had brought with him to the session, reminding him that the *Merck Manual* says that depression is due to lots of things and, therefore, was not due to the "total abject hopelessness of the real facts."

Session 144 (p. 17). The patient was very angry at the therapist and said he felt like "ripping out [the therapist's] bookshelf." His depression then lifted.

Session 172 (pp. 14–15). The therapist said, "You were in a lost state and all alone in relation to me," and the patient then asked, "What do you want me to do?" The therapist replied, "Pull out of the depression." The patient did. The technique here involved both interpreting the conflict specifically in terms of the relationship to the therapist and then using the patient's accessibility to direct him to pull out of his depression. A brief excerpt from the transcript of about 200 words before and 200 words after the shift illustrates the technique.

P: . . . longer ago than I thought. It's been bad since the last exam which I didn't do well in. I mean I did all right but I didn't take it feeling well.

T: Oh, you did all right and it sounds like ever since this uh . . .

P: Well . . .

T: . . . new girlfriend that you've been getting more worried.

P: Probably that's where it starts but, but--I--you know, what am I gonna do? I mean . . .

T: Well apparently the first thing is to see if you, you can't get out of this state you're in. The state in which you feel . . .

P: Well, sure.

T: . . . that nothing I say and nothing you say can be heard.

P: Yeah.

T: All that can be heard is this cry for help, kind of, thing: "There is nothing I can do." You've sort of given up almost.

P: Well, I don't know. I th--it's like I've been trying to forg--all this time and I--for 2 years and then I--I still don't seem to have the tools to be able to do anything about it.

T: It varies. It varies very much.

P: Hm. Yeah, but, I know it varies. For four months |³⁰⁰I could do what I wanted but then all of a sudden . . . May--I mean maybe I wasn't doing what I was wanted. I was messing around with some chick who meant nothing to me and, and who was just a good lay.

T: Well, once you get in this state then everything gets interpreted in terms of it. You say . . .

P: I know.

T: . . . everything!

P: Well, I don't, I don't know what to do. I'm lost. I really feel . . .

T: That's what I'm reacting to. You're in this kind of lost state where somehow you feel out of reach. You're crying all alone a lot.

P: Yeah. I am. I--I don't know that anyone can do anything. I mean I'm, I'm I'm at a lo--I uh--I feel like going now. I mean I don't know what to do. I mean I'm really not--I don't know. (pause) Okay. What do you want me to do?

T: See if you can't get this state under control so we can start to go over what's happening.

P: Okay. What do you want me to do? I'll stop it. $\downarrow^{400}$(SHIFT POINT)$\downarrow$ What?

T: Well, now let's go over what it is and see if it has some meaning to you. That all these--about 20 minutes or so, 25 minutes or so--you've been saying a lot but you haven't been able to listen to any of it somehow.

P: No.

T: Y'know, both of us can agree about a lot of it but it isn't meaningful somehow . . .

P: Right.

T: And you're saying you just can't stop it. The state can be called, kind of, crying alone. I don't know whether that--that seems to describe it to me. You're not with yourself and you're not with me. Neither one.

P: Yeah.

T: What--suppose you try and describe it. Does it say--it sounds like you're alone and it sounds like you're crying and you're saying someone else has to do something. There's nothing you can do. Doesn't it feel that way, like you've sort of thrown in the towel you've given up?

P: Yeah, that's exactly what I'm doing. You see I'm--now I'm trying not to but I . . . I don't know.

T: I know you're trying not to and it felt to me like somehow that part of you which had been obliterated suddenly asserted itself again. It said, Okay, here I am . . .

P: No, it was there all the time. I just didn't feel I should show it then, or something.

T: Why not?

P: I don't . . . 'cause I, I didn't ha--I don't know. Probably because I want to make you suffer or something like that. Because I'm trying to--to show you that you're no good or that I'm--that I'm--that I'm right or something like that.

T: All right. And I'm no good because, because you're no good, why . . .

P: Yeah.

T: I'm no good because I can't help you out of that state . . .

P: Exactly. Right. I mean th--th--th--th--uh--uh you can be depressed an' it's a wonderful weapon. I mean like if I left here depressed I--I don't know. I--I'm sure you'd learn how to deal with it but, I mean, you know, at least to my untrained eye, looking at it from my prospective view, if a patient leaves a doctor and he's still terribly depressed its an--and you're pissed off at him, it's a good way of getting at 'im, I mean . . .

T: All right. Okay.

P: I mean, I should suspect, you know, you know how to deal with that but, but, eh, at least it'ssss a weapon but all right, see, I'm . . .

T: Okay, now that you know . . .

P: . . . it's just general hostility.

T: Okay, now that you're back with yourself it really begins to make sense . . .

P: I could hate you . . .

Session 175 (p. 18). The therapist told the patient that things were not bad; it was just the way he saw them when he was depressed. Then when the patient was more accessible, the therapist said, "Enough of this." The patient then pulled out of his depression.

Excerpts Illustrating Shifts Toward Increased Depression

Session 135 (p. 5). The patient referred to a dream of himself and a girl he wanted, a girl who could be gotten by a much stronger man than he: "If it's me then I'm not strong enough." The patient then got depressed.

Session 135 (p. 11). The therapist referred to the patient's conception of the role of a patient with a therapist as a situation involving one person being inferior to the other. The patient's depression then increased. He explained that he was going to talk about his relationship with a divorced woman, where he felt inadequate in relation to her greater experience.

Session 138 (p. 11). The patient was thinking over whether he should or should not write to a girl whom he wanted to write to. He found himself unable to speak to the therapist about his decision for which he felt inadequate and then he got depressed.

Session 144 (pp. 21–22). The patient was speaking about hating his father. He began to get guilty and then depressed. The buildup of guilt was the patient's explanation for his depression. A brief excerpt shows this very clearly.

P: ... he [father] was poor (meaning the father had no money), $|^{250}$see, and I was always taught that they (poor people) were kind of bad. I was. Really!

T: By whom?

P: Guys like Johnny, or Robert, and, and, and, and Jane. You know what it was, I mean, really. He spit, too. I remember they said, "Your father spits." And, I mean, I don't know. I've $|^{200}$never know--I guess he does. But, I remember it, and I was a poor, and so was he. Well, I guess, that's something I could've forgiven him for maybe. I hated Sunday School. (pause)

T: It was too easy to forget that uh he was your father and that was too easy to think you could put him on his ass?

P: Well, I don't know. I probably just felt bad about it. I didn't want to fight $|^{100}$with him.

T: That's exactly what you did. You felt that you had to feel bad every time you thought of sticking him on his ass.

P: Yeah, but I never did.

T: You never did but you often wanted to.

P: Heh, no, I don't think I ever did wa--think of ... Y'know, I don't-- I mean--there was never anything to fight about. Well there was a thing--reasons to fight--okay, I guess I am s ... I hate 'im now sometimes but (sigh), $|^{50}$I mean, he never did a damn thing. He was useless. He made money. I mean, all right, I will consider him within the--his historical milieu and, and, blah, blah, blah and [economic] depressions and not having anything to eat and all that shit--But I--I--I don't know. ↓(SHIFT POINT) [0-word point] ↓ This--this just confuses me. This isn't doing me too much good.

T: Why not?

P: I don't know, 'cause I don't feel good now again.

T: Well what was--what did you say that made you not feel good right then?

P: 'Cause I just got all back and depressed again when I wasn't. I was out ten percent then.

T: That's right, you were. Then catch what made you feel all depressed again.

P: Something about my father, I guess.

T: Yes.

P: I don't know. I |[50]was fighting him or something.

T: Yes.

P: That I hated him.

T: Yes, yes.

P: Why I had to feel guilty about . . .

T: Yes.

P: . . . hating him?

T: Yes.

P: Well, I guess you do. You have to love your father, and all that shit.

T: Right. Yeah. And so if you hate him and you feel like fighting him and setting him on his ass, then you have to feel depressed about the whole damn thing.

P: And it's therefore I feel that way with all males|[93]

T: Honest to God you do.

Summary of Clinical Review Findings

One obvious preliminary generalization that fits all nine depressive shifts is that their context reflects stressful patient–therapist exchanges. The five shifts in which the patient decreased his depression were ones involving the therapist's interpretation about the relationship with the patient; the patient agreed with the interpretation, and the effect of the interpretation was to pull him into a closer positive relationship with the therapist. The increased positive response derived sometimes from the therapist's interpretation of the conflict in the relationship and sometimes from the therapist's fairly direct statement that the patient could or should put aside his depression.

The four instances in which the patient increased his depression were usually ones where the patient (rather than the therapist) was speaking before the shift. The immediate trigger for increased depression appears therefore, to be largely patient-determined—the patient came upon a theme that made him feel guilty, worthless, loss of self-esteem, hostility to himself, and then hopeless.[2] Usually the theme involved comparing himself with another man and feeling inferior and inadequate.

The two instances in Session 144 are good examples of what parts of the theme tipped the balance toward or away from depression. In the shift toward decreased depression (transcript p. 17), the patient felt angry and spoke of wanting to rip out the therapist's bookshelf; being able to speak in this way to express his anger and feeling good about it seemed to make him feel strong and so his depression decreased. In terms of one of Freud's concepts, his hostility was turned outward rather than turned inward.

In the other instance in the same session in which his depression increased (transcript p. 21), he had a similar thought in that it involved anger, but in this one it was at his father. He began to feel guilty, inferior, and hopeless because he had such thoughts, and then felt more depressed. In terms of another of Freud's concepts of symptom formation, it involved hopelessness and helplessness along with lowered self-esteem and hostility-inward—all clearly expressed in this instance.

After reading the same four examples of increases in depression, other clinicians who had slightly different emphases still had a core of agreement about the issue of competition with men and resulting feelings of helplessness and hopelessness. There are examples of the comments made to me by four outstanding psychoanalysts:

1. "He is mainly preoccupied with taking a woman from you; secondly, with helplessness."
2. "Whenever he feels 'hubris' (pride), he has a depressive shift, for example, in showing the therapist his wedding ring or speaking of throwing father on his ass."
3. "He has hostility to the therapist that threatens the narcissistic union with the therapist."
4. "Helplessness is outstanding in all the examples. Secondly, the pre-oedipal level sets the stage for the response to frustration on the oedipal level."

Method 2: Rated Variables in Symptom Versus Control Contexts

Ratings of each of the nine shift segments—the five toward decreased depression and the four toward increased depression—were made independently by two clinically trained judges who had had some training in the

---

[2]Freud's theory (1917/1957) involving hostility-inward is obviously much more complex than is represented by that one variable. For example, Freud also spoke about using the hostility to hurt the introjected object. This component of the theory seems to be represented in the patient's explanations after the instance in Session 172 (transcript p. 15) where the patient spoke (p. 16) of using the depression "to make you suffer" and commented, "It's a wonderful weapon."

rating of the 16 variables. Each rating was done on a graphic 5-point scale (with half-point divisions permitted). Both judges were aware of the usual clinical hypotheses about depression and of the time point of the depressive mood shift in the segments.

Agreement of Judges

Each judge rated the nine segments for each of the eight 100-word units of the patient's speech, that is, the four 100-word units before the shift and the four 100-word units after the shift. The correlations were based on an N of 72 (8 units within each of the 9 segments). This appeared to be an adequate method, because we wished only to know how these variables covaried; the loss of independence seemed preferable to the loss of information that would have resulted from combining all eight 100-word units for each segment. Therefore, we have not computed significance tests.

As was shown in Table 1, the interjudge correlations were generally satisfactory in level and somewhat similar to the levels of reliability obtained for those variables in other symptom-context studies (e.g., Luborsky et al., 1975). The highest of the reliabilities, .87, was for the criterion variable Depression; Helplessness was next highest, .81; Concern about Supplies was .77; Hostility to Self, .52; and Loss of Self-Esteem, .51.

Ratings Before and After the Depressive Mood Shifts and Their Intercorrelations

The main rating trends are depicted in a graph (see Figure 1) of the mean ratings for the two judges over the eight 100-word units—for the four segments with increased depression and the five segments with decreased depression. The shape of these curves for depression before and after the shift turned out to be what had been expected. The curve for increased depression shoots up at the end of the fourth segment and remains up. The decreased depression curve drops down at the end of the fourth segment and remains down.

The curves also reveal that in the segments in which the patient was most depressed, the ratings were just a little over 3.0, indicating only moderate depression. Therefore, it should be noted that in terms of the ratings, the shifts to increased depression are moderate and not really marked shifts—they are shifts from a mean of about 1.5 to a little over 3.0; the same occurs in reverse for the shifts toward lessened depression.

Note that the expected effects of the shift to increased depression (see Tables 2 and 3) occur just after the patient makes the statement about increased depression, "I am starting to get depressed now." The obvious comparison that should be made for this symptom occurs just *after* it is

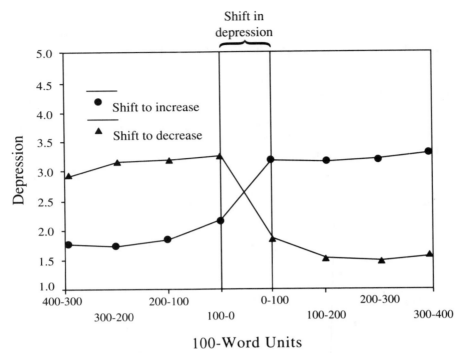

Figure 1. Ratings of Depression for 400 words before and 400 words after depression (means of two judges for each word unit).

TABLE 3
Rated Variables That Were Significantly Different Just After Shifts in Depression for Mr. Quinn

Variable	t (0-100 unit)	p (one-tailed)
Guilt	4.15	.002
Loss of Self-Esteem	3.33	.007
Hostility to Self	2.97	.011
Hopelessness	2.85	.013
Anxiety	2.43	.023
Blocked	2.41	.024
Concern about Supplies	1.99	.044
Oedipal Conflict	1.90	.050
Helplessness	—	+
Depression	—	+

Note. Helplessness and Depression are included in the table because, despite missing data, the existing data imply that they are significantly discriminating of symptom segments versus controls.

expressed. The differences (*ts*) for the 100-word units just after the symptom is expressed show eight discriminating variables, which are listed in rank order in Table 3 (see Figures 2, 3, and 4).

Helplessness (see Figure 5) is a variable that is very similar to depression in the shape of its curve (see Figure 1) and in its intercorrelations (see Table 4). Higher intercorrelations are shown for Depression and Helplessness ratings than for any other pair of variables: .95 (before) and .99 (after) for pooled ratings. Although the level of the Helplessness curve happens to be slightly higher in the third and fourth unit than the curve for Depression, this difference is not significant.

It is noteworthy, therefore, that the helplessness–hopelessness dimension is especially closely associated with the depression curve. Also every one of the variables that we listed as being associated with the three concepts of depression have curves that are similar to the depression curves. The remaining variables are less correlated with the depression curves.

Somewhat similar results are found by an analysis of variance comparing the four 100-word units before the shift to the four 100-word units after the shift (see Table 5).[3] The ranks of these for the ratings of increased depression segments in order are Loss of Self-Esteem, Helplessness, Depression, Hostility to Self (and the scored versions of two of these, Helplessness manual score and Hostility-Inward total). The mostly similar variables that were most discriminating for the five decreased depression segments were (starting with the most significant): Blocked, Guilt, Hostility to Self, Depression, and Hopelessness.

The intercorrelation of variables for the nine segments each with data averaged over four 100-word units before the shifts and four 100-word units after the shifts are presented in Table 4. A brief cluster picture is depicted in Figure 6. For simplicity of extracting the cluster a level of .8 was used. Helplessness correlated highly with Anxiety, Hopelessness, Blocked, Guilt, Reflective, Hostility to Self, Loss of Self-Esteem, the Helplessness manual score, and Explanatory Style.

Method 3: Scoring Variables

My colleagues and I used several systems to score eight variables, some of which were described briefly in the earlier section "Theoretical Bases."

---

[3]Significance tests were performed taking together rated and scored variables and using a two-factor analysis of variance in which type of segment (increased versus decreased depression) was considered a between-subject factor and location (before versus after the shift) was considered a repeated measures factor. The data were averaged over the four 100-word units before the shift and over the four 100-word units after the shift.

In order to understand the nature of the interaction effects, separate analyses of variance were computed for the increased depression segments and also for the decreased depression segments using location (before versus after the shift) as the only factor. The important changes are for those variables which significantly differ before versus after the shift in order of those with the highest *F*-ratios ranked first (see Table 5).

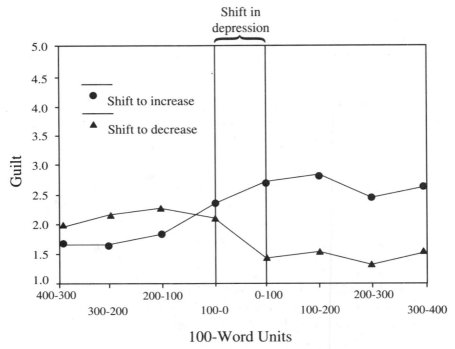

Figure 2. Ratings of Guilt for 400 words before and 400 words after depression (means of two judges for each word unit).

These scoring systems generally were not as significant in discriminating symptom segments (before shift to increased depression) from controls (before shift to decreased depression), in contrast to the rating system. In this section, I describe how each of the eight variables were scored.

Reference to Therapist

The number of References to the Therapist of any kind in each word unit were counted. The measure did not significantly discriminate symptom segments from controls, although the score correlated moderately well with the rated variable Involvement with Therapist—.60 before and .77 after the shift in depression (see Table 4).

Helplessness Manual

A scoring scale called Helplessness manual (Luborsky, 1976; see Table 6) was constructed for Helplessness, one of the most central variables theoretically, and its closely related variable, Hopelessness. The scale contained four categories of negative items, some derived from Engel and Schmale's (1967) giving-up, given-up complex: (a) feeling helpless; (b) describing the situation as too much, that is, too difficult to deal with; (c)

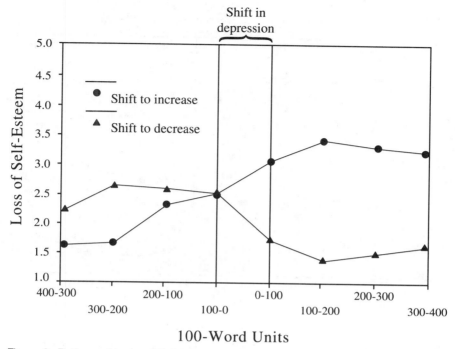

Figure 3. Ratings of Loss of Self-Esteem for 400 words before and 400 words after depression (means of two judges for each word unit).

believing that relationships can give no help or gratification; and (d) feeling hopeless and giving up efforts to cope. (The Helplessness manual also contains a positive pole that allows for a negative minus positive difference score; this was also used for the analyses presented in this chapter, although the results with it were similar to each pole separately.) The text of the transcript was divided into phrases, and every phrase containing a scorable item was underlined and the scores noted in the margin. Only the main score given to each phrase was summed for the present analyses. Interjudge reliability for scoring the Helplessness manual was high: $r = .86$ (see Table 1). The score did not show a significant difference between the increased depression and decreased depression segments in the 100-word unit after the shift (see Figure 7). The analysis of variance for the increased depression segments was significant (see Table 5).

Hostility-Inward

This variable, crucial to one of Freud's theories of depression (1917/ 1957), was independently scored on the Gottschalk and Gleser (1969) scoring system by Carolyn Winget, an expert on the scales. The value of

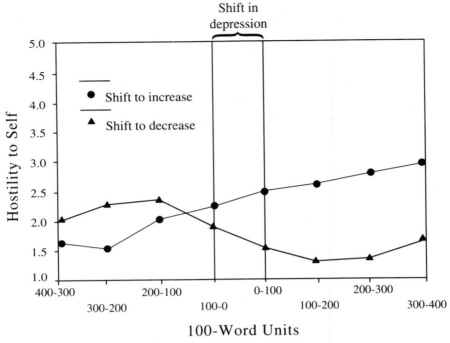

Figure 4. Ratings of Hostility to Self for 400 words before and 400 words after depression (means of two judges for each word unit).

these results was augmented by the fact that this expert only had the transcripts and knew nothing about our study. Her results provided an independent confirmation—the curves for her scorings in Figure 8 are of the same shape as those from our ratings.

The items in the Gottschalk-Gleser Hostility-Inward scale are composed of 11 subtypes. These, in turn, fit into three main subtypes, a, b, and c. The a and b consist of items that refer explicitly to anger at the self, that is, they are more directly an estimate of Hostility-Inward, whereas c refers to "disappointment, loneliness, discouragement, giving up hope, despairing, grieving, being depressed, having no purpose in life" (p. 34). In other words, these c items are more related to depression than are the a and b items. Moderate correlations between their Hostility-Inward scale (total) and various depression scales are reported in Gottschalk and Gleser (1969).

In our data, Hostility-Inward (c) correlated .61 with Depression ratings (see Figure 6), although Hostility-Inward (a + b) items correlated only .31 with Depression ratings (Luborsky & Alexander, 1989). In summary, the Hostility-Inward scores, especially the subtype c, appear to reflect depression and show the same main trends in relation to the shift points. Because this measure is completely independently assessed, it serves to im-

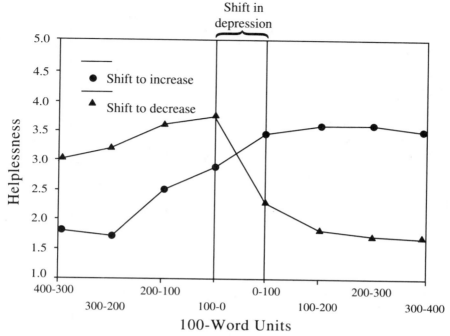

Figure 5. Ratings of Helplessness for 400 words before and 400 words after depression (means of two judges for each word unit).

prove the objectivity of the assessment of this variable. The analysis of variance (Table 5) turned up a significant result for Hostility-Inward (total) at $p < .05$.

Cognitive and Speech Disturbance

These measures (described in chap. 3) were used in an effort to assess likely facets of attention disturbance. For the 100-word unit after the shift, the speech disturbance measure showed a significant (.05) result in distinguishing symptom segments (increased depression) versus controls (decreased depression).[4]

Explanatory Style

This variable, as was mentioned briefly under Theory 4 earlier in the chapter, was derived from the reformulated learned helplessness theory (Abramson, Seligman, & Teasdale, 1978). As Peterson et al. (1983) hy-

---

[4]Detailed results for the first four scored variables are given in Table 7: Reference to Therapist, Helplessness manual (Difference score), and Cognitive and Speech Disturbance.

TABLE 4
Intercorrelations of Rated and Scored Variables With Each Other

Variable	1	2	3	4	5	6	7
			After				
Rated							
1. Concern about Supplies		11	11	74	76	72	01
2. Anxiety	73		09	04	−28	−41	−38
3. Separation Anxiety	07	−03		−16	−14	−11	−54
4. Helplessness	71	86	−19		92	78	11
5. Hopelessness	77	83	−24	91		89	29
6. Blocked	83	90	−15	97	94		42
7. Blocked by Therapist	60	42	−59	65	66	64	
8. Guilt	74	82	−23	93	95	99	61
9. Hostility	11	−38	−26	−15	−22	−21	40
10. Hostility to Therapist	39	18	−52	25	22	28	82
11. Reflective	84	78	−14	95	93	97	70
12. Reflective to Therapist	33	05	23	−19	10	−03	−04
13. Reference to Therapist	07	09	−61	−16	05	−05	26
14. Involvement with Therapist	57	46	−43	42	58	46	78
15. Hostility to Self	75	93	−11	89	94	93	49
16. Loss of Self-Esteem	78	94	−06	96	89	98	52
17. Oedipal Conflict	08	−30	68	−24	−20	−18	−42
Scored							
18. Hostility-Inward (total)	70	62	−38	69	89	73	76
19. Hostility-Inward (a + b)	49	79	02	69	81	70	26
20. Hostility-Inward (c)	63	30	−56	46	65	52	89
21. Helplessness manual score	74	79	−44	93	92	93	81
22. Explanatory Style	66	86	29	82	79	83	18
			Before				

continues

pothesized, explanations about negative events that are internal ("It is caused by me"), stable ("It will always be me"), and global ("It is generally me") will precede increased depressive symptoms, but external, unstable, and specific explanations will precede decreased depressive symptoms.

To test this theory, the same nine segments (800 words each) for Mr. Quinn were scored for explanatory style by four other independent judges (examples from Peterson et al., 1983, are provided in Table 8). Because the three explanatory style dimensions are known to be highly intercorrelated, a composite is typically used. The composite was reliably scored (.83) by the four judges (Peterson et al., 1983).

It is of interest for the validity of the measure that the explanatory style composite before the shift was highly correlated with the kinds of variables with which it would be expected to correlate (see Table 4). The correlations that were above .80 are Anxiety, .86; Helplessness, .82; Blocked, .83; Guilt, .82; Hostility to Self, .89; Loss of Self-Esteem, .88; and Hostility-Inward (a + b), .82. After the shift, the correlations tend to be

TABLE 4 (Continued)

Variable	8	9	10	11	12	13	14	15
				After				
Rated								
1. Concern about Supplies	55	−69	−25	73	−57	02	−19	78
2. Anxiety	−37	−49	−36	−10	29	−10	−50	09
3. Separation Anxiety	27	24	−43	−18	24	−36	−54	−07
4. Helplessness	58	−47	−09	99	−91	−23	−08	83
5. Hopelessness	68	−40	02	95	−95	−08	11	76
6. Blocked	61	−20	31	84	−81	17	35	62
7. Blocked by Therapist	−14	11	81	17	−22	78	92	−25
8. Guilt		−04	−24	65	−60	−28	−25	69
9. Hostility	−07		34	−40	30	00	28	−63
10. Hostility to Therapist	23	60		05	−05	74	94	−32
11. Reflective	95	−06	31		−95	−20	−01	82
12. Reflective to Therapist	12	15	11	02		25	−10	−74
13. Reference to Therapist	02	10	46	−14	39		77	−34
14. Involvement with Therapist	52	37	72	47	43	60		−35
15. Hostility to Self	95	−28	13	87	19	08	53	
16. Loss of Self-Esteem	93	−24	21	93	−01	−08	40	94
17. Oedipal Conflict	−30	−38	−51	−10	04	−61	−58	−28
Scored								
18. Hostility-Inward (total)	81	06	46	77	38	31	81	79
19. Hostility-Inward (a + b)	79	−29	−06	65	32	02	46	89
20. Hostility-Inward (c)	56	30	69	61	30	42	81	46
21. Helplessness manual score	90	−05	43	91	−13	14	62	84
22. Explanatory Style	82	−40	−20	78	08	−29	21	89
				Before				

continues

negative. The two most negative are Blocked, −.80, and Blocked by Therapist, −.83.

For each of the 800-word segments for Mr. Quinn's sessions, average composite scores were made for the units before and after the shift; the means are shown in Figure 9. The differences predicted by the helplessness reformulation were shown before and after the shifts—the more internal, stable, and global explanations preceded increased depression, whereas the more external, unstable, and specific explanations came before decreased depression. Some differences in types of explanations predicted by the theory were indeed present by an unweighted means analysis of variance (Winer, 1971) in which type of session (increased depression versus decreased depression versus control samples with no change in depression) was considered a between-subjects factor, and location (before versus after shift) was considered a repeated-measures factor ($F(2,9) = 33.12$, $p < .001$) as is reported more fully in Peterson et al. (1983).

TABLE 4 (*Continued*)

Variable	16	17	18	19	20	21	22
			After				
Rated							
1. Concern about Supplies	80	−22	58	11	59	62	−37
2. Anxiety	−22	−01	−29	−01	−30	−14	50
3. Separation Anxiety	14	79	−15	42	−21	−17	29
4. Helplessness	78	−46	88	22	89	97	−52
5. Hopelessness	82	−45	94	19	96	93	−72
6. Blocked	77	−42	73	00	76	79	−80
7. Blocked by Therapist	−20	−56	14	−58	22	16	−83
8. Guilt	75	21	72	75	65	65	−28
9. Hostility	−44	49	−30	05	−31	−29	01
10. Hostility to Therapist	−26	−50	−10	−50	−04	−04	−64
11. Reflective	81	−45	92	23	93	99	−59
12. Reflective to Therapist	−78	53	−97	−21	−98	−96	66
13. Reference to Therapist	−35	−33	−33	−59	−27	−28	−46
14. Involvement with Therapist	−25	−55	−03	−62	05	−02	−72
15. Hostility to Self	90	−30	75	49	72	77	−17
16. Loss of Self-Esteem		−18	77	40	75	76	−32
17. Oedipal Conflict	−21		−37	47	−45	−41	56
Scored							
18. Hostility-Inward (total)	66	−32		38	99	95	−58
19. Hostility-Inward (a + b)	74	−27	74		27	28	29
20. Hostility-Inward (c)	38	−26	87	31		95	−64
21. Helplessness manual score	87	−38	79	59	68		−58
22. Explanatory Style	88	02	51	82	12	66	
			Before				

Note. Intercorrelations of variables are based on nine segments, each with data averaged over four 100-word units before the shift and four 100 word units after the shift. Decimal points are omitted. Numbers below the diagonal were before the shift and those above the diagonal were after the shift. Adapted from Luborsky et al. (1984, p. 180) with permission.

The significant effect was for type of session. Explanatory Style did not yield significant effects for location or type of session-by-location interaction. This is the major difference between the explanatory style variable and the variables we used—explanatory style distinguished the type of segment but changed little over the shift points. It appears to be a kind of background trait; in contrast, the variables we used are very sensitive to the shifts into and out of depression.

The findings about Mr. Quinn's explanatory styles and the themes that were implicated in them suggest several conclusions. The themes center around helplessness and efficacy (Seligman, 1975), and they imply that attributional style concepts of depression are compatible with the psychodynamic concepts offered in this chapter. They also reveal that causal explanations are part of a broader pattern to be described under background factors in terms of the CCRT. Finally, the causal explanations were assessed

TABLE 5
F Ratios From Analyses of Variance Comparing Four 100-Word Units
Before Versus After Depressive Shifts

Variable	4 Increased depression segments	Rank[a]	5 Decreased depression segments	Rank[a]
Rated				
Concern about Supplies	4.38		11.88*	
Anxiety	2.47		16.69*	6
Separation Anxiety	4.42		<1	
Helplessness	46.68**	2	12.47*	
Hopelessness	9.63		22.25**	5
Blocked	12.84*	8	132.26***	1
Blocked by Therapist	6.40		3.46	
Guilt	9.64		52.07**	2
Hostility	<1		<1	
Hostility to Therapist	5.87		1.30	
Depression	36.77**	3	30.89**	4
Reflective	1.18		3.17	
Involvement with Therapist	15.71*	7	1	
Hostility to Self	20.50*	4	31.84**	3
Loss of Self-Esteem	54.98**	1	11.56*	
Oedipal Conflict	2.78		1.15	
Scored				
Reference to Therapist	1.71		1.27	
Helplessness manual score	17.18*	5	13.02*	7
Hostility-Inward (total)	17.13*	6	4.73	
Hostility-Inward (a + b)	7.78		4.38	
Hostility-Inward (c)	6.68		6.31	
Explanatory Style				

[a]For example, from before to after the shift in mood to increased depression, the loss of self-esteem was greatest of all the variables examined, therefore, it is assigned a rank of 1.
$p < .05$ $p < .01$ $p < .001$.

from naturally occurring statements in psychotherapy (Schulman, Castellon, & Seligman, 1989), rather than from the more usual attributional style questionnaire (Seligman, Abramson, Semmel, & von Baeyer, 1979).

Voice

To further examine what is shifting, we decided to go beyond inferences from the transcript and to determine whether shifts in affect could be recognized by listening to the tape recordings. A variety of emotions, such as grief and anger, have been shown to be judgeable from voice qualities (see, e.g., Costanzo, Markel, & Costanzo, 1969; Markel, Meisels, & Houck, 1964).

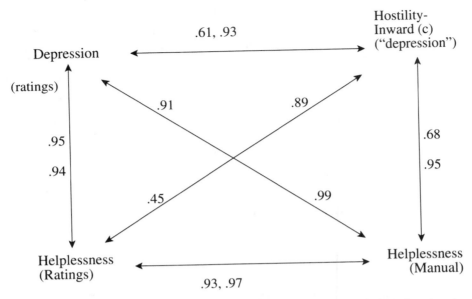

Figure 6. Cluster sketch of principal intercorrelations. The first correlation of each pair is before the shift, the second is after.

Two judges working independently listened to the tapes of the nine segments and rated the affect of depression. The first finding was that depressive tone in the voice could be recognized with a high degree of agreement by the two judges ($r = .89$). The next finding was that the depressive shifts were usually accompanied by recognizable shifts in depressive tone in the voice: For both judges, the ratings for only two of the nine segments did not include a shift in depressive tone, and for three more, the shift was only moderate. For the other four segments, the shift in depressive tone was commensurate with what had been inferred from the transcript alone. This analysis suggested that transcript analysis restricts the judges' access to cues to affective tone. It may be, therefore, that the results of such analysis overplay the cognition of helplessness as a main component of depression ratings and somewhat underestimate the affective component of depression.

Rate of Speech

We suspected that the rate of speech slowed as the patient became more depressed and speeded up as the patient became less depressed. Rate of speech, sometimes called fluency, is thought to change in relation to change in depressive mood (e.g., Cattell, 1950). Aronson and Weintraub (1967) compared improved depressed patients with unimproved depressed patients on a 10-minute sample of speech. As predicted, the improved

TABLE 6
Helplessness Versus Capability Scoring Manual

Negative pole: Helplessness		Positive pole: Capability	
Categories	Examples	Categories	Examples
a− *Feeling helpless* (Feeling unable to function and not confident of own ability)	I am not performing well. I don't know anything. I am unsure of myself. I can't do, respond, think. I feel inadequate. I feel ineffectual. I don't know what to do. I screwed everything up.	a+ *Feeling able to cope and not helpless*	I am doing well.
b− *Describing the situation as "too much"*	I am victimized or manipulated by (person). Things are too difficult to deal with.	b+ *Describing the situation as manageable*	The job is one I can handle.
c− *Believing that relationships can give no help or gratification*	Nobody helps. You can't or aren't helping me. I'm wasting time in treatment. I don't get enjoyment from it anymore.	c+ *Believing that relationships can give help and gratification* (Affiliative behaviors shown by relationships within treatment and outside of treatment; feels he or she is benefiting from treatment)	You (therapist) are able to help me. ___ is a person who can or who does help me.
d− *Feeling hopeless and giving up efforts to cope*	I have given up. What's the difference? What's the use? It's useless to try. There's no sense in doing anything. Nothing is worth it. Nothing works. I can't change.	d+ *Feeling hopeful and making efforts to cope* (Initiates activities)	I suppose if I keep going, things will get better.

Note. Adapted from Luborsky et al. (1984, p. 175) with permission.

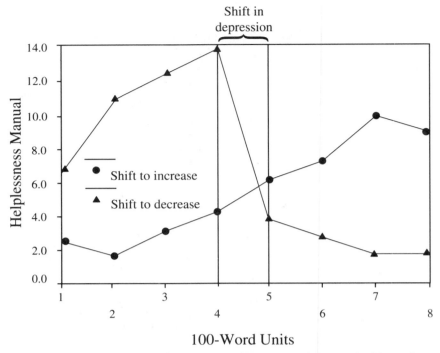

Figure 7. Scorings of Helplessness manual for 400 words before and 400 words after depression (score of one judge for each word unit).

patients spoke at a more normal rate of speech than did the less improved patients.

Our own observations were based on moment-to-moment shifts in depression in relation to the rate of speech, and they provided some evidence along the lines we expected. The curve for the eight 100-word units was examined for each of the nine segments in terms of the lowest point versus the highest point on the curve. All four of the increased depression segments showed their lowest point of speech rate after the shift. Three of the five decreased depression segments showed a point of increased speech rate after the shift. Taking the nine segments together, therefore, seven out of the nine showed consistency in these terms.

Another way to analyze the same data is in terms of the direction of the change in rate of speech. Of the four increased depression segments, all four showed a slowing in speech rate. The five decreased depression segments did not show the same consistency in terms of change in speech rate: from the third to the fourth 100-word unit, only one of the five showed increased speech rate, and from the third to the fifth, only two of the five showed an increase in speech rate.

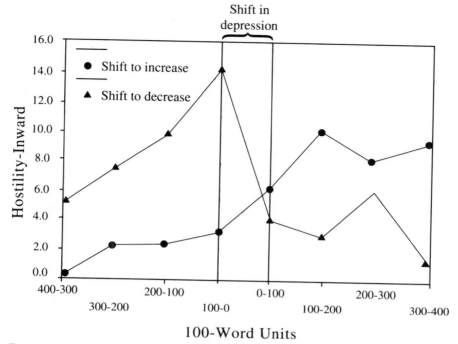

Figure 8. Scorings of Hostility-Inward for 400 words before and 400 words after depression (score of one judge for each word unit: Carolyn Winget).

Method 4: Evaluating the Broad Background Context

Our report so far has concerned the immediate psychological context of shifts in depressive mood and only tangentially touched on any background factors that might be involved. In other studies we have dealt with background factors that were revealed by examining much larger segments than we have done in the present study. Background factors are likely to emerge; for example, Beck (1967) stressed as major background factors negative attitudes toward oneself, the outside world, and one's future. These negative attitudes, which often begin early in a person's development, are set off by specific stresses, which is what we probably are measuring in the analyses presented in this chapter. The general level of stress is another background factor that makes some individuals more depression-prone at certain times than at others.

Comparison of the CCRT and the Symptom-Context Theme

The CCRT is based on the entire session and sometimes a series of sessions (Luborsky, 1977, in press). The symptom-context theme is based

TABLE 7
Scored Variables Within Word Units Before and After Shifts in Depression

	Word units before depressive shift						Word units after depressive shift					
	400-300		100-0		400-0		0-100		300-400		0-400	
Scored variable	t	p	t	p	t	p	t	p	t	p	t	p
Reference to Therapist	.74	.244	.61	.288	.56	.304	−.25	.407	−1.62	.091	−.20	.424
Helplessness manual (Difference score)	−2.79	.013	−3.14	.018	−4.01	.006	.59	.286	1.00	.195	1.38	.105
Cognitive Disturbance	1.23	.115	1.04	.154	.79	.219	1.01	.160	1.79	.042	2.25	.016
Speech Disturbance	−.56	.297	2.60	.018	1.54	.084	2.03	.041	1.20	.135	1.46	.093

Note. All *p* values are one-tailed.

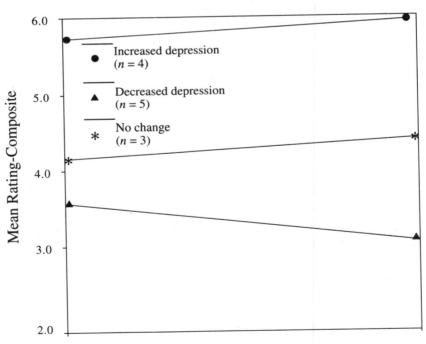

Figure 9. Means of internal, stable, and global ratings of attributions before and after mood shifts for different types of Mr. Quinn's sessions.

TABLE 8

Examples of Attribution Ratings for the Explanatory Style of Mr. Quinn

Event and attribution	Judge	Internality	Stability	Globality
I feel bothered—I'm comparing again . . . and she's stronger than me and brighter than me.	A	6	6	5
	B	7	7	7
	C	6	7	6
	D	6	7	6
I'm depressed—I studied a case for like 6 or 8 hours, and I couldn't get it in my mind.	A	7	3	5
	B	7	4	3
	C	7	1	1
	D	6	2	2
I was talking to D., and he was flirting with the idea of becoming a surgeon, and I found that tedious—We had a lecture on surgery today, and some of the things they do are awful.	A	1	3	4
	B	1	3	3
	C	1	1	1
	D	2	1	1
I feel mad at you—It's your trivial little bit of science fiction, of trying to make reality conform to the jargon you use in your trade.	A	1	6	2
	B	1	7	1
	C	1	7	1
	D	1	7	1
I was ashamed that I was held back in school—'cause I was a year behind my cousins, and I started out the same. I had to do a great deal of compensating to overcome it.	A	5	4	5
	B	1	4	4
	C	4	2	7
	D	5	2	3

Note. Internality, stability, and globality ratings were made on 7-point rating scales by Judges A, B, C, and D. Adapted from Peterson, Luborsky, & Seligman (1983, p. 99) with permission.

on only the immediate context in which the symptom appears. Yet, as was noted in chapter 3 on momentary forgetting, we might find parallels between the two themes. As an illustration, comparison was made between the CCRT for Session 144 and the symptom-context theme. The most obvious similarity is found between the CCRT's responses of self and the most differentiating variables between symptom segments and controls in the symptom-context theme. Some of this parallel is shown in Table 1 of chapter 15 on the therapeutic uses of the symptom-context method.

Comparison between the most significant rated variables for shifts to increased depression versus shifts to decreased depression show that the top qualities were very similar to the top responses of self: (1) Guilt in the symptom context with response of self "to blame himself," (2) Loss of Self-

Esteem with response of self "to feel inadequate," (3) Hostility to Self with response of self "to feel ashamed," and (4) Hopelessness with response of self "to feel hopeless and depressed." It should be emphasized that these analyses leading to comparisons of the symptom-context theme with the CCRT were done completely independently at different times by different assessors.

Integrating Quantitative and Clinical Analyses

I have presented inferences derived from ratings and scorings of the context of Mr. Quinn's shifts in depressive state. To achieve broader dimensions of understanding, these inferences have to be reembedded in the larger framework of the clinical analyses, even though clinical analyses are not as easily subjected to reliability tests. For inference-making, a profitable mutual interaction of the clinical and the quantitative should exist: The clinical analyses suggest variables that may be objectively measured; quantitative results with these variables derive added meaning from the clinical framework.

Further inspection of Mr. Quinn's interactions with the therapist around the shift point revealed that the moments of shift in mood were embedded in moments of shift in the patient–therapist relationship. In instances with a shift to decreased depression, the patient moved to a more positive relationship with the therapist. Mr. Quinn often expressed this through a greater inclination to agree with what the therapist had just said. In instances with a shift toward increased depression, there were signs that the patient had become more negative toward the therapist. It was clearest in three of the four instances (and maybe was implicit in the fourth as well) in which the patient compared himself with another man, often the therapist, who seemed to him more capable of attracting and dealing with a woman. After that thought he experienced a Loss of Self-Esteem and felt put down and Helpless (the analysis of variance p-value was greatest for Loss of Self-Esteem and increased Helplessness). This theme probably also reflects Oedipal Conflict (although the agreement of judges in rating Oedipal Conflict was low, most likely because it was hard for the judges to recognize this variable in such small samples).

A SUMMARY OF FINDINGS ABOUT THE PATIENT'S SHIFTS IN DEPRESSION

The Immediate Symptom Context

For this depression-prone patient, the variables in the symptom's context that changed most before and after the patient-identified shifts in depression were those related to the four theories of depression. The variables included Hopelessness and Helplessness (related to Theory 2), Loss of Self-Esteem (Theory 3), Blocked by Therapist (probably related to Helplessness and Hopelessness), Guilt and Hostility to Self (both associated with Theory 1), and Explanatory Style (associated with Theory 4). The temporal associations of these variables with depression are obvious from inspection of the curves for these variables: They shift markedly in relation to the patient-identified shifts in depression in the direction that would be expected from the increased versus decreased depression segments. In essence, the variables selected from the four theories were prominently represented in the symptom context for this patient, even though each was chosen from a different theory of the onset of depression. This result is not entirely unexpected—each theory reflects a special emphasis, but in this patient, and probably in others as well, the qualities related to the shifts in depression are multifaceted.

Intercorrelations Among Variables

The main variables that shifted as the shift points approached appear to be part of a complex constellation, as is revealed by their intercorrelations (Table 6), but is even more easily seen in a cluster sketch of a few main theory-related variables (Figure 6). Ratings of Depression and Helplessness correlated very highly with each other (.95 before; .99 after). The other theory-related ratings also correlated highly with the more objective Helplessness manual scores, which suggests much overlap in what they measure.

The Temporal Association of Helplessness and Depression

The high correlation level of .95 (before) and .99 (after) between Helplessness and Depression ratings supports the view of those who claim that judgments of Helplessness and judgments of Depression are almost indistinguishable. Nevertheless, the temporal relationships of Helplessness and Depression ratings as well as those of their more objective counterparts, the Helplessness manual scores and Hostility-Inward (c) scores, appear to show a slight *prior* slope of the onset for the Helplessness curve (Figures 1 and 5).

An even more precise analysis allowed an even closer comparison: The two rated measures and their two scored counterparts were converted to standard scores and replotted on the same graphs (Figures 10 and 11). The increased depression segments are the ones of greatest interest, only because theories of depression pay so much more attention to explaining increased depression than to explaining decreased depression. The graphs illustrate (a) a considerable correspondence in the shape of the curves; (b)

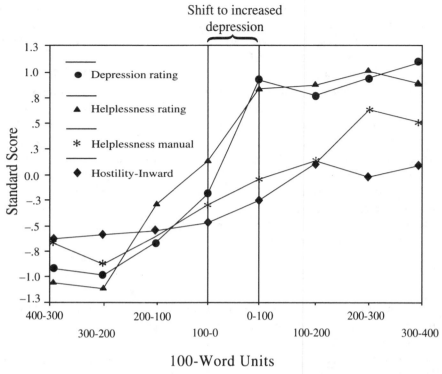

Figure 10. Standard scores of different variables for four 100-word units before and four 100-word units after increased depression.

that the changes in Depression and Helplessness have already begun to occur between 100 and 200 words before the reported shift; (c) that the Helplessness ratings do antecede the depression ratings at the 300- and 400-word units, but nonsignificantly; and (d) that the Helplessness manual scores antecede the Hostility-Inward c scores (depression) at the 400- and 500-word units, but nonsignificantly; however, they are reversed at the 200-word unit.

For the decreased depression segments, the curves are the reverse of the curves for the increased depression segments. There is considerable synchrony in the four measures; as a whole it is the agreement that is more impressive than the slight temporal differences. If the theory expects increased helplessness before increased depression, then the reverse should be true for decreased depression. And it *is* true: The Helplessness manual score decreases before the depression score (the Hostility-Inward c score), although only nonsignificantly.

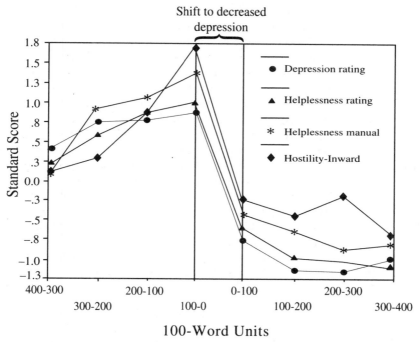

Figure 11. Standard scores of different variables for four 100-word units before and four 100-word units after decreased depression.

THE LIMITS AND POTENTIAL OF USING THE SYMPTOM-CONTEXT METHOD FOR RESEARCH ON DEPRESSION

I will conclude by posing and responding to questions that have been asked about the limits of the symptom-context method and its potential for further application in research on depression.

Question: Do patients know when they are depressed?

Answer: A possible limit to the method's applicability to depression research was pointed out by Erik Erikson after a presentation on this topic (personal communication, June 1970): "Psychoanalytic research has a tendency to take a patient's description of an affect as a natural observation ... but how much true observation is there in the patient's statement? It is not clear what the affect is even when the patient affirms it as depression and the observer believes it is depression."

Answer: Fortunately, the method and its results provide a positive answer to Erikson's question. There is evidence that the patient's statements are based on some valid observations. First, the context for patient-identified shifts in depression were independently judged to show changes in the appropriate direction (as is shown in Figure 1): When the patient made a statement that he had shifted to more depression (the shift point), the observers rated the subsequent material as showing more depression; when the patient said he had shifted to less depression (the shift point), the observers rated the subsequent material as reflecting less depression. Second, the related objectively scored measure, the Hostility-Inward manual score and its depression-related component, c (Figure 8) also changed after the shift point in appropriate directions. Third, observers listening to tape recordings of sessions could identify the mood shifts in terms of voice quality as well as in the content of the statement. Fourth, the patient appeared to the therapist to be depressed at the time he said he was depressed and less depressed when he said he was less depressed.

Question: Mr. Quinn was not asked to say when the shifts in depression occurred; he said this spontaneously. Could his statements have been more than a self-description? Might they have had a social communication function as well?

Answer: Yes, they also appear to reflect a communication to the therapist. When the patient says, "I am getting more depressed," the implied communication often is "help me, tell me what to do now." Such a communication was partly explicit in a few of his shift segments (the social communication meaning of depression was discussed by Whybrow et al., 1984, p. 19).

Question: Might the shifts in depression studied be relatively minor ones and based on other factors than those that caused Mr. Quinn's more major and long-lasting depressions?

Answer: The antecedents to his long-term depressions have not been as well established as the context of his shifts. Yet we have come to a tentative conclusion: The brief shifts and the long-term shifts appear to have similar preconditions. However, the major difference may be that the preconditions for the long-term shifts were more powerful and that his usual defenses were less effective than for the brief shifts.

Question: Would all forms of depression necessarily show the same conditions for their onset?

Answer: As Schmale (1972) emphasized, types of depression are diverse, but they can be integrated into one dynamic framework. He stressed the importance of distinguishing each form of depression in order to know whether it involves a "biological threshold phenomenon, an affect with somatic components, a character style, or a defensive symptom formation that protects with varying degrees of success against an unresolved deprivation with fixations related to repressed infantile separation or castration trauma" (p. 349). Mr. Quinn's depression is probably best described as a moderately severe neurotic depression. In terms of Schmale's (1972) classification, it is both an affect and a defensive symptom formation.

Question: How exact is the location of the shifts?

Answer: It is difficult to be precise about the moment when a depressive mood shift occurs, but we have taken the precautions already described in order to be as exact as possible. Precision also increases with greater precipitousness of the patient's mood shifts, and, the larger the shifts, the easier it is to recognize them. Concurrent physiological indices can also be helpful as long as these can be shown in each patient to be depression-related.

Question: What kinds of psychophysiological analyses should be tried?

Answer: We have mainly focused so far on the psychological level of symptoms in this study, but we hope to find some patients with a high frequency of large precipitous depressive shifts who can be studied with concurrent psychophysiological measurements, especially psycho-endocrine ones, to expand on the work of Bunney, Murphy, Goodwin, and Borge (1972), who were able to study shifts but only within hours of their occurrence.

CONCLUSIONS

■ This study reveals an essential fact about the relation of a patient's self-report of shifts in depression to the levels of depression in the context surrounding its shifts. As Figure 1 shows, the increased depression curve shoots up at the end of the fourth segment, and the decreased depression curve drops down at the end of the fourth segment and remains down. These curves appear to support the meaningfulness of the patient's self-reports of precipitous shifts in depression.

- A related question of interest, as was noted in the introduction to this chapter, was the degree to which the curve for depression paralleled the curve for helplessness. The parallel is easily seen in a comparison of the ratings of Depression and Helplessness and scorings of the Helplessness manual and Hostility-Inward (Figures 1, 5, 7, 8, and 10). The parallels are easier to see after converting all of these to standard scores, as is shown in Figure 10 for increased depression and in Figure 11 for decreased depression. The correlations within Table 6 also show the parallels in another way. In addition, there is a nonsignificant anticipation of the shift to increased depression on the part of the helplessness rating (in Figure 10).
- An inspection of these data shows that relatively less of the action occurs *before* the shift; the curve for the ratings shows this and Table 2 shows this for the significance of the differences for variables (the mean of two judges) between ratings of segments before shifts to increased depression versus before shifts to decreased depression. In the 100-0 unit before the shift, the only variables that are significant in a positive direction are oedipal conflict, separation concern, anxiety, and reflective (with marginal significance).
- The usual qualities of symptom contexts mostly appear just *after* the shift to increased depression (as is easily seen in Tables 2 and 3 and in the graphs). As Tables 2 and 3 show, Guilt, Loss of Self-Esteem, Hostility to Self, Hopelessness, Anxiety, Blocked, Concern about Supplies, Oedipal Conflict, Helplessness, and Depression are significantly different between shifts (similar results are shown by the analysis of variance comparing the four 100-word units before the shift and the four 100-word units after the shift, in Table 5). The most significant differences (in order) are: Loss of Self-Esteem, Helplessness, Depression, Hostility to Self, and the scored versions of these ratings, the Helplessness manual and Hostility-Inward (total).
- The findings appear to be consistent with all of the four theories about the context for the emergence of depression. For Theory 1 about anger turned onto the self, both the rating of Hostility to Self and Guilt (see Table 3) are significantly different between shifts to increased depression versus shifts to decreased depression. For Theory 2, designated as Freud's helplessness theory, the rated variables (see Table 3) give a prominent place to Hopelessness and Helplessness. For Theory 3, the Loss of Self-Esteem theory (Table 3) also has a high place for Loss of Self-Esteem. For Theory 4 on the pessimistic ex-

planations for negative events, the data are clearly supportive. The analysis of shifts before to after (see Figure 9) shows that the causal explanations fit with the mean rating of the composites of the explanatory style. For example, the shift from before to after for the four increased depression shifts show the increase in the mean composite ratings of explanatory style. In summary, the changes in the context of the depressive shifts are complex enough so that all four of the theories find a place.

- The symptom-context theme also has a parallel with the CCRT. The most significant rated variables for shifts to increased depression versus shifts to decreased depression show that the top qualities are very similar, especially to the top responses of self in the CCRT.

The benefits from the symptom-context method come from its high-powered controlled focus on the contexts for current precipitous shifts in depressive mood in psychotherapy. Consequently, reliance on the method increases our skill at finding the fit of our findings with each of the four main theories about the conditions for depression. The continued success of the method for research on depression depends on finding additional patients with clear depressive mood shifts. Then we will expand our exploration into the broader background factors for these shifts and expand our range of measures to include the psychophysiological level.

REFERENCES

Abramson, I. Y., Seligman, M. E. P., & Teasdale, J. D. (1978). Learned helplessness in humans: Critique and reformulation. *Journal of Abnormal Psychology, 87,* 49–74.

Aronson, H., & Weintraub, N. (1967). Verbal productivity as a measure of change in affective status. *Psychological Reports, 20,* 483–487.

Beck, A. T. (1967). *Depression: Clinical, experimental, and theoretical aspects.* New York: Hober.

Beck, A. T. (1972). *Depression: Clinical, experimental, and theoretical aspects* (Rev. ed.). New York: Harper & Row.

Beck, A. T., Rush, A. V., Shaw, B. F., & Emery, G. (1979). *Cognitive therapy of depression.* New York: Guilford Press.

Bibring, E. (1968). The mechanism of depression. In W. Gaylin (Ed.), *The meaning of despair* (pp. 154–181). New York: Aronson.

Bunney, W., Jr., Murphy, D., Goodwin, F., & Borge, G. (1972). The "switch process" in manic depressive illness: I. A systematic study of sequential behavioral changes. *Archives of General Psychiatry, 27,* 295–302.

Cattell, R. B. (1950). *Personality*. New York: McGraw-Hill.

Costanzo, F., Markel, N., & Costanzo, P. (1969). Voice quality profile and perceived emotion. *Journal of Counseling Psychology, 16,* 267–270.

Engel, G., & Reichsman, F. (1956). Spontaneous and experimentally induced depression in an infant with fistula: A contribution to the problem of depression. *Journal of the American Psychoanalytic Association, 4,* 428–452.

Engel, G. L., & Schmale, A. H. (1967). Psychoanalytic theory of somatic disorder: Conversion, specificity and the disease onset situation. *Journal of the American Psychoanalytic Association, 15,* 344–356.

Freud, S. (1957). Mourning and melancholia. In J. Strachey (Ed. and Trans.), *Standard edition of the complete psychological works of Sigmund Freud* (Vol. 14, pp. 243–258). London: Hogarth Press. (Original work published 1917)

Freud, S. (1959). Inhibitions, symptoms and anxiety. In J. Strachey (Ed. and Trans.), *Standard edition of the complete psychological works of Sigmund Freud* (Vol. 20, pp. 87–174). London: Hogarth Press. (Original work published 1926)

Goldstein, K. (1939). *The organism*. New York: American Book.

Gottschalk, L., & Gleser, G. (1969). *The measurement of psychological states through the content analysis of verbal behavior*. Berkeley: University of California.

Horney, K. (1957). *The neurotic personality of our time*. New York: Norton.

Leff, M., Roatch, J., & Bunney, W. (1970). Environmental factors preceding the onset of severe depression. *Psychiatry, 33,* 293–311.

Luborsky, L. (1971). Perennial mystery of poor agreement among criteria for psychotherapy outcome. *Journal of Counseling and Clinical Psychology, 37,* 316–319.

Luborsky, L. (1976). *A helplessness rating scale and manual for verbal samples*. Unpublished manuscript.

Luborsky, L. (1977). Measuring a pervasive psychic structure in psychotherapy: The core conflictual relationship theme. In N. Freedman & S. Grand (Eds.), *Communicative structures and psychic structures*. New York: Plenum Press.

Luborsky, L. (1984). *Principles of psychoanalytic psychotherapy: A manual for supportive–expressive (SE) treatment*. New York: Basic Books.

Luborsky, L. (in press). The Core Conflictual Relationship Theme (CCRT): A basic case formulation method. In T. Eells (Ed.), *Handbook of psychotherapy case formulation*. New York: Guilford Press.

Luborsky, L., & Alexander, K. (1989). [Depression analyses]. Unpublished raw data.

Luborsky, L., Docherty, J. P., Todd, T. C., Knapp, P. H., Mirsky, A. F., & Gottschalk, L. A. (1975). A context analysis of psychological states prior to petit mal EEG paroxysms. *Journal of Nervous and Mental Disease, 160,* 282–298.

Luborsky, L., Mark, D., Hole, A. V., Popp, C., Goldsmith, B., & Cacciola, J. (1995). Supportive-expressive dynamic psychotherapy of depression: A time-limited version. In J. P. Barber & P. Crits-Christoph (Eds.), *Psychodynamic psychotherapies for psychiatric disorders (Axis I)* (pp. 13–42). New York: Basic Books.

Luborsky, L., Singer, B., Hartke, J., Crits-Christoph, P., & Cohen, M. (1984). Shifts in depressive state during psychotherapy: Which concepts of depression fit the context of Mr. Q's shifts? In L. N. Rice & L. S. Greenberg (Eds.), *Patterns of change* (pp. 157–193). New York: Guilford Press.

Markel, N., Meisels, M., & Houck, J. (1964). Judging personality from voice quality. *Journal of Abnormal and Social Psychology, 69*, 458–463.

Mendels, J. (1970). *Concepts of depression*. New York: Wiley.

Mendelson, M. (1974). *Psychoanalytic concepts of depression* (2nd ed.). New York: S. P. Books.

Muran, J., Gorman, B., Safran, J., Twining, L., Samstag, L., & Winston, A. (1995). Linking in-session change to overall outcome in short-term cognitive therapy. *Journal of Consulting and Clinical Psychology, 63*, 651–657.

Peterson, C., Luborsky, L., & Seligman, M. E. P. (1983). Attributions and depressive mood shifts: A case study using the symptom-context method. *Journal of Abnormal Psychology, 92*, 96–103.

Schmale, A. H. (1972). Depression as affect, character style and symptom formation. In R. Holt & E. Peterfreund (Eds.), *Psychoanalysis and contemporary science* (pp. 327–354). New York: International Universities Press.

Schulman, P., Castellon, C., & Seligman, M. (1989). Assessing explanatory style: The content analysis of verbatim explanations and the attributional style questionnaire. *Behavior Research and Therapy, 27*, 505–512.

Seligman, M. (1975). *Helplessness: On depression, development and death*. San Francisco: Freeman.

Seligman, M. (1990). *Learned optimism*. New York: Pocket Books.

Seligman, M. E. P., Abramson, L. Y., Semmel, A., & von Baeyer, C. (1979). Depressive attribution style. *Journal of Abnormal Psychology, 88*, 242–247.

Seligman, M., Maier, J., & Geer, J. (1968). Alleviation of learned helplessness in the dog. *Journal of Abnormal Psychology, 73*, 256–262.

Viney, L. L. (1983). Assessment of psychological states through content analysis of verbal communications. *Psychological Bulletin, 94*, 542–563.

Whybrow, P., Akiskal, H., & McKinney, W. (1984). *Mood disorders: Toward a new psychobiology*. New York: Plenum Press.

Winer, B. J. (1971). *Statistical principles in experimental design* (2nd ed.). New York: McGraw-Hill.

6

STALKING THE ELUSIVE CONTEXTS OF A PHOBIA WITH A MODIFIED SYMPTOM-CONTEXT METHOD

LESTER LUBORSKY, LOUIS DIGUER, SUZANNE JOHNSON,
DAVID A. SELIGMAN, SCOTT FRIEDMAN,
and RACHEL KASABAKALIAN-MCKAY

This is a narrative about the outfitting and the outcomes of an expedition aimed at tracking down the instigators of a phobia. What makes tracking this type of symptom a challenge is that it does not usually have what the other symptoms in this book have: a clearly concurrent moment of onset and an onset that always occurs within the therapy session. Instead, most of the onsets of the phobic symptoms occur outside of the session, so that the accounts of the symptom in the session do not necessarily correspond with the intensity of the symptom described in the session. This journey required field testing of these essential items of equipment: a modified version of the symptom-context method to assess the accounts in the session of the behavior outside of the session and the CCRT method to be used as a broad background context measure.

The usual form of the symptom-context method is not adequate to deal with the usual form of episodes of phobic behavior because of the two related limits: the phobic states do not have clear on–off points within the sessions, and the symptom appearances in the session are almost all retrospective accounts of episodes outside the session. I dealt with these limits by devising a modified symptom-context method by which I could still be able to track down many of the essential conditions for the onset of the phobia.

THE PATIENT AND THE PROCEDURES

Psychotherapy sessions are the preferred milieu within which to ex-plore the increases and decreases in the phobic symptoms because of psy-chotherapy's largess in generating vital concepts about symptom formation (see chap. 16) and because it offers occasional instances of recurrent symp-toms. The sessions for this study were drawn from the very successful time-limited (24 sessions) psychoanalytic psychotherapy of Mr. John Alton, then in his early 30s. His main goal in starting psychotherapy was to overcome severe phobic symptoms that had been increasingly interfering with his work and with his marriage about three years earlier (Luborsky & Crits-Christoph, 1989). His phobic symptoms included anxiety and phobic re-strictions, and they had put much strain on his relationship with his wife, who was also a partner in their small law firm. In his original family he was the middle child of professional parents.

Diagnostically, in terms of the *DSM-IV* (American Psychiatric As-sociation, 1994), his symptoms are best described as those of agoraphobia (300.22), without history of panic disorder: Mr. Alton had a cluster of situations that he was fearful in or about, including, but not limited to, air travel, highway travel, and unfamiliar restaurants. In these situations he felt trapped and worried that he would have physical symptoms, such as gastrointestinal problems, or would lose control or go crazy. He was very distressed when in these situations and when he was not able to avoid them. The diagnostic criteria for agoraphobia are paraphrased as follows: (a) anxiety about being in situations where escape might be difficult or embarrassing in the event of panic-like symptoms (in Mr. Alton's case, gastrointestinal problems, losing control, or going crazy), and there is typ-ically a cluster of situations; (b) situations are avoided or endured with marked distress; and (c) anxiety and phobic symptoms are not better ac-counted for by another disorder.

The main sample of the 24-session psychotherapy to be used for the analyses in this chapter were Session numbers 2, 3, 4, 8, 17, and 18, a fairly representative sample of the sessions, except for the purposeful exclusion of the session at the very beginning and the last six at the end of the psychotherapy. Three facets of the symptom reports that were accepted in this study as the main symptom-related behaviors were in fact found to be temporally associated: (a) reports of intense anxiety (such as "I got really uptight"); (b) reports of intense anxiety that are associated with physical sensations, usually bowel and other gastrointestinal symptoms; and (c) re-ports of concerns and fears about traveling, to which he reacted by trying to restrict his traveling, and reports about feeling confined (such as "I did not go on a trip" or "I did not go to a restaurant"). The restrictions served his efforts to contain his anxiety. These are fairly common phobic behav-iors that fit with the criteria for the *DSM-IV* diagnosis. As the examples will illustrate, the majority of the phobic behaviors were described as part of past instances of phobic behavior, rather than being part of current instances in the session.

Because these phobic behaviors were presented as either increasing or decreasing, a sample of each was selected: eight instances of increased phobic behaviors and six instances of decreased phobic behaviors. In addition, eight instances were selected of the usual controls with no phobic behaviors; these were located in sessions with no increased phobic behavior. Three severity components of each of the eight increased phobia and six decreased phobia instances were independently rated by two judges with 5-point rating scales for each component of the phobic behaviors (mean agreement correlations were anxiety, .82; physical distress, .48 (just misses significance); and restriction of space, .54). Table 1 summarizes these 14 contexts and the judges' ratings.

Fifty-word units of the immediate context for each instance of the phobic behavior were counted off to be rated and scored with variables that were similar to those for the other symptom studies in this book. To reduce the large amount of work of making ratings, only four 50-word units were rated before and after each instance. Finally, the broader background context was assessed from a sample of whole sessions (4 and 17) in which the phobic behavior appeared; these whole sessions were taken together as the unit for deriving the CCRT.

METHODS FOR UNDERSTANDING THE PATIENT'S PHOBIAS

Method 1: Clinical Review of Contexts

I based this clinical review of Mr. Alton on brief segments before the appearance of the report of the phobias. I first reviewed the context for three of the eight session segments that showed increases in phobic behavior. In the following excerpts, statements of the phobic behavior are bounded by arrows and are underlined; the context is divided into 50-word units. After reading this sample of contexts, the qualities that appear before increases in the symptom should be easier to understand.

Session 2 (p. 17)

P: I ^{100}|said "Don't tell anyone, but I (laugh) am enjoying myself." And we'll even stop off the unplanned route." Which is,

T: is *verboten*

P: is *verboten*. And we stopped and went to a motel and went out to dinner, just at a coffee shop, had a good time, relaxed, went out and did some things. ^{50}|And I have to admit it was really enjoy-

TABLE 1
Summary of 14 Instances of Temporally Related Phobic Behaviors for Mr. Alton

Session: page no.	Patient's statement or behavior	Two judges' ratings			Circumstances of instance
		Anxiety	Physical distress	Restriction of space	
	Instances of increased phobia				
2:17	"I got really uptight; I can't go in the crowd"	3 4	1 1	5 5	Pressure from wife (to go to theater) (Feels he can't oppose directly, although here he does)
3:2	"I got this real physical feeling of fear . . . sick . . . feeling," feel trapped; can't leave	5 5	5 5	3 4	Pressure to get ready for guests
3:4	"I just feel very anxious" (current)	4 5	2 1	1 1	Pressure to come to therapy on time when his wife caused a delay by needing the car
3:20	"I was incapacitated, nauseous; had only to go 3 blocks"	5 5	4 5	3 1	Had to do a presentation at a meeting
17:1	"I couldn't deal with (scared) going on an airplane trip"	3 3	1 1	5 4	Pressure to go on airplane trip with wife and partner
17:3	"I was really nervous. I was off the wall"	4 5	1 1	4 1	Pressure because therapist ended the session at 60 minutes and he could do nothing about it; felt anger
17:6	"I have a headache because I'm nervous" (current)	4 3	1 4	2 1	Does not know what to do, what to talk about, needs direction
17:12	"I really started feeling ill" (in restaurants) so not do it	4 4	1 5	5 4	Pressure to fill the role the girl (fiancée) assigned to him (Feels he can't oppose it directly)

Entry	Increased phobia statement			Instances of decreased phobia		
2:7	"An absolute pit in my stomach"	4	4	Anxious about leaving parents' house and driving, but after first hour it was all right	3	5
4:3	Started to feel panicky but controlled it	2	2	Went to a restaurant. Able to be assertive in relation to self. Able to reassure self he *could* leave	4	3
4:4	Started to get a little nervous but controlled it	2	2	Went to a movie, I just said (to wife) "I'm going." Able to be assertive and define self	3	2
8:6	Was very anxious; "then all of a sudden, the anxiety just went away"	4	5	Wife proposed going to a restaurant. He turned her down (he countered her pressure). Wife started to cry: "I can't stand it, I'm tired." (She now became the weaker one and he the more assertive giver of advice.)	3	1
18:2	I had points of being nervous and then calm	3	4	Incredible pressure at work to do things	4	1
18:11	"I was very nervous and my stomach was very upset . . . It subsided, you know you are all right"	4	5	Wife said, "I want to see my grandparents." Driving back from trip with wife, "Soon as came near home, anxiety left me"	4	4

Note. Mean ratings for instances of increased phobia: 4, 2, 3.5 and 4.3, 2.9, 2.6. Mean ratings for instances of decreased phobia: 3.2, 2.2, 3.5 and 3.7, 1.3, 2.7.

able. It was, if could have more of those, that's (slight laugh) that's a good goal to achieve. But I came back and, it was a, Monday or Tuesday of last week, and (my wife) says I want to get tickets to see (a play). ↓[Phobic behavior:] And my first reaction was just "No, I can't go. I can't go to that theater. I can't go in the crowd." And I, and I had, that was the first reaction I had. And I got really uptight↓ and I sort of snapped back at her, like, "No, I can't. I've got work. What, are you crazy? We got so much," and we really do have a lot of work, but it's only 2 hours (laughs), uhm, but the, what I was really annoyed at myself, and I said ⁵⁰|to her, I said, I don't understand why I snapped back. Because if I learned anything from my trip, I mean, I went over 1,200 miles and I didn't, I didn't go crazy. A-, in fact, even one night I, I sat in this fancy French restaurant and had five courses ¹⁰⁰|of dinner and made it all the way through.

Session 3 (p. 2)

P: ¹⁰⁰|this morning (laugh), and I had to borrow a car to get her (wife) a ride, so, not bad (laugh), 10 minutes late. I started to take notes, and uh, you asked me to write down the sequence in that uneasy feeling.

T: Right. As the anxiety begins and starts to

P: Uh-huh

T: increase.

P: One thing I noticed, that in writing it down it ⁵⁰|begins to subside.

T: That's interesting.

P: (several words inaudible). I really only had one event last week.

T: I'd be interested to hear about it.

P: And it came on very quickly. I was getting ready for a party Sunday night, my, uh, birthday, and invited 30 people over, and I'd been cooking for about 2 days, and about 2 hours before everyone was supposed to arrive ↓[Phobic behavior:] I got this real feeling of fear, of, and it, and it, and these feelings come very quickly. A feeling of fear about what is going to happen, and not specific on that evening, that things, uhm, might be out of control. Uhm, I got a very physical, sick kind of feeling, nauseous or uhm, kind of intestinal feeling. And then that is coupled with an extreme feeling of fatigue, just an absolute like, how am I ever going to do this. I can hardly pick up my arms now, like a lot of weight.↓

T: Mmm hmm

P: And that, that just comes like that (snaps fingers twice) first. I can know, that's the sequence of feelings that come in 30 seconds, 40 seconds.

T: And did it begin with the thought that somehow you'd be having difficulty maintaining control in the evening?

P: Yeah. Yeah.

T: And what's the details of that? What, what kind of fantasy

P: (sigh)

T: of loss of control?

P: What happens if I just get sick and ill and have to (2-s pause) you know, all these people will be here, and something happens to me. [50]|It's not like I can leave the party. Uhm, it's my house. Uhm, a feeling of trapped, and uh, something will happen, and I just, I'll feel ill and, and uh, I was tired. I mean, I was physically tired because the week had been pretty exhausting. Uh, and then even when I [100]|came to eat

Session 3 (p. 4)

P: But I [100]|gave, I began to relax, and sort of (2-s pause), it subsided by going down. I sort of ran down the hallway and wrote it down. I got a hot one here and finally I just decided to, whatever's going to happen is going to happen, and I couldn't stop 30 people [50]|from coming in the house. Uhm

T: Okay. So your initial anxiety was that 30 people are coming, and you could find yourself stuck in a situation where you felt ill, by which I gather you mean ill intestinally, again.

P: Yeah. That or physically, that intestinally, yeah, or nauseous.

T: Nauseous or, or vomiting

P: Uh-huh

T: or diarrhea

P: Uh-huh

T: something like that.

P: Uh-huh

T: Anything else, or is it mostly in that whole system, nausea, vomiting, and diarrhea?

P: Well, some-, sometimes I just get this sort of like physically tired, just heavily fatigued, and like I just, I have to go lay down and take a nap.

T: Okay. So that your fear would be that that would happen when you had to be available as the host for your birthday party.

P: Yeah. Uh-huh.

T: And then the anxiety builds as you anticipate, uh, the situation of being stuck

P: Mmm hmm

T: with being ill, but yet not being allowed to escape from that situation.

P: ↓[Phobic behavior] Mmm hmm. I sort of have that feeling now. It's, uh, one, I had to borrow somebody else's car, I had to race out here, uh, uh, (sigh). You know, I didn't want to be late, uh, it's a very sort of unsettling kind of feeling.

T: You feel a bit anxious right now.

P: Yeah

T: Any more details to the anxiety you're feeling right now?

P: It's (5-s pause), I just don't feel (2-s pause) that I'm in control as much as I could be. I just feel very anxious. I guess, that's what it is right now. Just anxious about, uhm, if I can really hold on to today.↓ One, I'm tired. I had a long meeting last night, and uh, uhm

T: Mmm hmm. So you feel a bit tired and a bit harassed from having to organize yourself.

P: Yeah. It's sort of this last-minute organization of running around and trying to figure out, you know, at 11:00 at night how we're going to get cars and people moved around, and, and uh, yeah, I'm annoyed, harassed, and [50]|that, that sense of anxiety now, because everything's sort of crazy.

T: What do you feel of annoyance?

P: Well, I've, I meant, I like to know certain things in advance, a little preplanning. That's the one thing that my wife and I can't, I can't really talk to her about it. That's the one thing that she's never [100]|done

Summary of Clinical Review Findings

Within these three instances and within the other instances, several frequent conditions for increased phobic behavior appeared for Mr. Alton:

1. He felt increased pressure, usually through a demand from a person to whom he was close and with whom he was intimately involved. Most often the people who had been sources of pressure were his wife, his former fiancée, or his father.
2. He felt helpless to oppose the pressure directly because he felt attached to and needed the other person. Another strongly associated fear was that he felt it would drastically hurt the other person if he directly and explicitly expressed opposition.
3. He consciously feared and became anxious about being in situations of being unprotected, usually by another person. This fear may have been increased because he also wished to oppose and to throw off the control from these sources of pressure who were also sources of protection.

The following four conditions applied when an imminent symptom outbreak was *decreased* by being avoided or aborted:

1. He countered the pressure by being able to be assertive.
2. He defined himself better in relation to the other person so that he was able to see himself as a more distinctively separate person.
3. He was able to change the power balance by seeing himself as the stronger one, with the other person as the weaker one who needed his advice and help.
4. His phobic avoidance of travel served to help him to keep his anxiety down.

Method 2: Rating Variables in the Symptom Versus Control Contexts

For the 22 contexts that were selected for study (8 instances of increasing phobia, 6 of decreasing phobia, and 8 control contexts), 12 variables were independently rated by two judges, including 3 from CCRT categories. Most of these variables are the same ones used in the other symptom-context studies described in this book that had differentiated symptom segments from controls, but a few were suggested by our clinical review of the accounts of the phobia. The 12 variables rated were (a) Helplessness; (b) Hopelessness; (c) Anxiety; (d) Involvement with Therapist; (e) Concern about Supplies, separation anxiety; (f) Blocked, rejected; (g) Depression; (h) Feeling bold, assertive, aggressive, critical, or hostile to others; (i) Feeling self-blaming, ashamed, guilty; (j) CCRT Wish: To assert independence, overcome domination; (k) CCRT Response from Other: Dominates, controls, interferes; and (l) CCRT Response of Self: Anxious, helpless.

Agreement of Judges

The two judges showed only moderate agreement in terms of their mean general correlation with each other (.50, $p = .0001$), but somewhat better agreement in terms of their mean percentage agreement (see Table 2). Percentage agreement, however, may give a better estimate of agreement than correlations, because the data to be correlated have only a small variance.

Comparison of Ratings

The results of the ratings are presented in three ways: for each of the eight 50-word units that were significant (Table 3) and in terms of only *the units before* and only *the units after* phobia increases (see Tables 4, 5, and 6). The significance of the differences in ratings were based on the eight symptom (increased phobia) segments versus the eight control segments.

Our initial lack of confidence that significant differences would be found between symptom versus control segments was based on the fact that the symptoms did not usually appear directly in the session but were mostly accounts of the symptom that appeared outside the session. Yet, as it turned out, there *were* more significant differences between the symptom and control segments than had been expected, and the level of significance and the types of rating scales that were significant were much like those found in other symptom studies. For example, the 50-word unit just before the phobic behavior tended to show significant differences for these rating scales more often than did other 50-word units: Helplessness (.003), Concern about Supplies (.011), Hopelessness (.017), Anxiety (.015), Blocked (.021), and Response of Self of anxious and tense (.041).

TABLE 2
Agreement of Two Judges' Ratings for Mr. Alton's Phobia

	50-Word units	Correlations	% Agreement
Before phobia	1	.54	85.9
	2	.53	82.6
	3	.47	82.6
	4	.50	87.7
Phobia onset →			
	5	.56	83.3
	6	.48	79.6
	7	.51	83.4
After phobia	8	.49	83.7
M		.50*	83.6

*$p = .0001$

The larger 200-word unit shows mostly similar results (Table 5). Figures 1, 2, and 3 depict the shape of the curve for Helplessness, Hopelessness, and Anxiety for all of the immediate segments. There were about as many significant differences for the 200-words before-symptom as compared with the 200-words after-symptom segments (see Tables 5 and 6), but the after units were even more significant than the before units.

Comparison of Current and Past Phobic Behavior

Of the eight increases in the phobic behavior, two occurred in the session and six occurred outside the session (see Table 1), which gave me a rare opportunity for comparison. The first of these current phobic behaviors occurred in session 3, where Mr. Alton explained, "I just feel very anxious (now)," because he felt pressure to be able to come to therapy on time after his wife had delayed him by needing the car. The second example is from session 17, where the patient reported a headache "because I am nervous (current)." This appeared in the context of the stress of not knowing what to talk about in the therapy and the need for direction from the therapist.

One way to see whether these two instances with current symptoms differ from the six with accounts of past phobic behavior is to actually run significances of differences between the two subgroups. We tried this and found that the subgroups were not usually significantly different, but a very few of these were in the direction that implied, as would be expected, that the current instances had more of the 12 main variables than did the past instances. For example, for the 50-0 unit before the symptom, Hopelessness was significantly greater for the two instances as compared with the six past instances ($p < .03$). There were also two variables at the 200-150 unit that showed advantages for the two current instances, Helplessness and Response of Other: dominating. Two obvious dimensions in which these two current phobic behavior symptoms appear to be similar to the usual current symptom contexts reported in other chapters are that they both involve a sense of Helplessness about how to manage, and they both involve a clear Reference to Therapist.

Intercorrelations of Variables

The rated variables that significantly discriminated between increases in phobic behavior versus controls had mean intercorrelations that were only modest to moderate (see Table 4). The highest of these was .44 for the Response of Self: anxious and tense; the next was Hopelessness .41, and the next was Blocked .40.

TABLE 3
Significances of Differences Between Two Judges' Mean Ratings of Variables Before and After Increased Phobia Versus Control Contexts for Mr. Alton

Variable	50-word units[a] 1 to 8	Before or after phobia	Mean contexts Control	Mean contexts Increased phobia	t[b]	F	p	Rank of unit 4
Helplessness	4	Before	1.13	2.64	3.97	6.6	.003	1
	5	After	1.19	2.75	3.70	7.7	.003	
	6	After	1.31	2.19	2.40	9.1	.020	
	7	After	1.44	2.12	1.87	14	.042	
	8	After	1.44	2.38	2.33	14	.018	
Hopelessness	1	Before	1.00	1.58	3.40	12	.003	4
	4	Before	1.06	1.64	2.65	7.1	.017	
Anxiety	3	Before	1.44	2.43	3.28	13	.003	3
	4	Before	1.25	2.79	2.78	6.4	.015	
	5	After	1.19	2.38	2.53	7.6	.019	
	6	After	1.25	2.31	2.46	8.5	.019	
	8	After	1.56	2.37	1.96	14	.035	
Concern about Supplies	1	Before	1.62	2.25	1.84	12	.045	2
	4	Before	1.38	2.14	2.60	13	.011	

Blocked	1	Before	1.19	2.33	3.01	6.4	.011	
	4	Before	1.13	1.86	2.49	7	.021	5
CCRT: wish, independence	1	Before	1.69	2.75	2.23	12	.023	
CCRT: response from other, dominating	5	After	1.38	2.56	2.41	14	.015	
CCRT: response of self, anxious, tense	3	Before	1.19	1.86	1.92	8	.045	6
	4	Before	1.12	2.14	2.07	6.3	.041	
	5	After	1.00	2.75	6.17	7	.000	
	6	After	1.31	2.06	2.02	7.9	.039	
	7	After	1.37	2.00	1.85	14	.043	

Note. Judges: RM and SF.
[a]Combined ratings of two judges for each of the eight 50-word units—four before and four after—numbered in order from 1 to 8. Unit 4 is the 50-word unit just before the phobic behavior.
[b]The *n*s for the controls are all 8; the *n*s for the increases are almost all 7 or 8.

TABLE 4
Intercorrelations of Rated Variables That Significantly Discriminate Between Increased Phobia Versus Control Segments 50 Words Before Phobia for Mr. Alton

Variable	1	2	3	4	5	6	M^a	$M2^b$
1. Helplessness	—	.72	.55	−.26	.20	.38	.32	.42
2. Hopelessness		—	.10	.14	.66	.43	.41	.41
3. Anxiety			—	−.35	.04	.74	.22	.36
4. Concern about Supplies				—	.49	.06	.02	.26
5. Blocked					—	.59	.40	.40
6. Response of Self, anxious, tense						—	.44	.44

[a]M = mean of the correlations for that variable.
[b]$M2$ = a mean of the absolute value of each correlation for that variable.

TABLE 5
Rated Variables Within 200-Word Units Before and After Phobic Behavior

	Word units before phobia				Word units after phobia			
	200-150		50-0		0-50		150-200	
Variable	t	$p <$	t	$p <$	t	$p <$	t	$p <$
Helplessness	1.73	.068	3.97	.003	3.70	.003	2.33	.018
Hopelessness	3.40	.003	2.65	.017	1.65	.060	1.13	.139
Anxiety	1.54	.075	2.78	.015	2.53	.019	1.96	.035
Involvement with Therapist	.180	.430	.06	.477	.24	.406	1.37	.102
Concern about Supplies	1.84	.045	2.60	.011	.31	.379	.15	.440
Blocked, rejected	3.01	.011	2.49	.021	1.23	.119	.34	.368
Depression	1.58	.087	.09	.463	−1.00	.175	.40	.346
Bold, hostility to others	−.12	.453	−1.17	.131	.78	.224	1.21	.128
Self-blame, guilty	.58	.291	1.55	.086	.92	.190	.61	.274
Wish: independence	2.23	.023	.24	.409	.89	.195	.59	.281
Responses from Other: dominating	.26	.401	−.39	.350	2.41	.015	.97	.174
Responses of Self: anxious, tense	1.30	.121	2.07	.041	6.17	.000	1.35	.104

Note. 16 sessions used: Increases: 2 (p. 7), 3 (p. 2), 3 (p. 4), 3 (p. 20), 17 (p. 1), 17 (p. 3), 17 (p. 6), 17 (p. 12). Controls: 1 (p. 4), 1 (p. 7), 1 (p. 9), 1 (p. 11), 4 (p. 6), 4 (p. 11), 4 (p. 8), 18 (p. 12). All *p* values are one-tailed. Judges: SD and RM.

TABLE 6
Scored Variables Within 200-Word Units Before and After Phobic Behavior

	Word units before phobia						Word units after phobia					
	200–0		200–150		50–0		0–50		150–200		0–200	
Variable	t	p	t	p	t	p	t	p	t	p	t	p
Reference to Therapist	0.00	.500	−1.50	.104	0.00	.500	0.00	.500	.41	.352	.95	.197
Cognitive Disturbance	−2.44	.010	−1.82	.039	−.44	.331	.23	.412	−1.22	.115	.18	.431
Speech Disturbance	−1.79	.058	−1.34	.111	−.94	.191	−1.00	.176	−.50	.317	−.89	.201
Helplessness (Difference score)	2.12	.030	1.41	.090	2.65	.017	1.00	.175	N/A		1.00	.175

Note. 16 sessions used: Increases: 2 (p. 7), 3 (p. 2), 3 (p. 4), 3 (p. 20), 17 (p. 1), 17 (p. 3), 17 (p. 6), 17 (p. 12).
Controls: 1 (p. 4), 1 (p. 7), 1 (p. 9), 1 (p. 11), 4 (p. 6), 4 (p. 11), 4 (p. 8), 18 (p. 12).
All p values are one-tailed. Judges (in order): SJ, KB, KB, SJ, SJ.

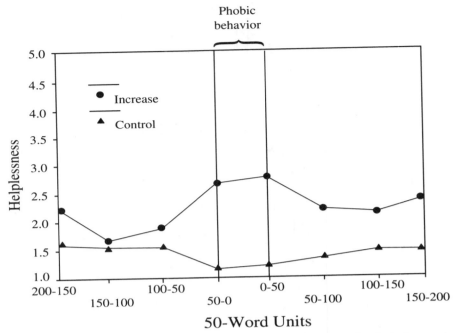

Figure 1. Mean ratings of Helplessness for Mr. Alton, four 50-word units before and four 50-word units after phobia.

Method 3: Scoring Variables

The scored variables that were used for this study are those used for the other studies presented in this book: Reference to Therapist, Cognitive Disturbance, Speech Disturbance, Helplessness manual, and Explanatory Style. These scores are presented in Tables 5 and 6. The results were usually not significant, and when they were for Cognitive Disturbance and Speech Disturbance, the increased phobia segments were less rather than more, as compared with the controls. The main exception was the Helplessness manual score, which was significant at the .017 level.

Method 4: Evaluating the Broad Background Context

CCRT Results

The CCRT analysis (Luborsky & Crits-Christoph, 1989) of the whole psychotherapy sessions of Mr. Alton offers insights into the broad background context of the symptoms. The standard category system used for these analyses was "Edition 1," which was based on the CCRTs of 16 patients (assembled by Luborsky, 1985, and included in Barber, Crits-

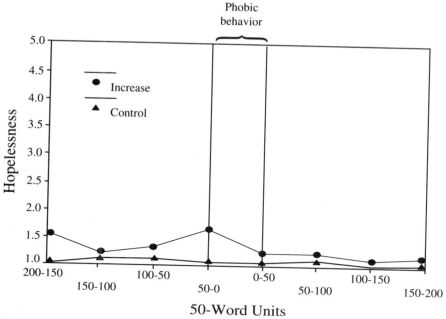

Figure 2. Mean ratings of Hopelessness for Mr. Alton, four 50-word units before and four 50-word units after phobia.

Christoph, & Luborsky, 1990). CCRT results are given in more detail in Luborsky and Crits-Christoph (1989).

Three judges tended to agree in their scoring of the CCRT variables from sessions 4 and 17 with Mr. Alton (see Table 7). For the wish component of the CCRT, all three judges selected two categories about equally and with higher frequency than other categories: "to assert one's independence and autonomy" and "to overcome other's domination; to be free of obligations imposed by others." Two other categories were selected by the three judges with slightly lower frequencies: "to achieve, be competent, be successful" and "to get help, care, protection, and guidance from others." Two of the judges selected with highest frequency the same negative response from other category, "dominating, controlling, interfering, intimidating, intruding." This category was the second highest frequency for the third judge. For the positive Response from Other, all three judges selected "accepting, approving" most frequently. For the negative Response of Self, "anxious, tense, upset" was selected most frequently by all three judges; the positive Response of Self category "assertive, express self assertively, gain control" was selected with highest frequency by all three judges. Not only did the judges agree with each other in their CCRTs, but their CCRTs were similar to the formulations used very effectively by the therapist (as

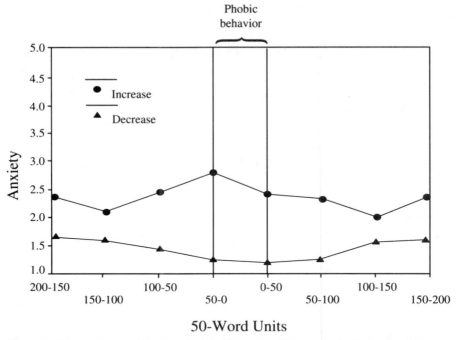

Figure 3. Mean ratings of Anxiety for Mr. Alton, four 50-word units before and four 50-word units after phobia.

is reviewed in the guide to clinical use of the symptom-context methods in chap. 15).

Comparison of the CCRT and the Symptom-Context Theme

The results of the immediate symptom-context analyses and background CCRT analyses appear to be similar. The CCRT method identified a relationship schema with a relatively stable structure; the immediate symptom-context method also identified a stable schema whose components also appeared in the CCRT. When these schemas are activated in this patient, the phobic symptoms may form. As was summarized in the clinical review, the symptom context for phobic symptoms includes experiencing pressure from another person; this in turn arouses simultaneously activated conflicting components of the inclination to oppose and be angry versus the inclination to suppress one's opposition for fear of hurting or displeasing the other person. The conflict may result in a helpless state before the symptom appears. Some of these results also overlap with the more extensive Role Relationship models method (Horowitz, 1989).

The comparison between the CCRT and the symptom-context theme is simplified in the CCRT column in Table 7. The most likely alignment

TABLE 7
Pervasiveness of CCRT Standard Categories in 10 Relationship Episodes
in Sessions 4 and 17 for Mr. Alton, According to Three Judges

CCRT component and standard categories	Pervasiveness in RE per judge[a]			Mean pervasiveness	Symptom-context mean p
Wish A					
to assert my independence and autonomy	7	7	10	8.0	
to overcome other's domination; to be free of obligations imposed by others	7	7	9		
to not be put down by others					
to achieve, be competent, be successful	5	4	4	4.3	
Wish B					
to get help, care, protection and guidance from the other person	4	3	5	4.0	
to please the other person	4	4	2		
to avoid hurting the other person					
Negative responses from other					
dominating, controlling, interfering, intimidating, intruding	6	5	3	4.7	
Negative responses of self					
anxious, tense, upset	5	7	10	7.7	2.46
helpless, less confident, ineffectual ("I do not know how to do things")	5	5	8	6.0	2.19
frustrated	2	6	4	4.0	2.13
angry, resentful, hating	2	5	5		
Positive responses of other					
accepting, approving	3	2	2	2.3	
Positive responses of self					
assertive, express self assertively, gain control	4	5	6		
gain self-esteem, feel affirmed, self-confident	3	4	4		

Note. Adapted from Luborsky & Crits-Christoph (1989, p. 257) with permission.
[a]Judges: LL, JM, and CP.

is between the CCRT's negative Response of Self with the ratings that were most highly significantly different for symptom segments versus controls. The most significantly discriminating rating for symptom segments versus controls (see Tables 4, 5, and 6) were Helplessness, Hopelessness, Anxiety, Feeling Blocked, and the CCRT Response of Self (anxious and helpless). That is an impressive area of probable overlap. (We did not happen to include symptom-context rating scales to try to match with the wish to assert independence or scales to match with the negative Response from Other, dominating and controlling.) It should also be noted that the symptom context was rated from small samples of sessions that were selected across a broader sample of sessions than just sessions 4 and 17 on which the CCRT is based.

Such dovetailing of findings from the CCRT and from the symptom-context theme has been noticed in previous research, for example, in comparison of the themes in the antecedents to forgetting versus in the CCRT (Luborsky, 1988) and in the antecedents to stomach ulcer pains in relation to the activation of the "surgent" state—both of these are summarized in the final chapter.

CONCLUSIONS

I have tracked down and inspected the conditions for a patient's phobic behaviors with the help of a modified version of the symptom-context method that is appropriate for narratives about the patient's phobic episodes. Now I am ready to do what travelers do who have returned to tell the tale—talk over the trip's memorable discoveries about the sources of this phobia.

- *Positive results were found despite the modified method.* The modified symptom-context method turned up information about the components that were activated just before the appearance of the phobic symptoms, even though these had been described as past events outside of the session.
- *Each data-analytic procedure showed some of the usual onset conditions.* The clinical review of the eight increases in phobic behavior showed that the conditions were part of an interaction with another person in which the patient experienced pressure from and expected domination from the other person to get the patient to agree with the other person. The conflict resulted in the phobic behavior with its anxiety, physical effects, and restriction of space. In contrast, decreased phobic behaviors appeared in those six instances in which the phobic anxiety was aborted; in these, the patient was able to be assertive in his attitude to himself or to the other person.
- The style and results of the clinical review have a kinship with the style and results of Freud's clinical case studies for patients with phobias, such as Freud's (1909/1955) famous case of Little Hans and the discussion of phobias in Barber and Luborsky (1991). Part of Freud's research strategy for understanding, treating, and then presenting this case history was to identify the context for the occasions in which Little

Hans' symptom increased and to identify the context for the occasions in which it decreased. According to the child's father, to the child, and to Freud (1926/1959) himself, the focus of the increased fear was the dangerous idea that a horse will bite him in the street.

This fear *increased* under the conditions summarized here: (a) by the appearance of the phobia after once seeing a horse fall down in the street; (b) by fearfulness in the evening before going to bed; (c) by fears of being separated from his mother, which may have started with his mother's confinement at the time of the birth of his sister (pp. 136ff); (d) by the warnings he was given against masturbation; and (e) by the possible association of these with his anger at his father and his desires toward his mother.

The phobia *decreased* under certain conditions: (a) by the calming effect of being taken into his mother's bed; and (b) by his own restriction on his freedom of movement, which appears to have been his way of decreasing his fear—"he produced the inhibition of not leaving the house so as not to come across any horses" (p. 126).

- From the ratings of Mr. Alton's sessions, significant differences were found in the segments before the phobic behaviors (in the 200 words) versus in the segments before the controls (in the 200 words) for variables that were much like those of the other recurrent symptoms in this book. The significant variables were Hopelessness, Helplessness, Blocked, Anxiety, and the CCRT Response of Self (anxious and helpless). The ratings were even more significant after the phobic behavior. From the scorings, only the Helplessness manual showed significant increases in Helplessness.

- *Two of the instances were really examples of current phobic symptoms.* They suggested that the context for the current phobic behaviors and the context for the past accounts of phobic behavior had much in common.

- *The background conditions showed parallels with the immediate conditions.* The CCRT method provided information about the broader background context. Interjudge agreement was found among the three independent judges after their CCRTs were translated into standard categories. As Table 6 showed, the standard category CCRTs were as follows (the mean frequency across REs of the component across 10 REs appears in parentheses): wish A (8), to assert my independence and to overcome the other person's domination; wish B (4), to get help and to please and to not hurt the other person; negative response from other (5), the other person is dominating; positive response from other (2), the other person is accepting; negative response of self (7), I am anxious and helpless; and positive response of self (5), I am assertive and gain control (see Table 7).

- *The experience of formulating both the CCRT and the symptom-context theme strengthened the realization of their similarities.* In general terms, both schema-generating methods—the symptom-context theme and the CCRT—suggested that the symptom can be understood as a resultant of the conflict between opposed wishes. The more expressed wish (labeled A in Table 7) collides with an opposed less expressed wish. Another form of conflict was between the potential expression of opposed wishes between the Responses from Other and Responses of Self.

The results of this modified symptom-context analysis for the phobia had not been expected to show as much discrimination between symptom versus control as was shown by the other symptoms analyzed by the usual symptom-context method. The basis for this expected reduced discrimination is obvious: In the modified symptom-context method, the symptom is described retrospectively; it is not actually present at the moment. Yet the findings based mostly on accounts of the past symptom outbreaks still show some of the most central aspects of the presymptom conditions as were found through the usual symptom-context analyses!

REFERENCES

American Psychiatric Association. (1994). *Diagnostic and statistical manual of mental disorders* (4th ed.). Washington, DC: Author.

Barber, J. P., & Luborsky, L. (1991). A psychodynamic view of simple phobias and postscriptive matching: A commentary. *Psychotherapy, 28,* 469–472.

Barber, J. P., Crits-Christoph, P., & Luborsky, L. (1990). A guide to CCRT standard categories and their classification. In L. Luborsky & P. Crits-Christoph (Eds.), *Understanding transference—The CCRT method* (pp. 37–50). New York: Basic Books.

Freud, S. (1955). Analysis of a phobia in a five year-old boy. In J. Strachey (Ed. and Trans.), *The standard edition of the complete psychological works of Sigmund Freud* (Vol. 10, pp. 5–149). London: Hogarth Press. (Original work published 1909)

Freud, S. (1959). Inhibitions, symptoms and anxiety. In J. Strachey (Ed. and Trans.), *The standard edition of the complete psychological works of Sigmund Freud*

(Vol. 20, pp. 87–174). London: Hogarth Press. (Original work published 1926)

Horowitz, M. J. (1989). Relationship schema formulation: Role–relationship models and intrapsychic conflict. *Psychiatry: Interpersonal and Biological Processes, 52*, 260–274.

Luborsky, L. (1985). An aid to reliability studies of the CCRT: Standard scoring categories (2nd ed.). Unpublished manuscript.

Luborsky, L. (1988). Recurrent momentary forgetting: Its content and context. In M. Horowitz (Ed.), *Psychodynamics and cognition* (pp. 217–245). Chicago: University of Chicago Press.

Luborsky, L., & Crits-Christoph, P. (1989). A relationship pattern measure: The Core Conflictual Relationship Theme. *Psychiatry, 52*, 250–259.

III

THE ONSET CONDITIONS FOR PSYCHOSOMATIC SYMPTOMS

7

THE CONTEXT FOR STOMACH ULCER PAINS

LESTER LUBORSKY

During psychotherapy sessions, Mr. Paul Rycheck would interrupt himself in the course of free associating to report that he was suddenly experiencing an acute stomach pain at the site of his past ulcer. He would blurt out words like these, "there goes my stomach—it's kicking me again." I built a study around these reports of pain, because it focused on how the pain reports could be understood through an analysis of the patient's thoughts immediately before the pain and by the broader background of personality factors assessed by daily tests given before each session. Although the pain was intrusive, the treatment itself was not aimed at relief of his pain but on his goal to improve his personal adjustment and school problems. His reports of pain were spontaneous—during the treatment no instructions were given to the patient about reporting these pains. Even this research on the context for the pain was begun only after treatment was over.

With thanks for critiques of the original paper by Robert R. Holt and Robert Wallerstein. With my lasting gratitude to Raymond Cattell for his innovation of the P-technique and collaboration in this first study of P-technique for a patient in psychotherapy. With appreciation to Marilla Logan of the University of Illinois, who assisted with the factor analysis.

THE PATIENT AND THE PROCEDURES

The patient's peptic ulcer had been surgically treated about a year before the psychotherapy, yet the pains were at the same site as the ulcer had been. It was never entirely known what the substrate for the stomach pain was, but the patient's description of his pain fit closely with that given by Netter (1959) on the neuroregulation of gastric activity:

> The effective stimulus for visceral pain is tension transmitted to the nerve endings by strong muscular contraction, by distention, or by inflammation. Normal peristaltic movements of the stomach do not ordinarily give rise to any sensation, but forceful contractions may be perceived as a feeling of gnawing and tension, or as actual pain in the abdomen, particularly in the presence of an inflammatory or ulcerative process. (p. 85)

The patient described the pain as severe and sudden, so that when a pain report was made it appeared to correlate with real pain. It is still possible that on some occasions the pain was present and not reported, although it is unlikely because there is no evidence about this in any of the sessions. The patient was under considerable stress during this period of his life and the level of stress could have played a part in the pains— psychological factors such as stress could have been found to worsen such ulcers (Murray, 1982).

Mr. Rycheck was an ambitious hard-driving 25-year-old college student who had completed two semesters and had just been dropped from college because of low grades. The failures seem to have evolved from a neurotic conflict with a teacher who "like my father did not care whether I learned, and would not take arguments." In addition, although he was apparently physically robust and of athletic build, he had been rejected from the army a year before with a diagnosis of a peptic ulcer.

Mr. Rycheck was brought up on a small farm in a northern central state. He already had been an unusually successful farmer on a farm of his own. But he had sold out completely (land, house, barns, tractors, and airplane), against his family's advice, to get a higher education, even though this meant starting afresh, as he called it "at the bottom of the ladder." He became very active in campus activities, especially the YMCA and church groups, in which he held a very large number of small offices. He impressed most people, particularly casual acquaintances, as being a genial good mixer, friendly, and self-assured. His passage across the campus was always interrupted by more than an average number of warm greetings to friends.

His parents were both American-born of Bohemian and Czechoslovakian origin. The family was Catholic, but just before the study, Mr. Rycheck left the church and joined a Protestant sect. During his growing up, he received more responsibilities and criticism than his younger brother and two sisters, and the parents tended to favor the younger brother. Although all members of the family were strongly loyal to each other, they failed to establish warm relationships. The mother had demanded payment from him for food consumed and rent during visits home after the age of 21, saying, "My own mother never helped me any." During his early childhood, he recalled, his mother kept him tied up with a rope on the porch while she did her work. There was a great deal of friction between the father and mother, which Mr. Rycheck partly attributed to the father's patriarchal conception of the wife's role in the family.

The patient's purpose in volunteering for this unpaid treatment study grew partly out of his having been dropped from school—he had visited the college's guidance bureau for counseling and was referred to our treatment study. In return for helping with our research, he was to have the opportunity to profit from treatment. He explained that he was especially concerned about his schoolwork and hoped that he would be readmitted the following semester. He was also glad that he could "make a contribution to science." He revealed in his associations during treatment that his goals were to "find the sources of help on the campus," "make contacts with people," and "make myself stronger."

What happened within the treatment and as a result of it cannot be related solely to the treatment, because it was based on a mixture of products of therapy and other influences. Although before treatment the patient had just been dropped from school and was in the throes of deciding what to do with his life in the face of this almost catastrophic blow, after treatment he reentered school and made passing grades. He was married a year later and from external appearances continued to do well (as of 5 years after treatment). To my knowledge, he has not had another full-blown ulcer relapse. Much of this probably was attributable to the treatment, but as with any such treatment, these changes could have occurred without therapy.

To further complicate the problem of causality, after the 54-session experimental period of daily psychotherapy sessions, he was seen in even more active therapy for 10 more sessions and then twice in the next 2 years. As a conservative estimate, the treatment gave him support during a trying period of his life. Although his personality structure appeared at the end of treatment to be similar to his initial structure, there were two likely gains: more clarity about what courses he wanted in school and in the direction of his life, and slightly more ability to say no to people who would impose on his good nature. Diagnostically, his symptoms do not warrant a specific mood or anxiety Axis I disorder nor an Axis II disorder. The best-fitting *DSM-IV* (American Psychiatric Association, 1994) diagnosis is Psychological Factors Affecting Medical Condition (Stomach Ulcer Pain, 316).

The patient was seen in the treatment study 5 days a week, for 54 sessions over a period of 12 weeks. The first hour of each session consisted of psychological testing, followed by a second hour of recorded free association that included the recounting of dreams, associations to the dreams, and unguided free association. The same tests or alternate forms of them were repeated daily in the hour before each session of psychotherapy. Measures were derived from objective personality tests, physiological tests, dreams, free association, and self-observation. Forty-six variables were extracted from the tests (Table 1), their scores intercorrelated, and the correlation matrix factor analyzed by the centroid method to find factors through the P-technique. More about the method (Cattell, 1943), measures, and statistical results for this patient can be found in other articles (Cattell & Luborsky, 1950; Luborsky, 1953, 1993, 1995).

METHODS FOR UNDERSTANDING THE PATIENT'S STOMACH PAINS

Method 1: Clinical Review of Contexts

In 23 of the 54 sessions, 26 instances of reports of stomach pain were located in the verbatim records of the sessions. The contexts of the 100 words immediately before and 100 words immediately after the report of pain were marked off in the transcripts. These pain reports and their contexts were surveyed to find common elements from one to the next. The reader can also engage in a clinical review by reading these examples of three stomach pain contexts, with the report of the stomach pain in italics.

Session 8: Stomach Pain Context

P: And I'm expecting that it's going to be good, and hoping that there's going to be a lot of people to be there and take advantage of it. I'm thinking about the experience that this committee and these other committees |[50] will give me, and in a year, oh, perhaps a year, I can be shooting for the presidency of the YMCA. And yet, one or two main activities I'll take care of, rather than experiencing these various functions of the whole organization--[I'll be] on the tail end of the circle of authority ↓(pause). *Right now my old stomach is kicking around.↓* It seems to do that every time I lie down on this couch (pause). It seems as though it is squirting something out. I have noticed it do that before on occasions, but not very often. I just wonder why it does that. It seems to do that more when I'm hungry |[50] than when I'm not (pause). About Beth (girlfriend), I've been wondering what progress or bent her thinking has taken in the last 3 or 4 days (pause). And I kind of wonder about my mother and dad at home and wondering how agitated

TABLE 1
Variables Derived From Daily Assessments of Mr. Rycheck

Number	Variable
	Physiological: biochemical
30	Glucose concentration in the blood (Shaffer-Hartman-Somogyi method)
31	Calcium level (serum calcium: Clark Collip method)
32	White corpuscle count (absolute)
33	Red corpuscle count (absolute)
44	Neutrophil count % of total white from blood smear
45	Lymphocyte count % of total white from blood smear
11	Salivary pH (alkalinity of saliva)
12	Salivary quantity (secretion in 2 min)
	Physiological: total organism
15	GSR mean magnitude of deflection to stimuli (as % fall)
14	GSR initial resistance (absolute) of skin
13	GSR frequency of spontaneous deflections in 3 min
41	Frequency of urination
42	Frequency of stomach awareness, i.e., of reported pains and discomfort[a]
17	Negative alter-image; length of duration after standard exposure
40	Hours of sleep
	Psychological: objective measurement
8	Myokinesis, mean length of movements intended to be 1″
9	Myokinesis, mean length of movements intended to be 2″
10	Myokinesis, drift in either direction for intended line of drawing
5	Speed of writing and multiplying (correctly)
6	Perseveration (disposition rigidity) by visual motor test
7	Inability to acquire new mental set (substitution multiplication)
2	Reaction time to light, mean of 20 reactions with regular and irregular
1	Reaction time ratio, time for regular warnings over time for irregular
3	Fluency of association, verbal, sentence completion and two T.A.T. cards
4	Fluency of association, drawing (unrestricted nonverbal fluency)
37	Amount of dreaming recalled, indicated by number of words of description
38	Feeling at end of dream, scored low for happiness, high for frustration or fear
39	Completeness of dream, extent to which dream action seemed achieved, (scored low for completeness)
43	Frequency of recorded laughter during daily interview
18	Funniness of jokes as rated by subject (22 jokes)
16	Number of words remembered from a word list; deliberate memorizing
46	Serial order number of test session
19	Cooperative vs. obstructiveness
20	Emotionality vs. calmness, steadiness

continues

TABLE 1 *(Continued)*

Number	Variable
21	Attention-getting behavior vs. self-sufficiency
22	Self-confidence and aggressiveness vs. retiring submissiveness
23	Cheerful contentedness vs. worryingness, anxiety
24[b]	Persistent in desires, strong-willed vs. not insistent, quitting
25	Friendly interest in people vs. shyness, caution
26[b]	"Lively," jumpy, restless vs. quite, poised
27	Vigor, orderly mind vs. languidness, absentmindedness
28	High intellectual interest vs. lack of interest in work and discussion
	Psychological self-rating
29	Distractible, dependent vs. absorbed, self-sufficient
34	Strength of interest in food
35	Strength of interest in sex activity
36	Strength of interest in social activities

Note. Adapted from Luborsky (1953, p. 391) with permission.
[a]From the psychotherapy sessions.
[b]Variables 24 and 26 were intended to represent respectively G factor (as persistent vs. quitting, fickle) and I factor (as sensitive, jumpy vs. stolid, poised), but the meanings given by the raters were found to be as now labeled. The daily raters included Luborsky and three friends of the patient.

they are about all this stuff (laughs). It rather amuses me |[100] at times (laughs), but I don't mind.

Session 14: Stomach Pain Context

T: Tell me what you think this dream might mean.

P: Oh, it might mean another crack back at Beth again (i.e., to try to win his girlfriend again) (pause). In a way, I think I'm wishful thinking in a way. If it could really work out, or [I'd get] another kick in the slats, so to speak (laughs), |[50] of course (pause). The plan might be, have something to do with a part of my earlier plan to get myself set up, too. Pretty darned busy until this pressure gets off of it -- until I get back, you might say, to normal -- if I ever was normal (laughs) -- normal for me. ⌊My *old stomach kicks me again for some reasons or other* (pause)⌋. It seems as if there would have to be a pretty darned good reason for me to try anything like that soon (pause). In other words, she would have to show some reasonable signs of being interested before I would try it again, at least openly. I might work subversively for |[50] a while (laughs). Right now, it's hard to bring myself to do it, but I'm beginning to take out the other girls a little bit. It might do her a lot of good, and it might do me a lot of good.

Session 19: Stomach Pain Context

T: If you could get the lady situation cleared up, you would feel better?

P: (pause) I think that would tend to be so (pause). I know that there would be the problem just the same, but if I could find the fellowship or comradeship, you might say, the appreciation, or give-and-take I'm hoping |[50] for--I don't believe I'm hoping for too much--and then have that possibility of not winning, but as long as you know you are still in the running--running in a contest for a long time, just begin to wonder how the darned thing is going to work out ↓--*there goes my stomach again*--↓ largely seems to be a matter of sharing things--I share things with people all around me--that's one thing that people say about me--I believe it's so, might as well admit it (laughs). Usually I add something--like in a discussion or just a social gathering, and I enjoy |[50] sharing things with people--I wish I had someone closer to me personally to share things with--things have more meaning. I've always had the idea for just myself alone--I can't see much in that--heck, I'd do out and be a beggar or a tramp--any number of |[100] ways I could get along--roaming farmhand, or something like that.

Summary of Clinical Review Findings

Two qualities that appear across these three examples seem to be most prominent before the pain: (a) a feeling of pressure to win what he wanted (a high position or a positive response from a girl) and (b) an afterthought about his helpless feeling and his own inadequacy to win. The presence of these common qualities can be recognized by rereading the contexts, but they can be better understood after the discussion of the other methods.

Method 2: Rating Variables

Method 2A: Sorting Real Versus Control Sentence Pairs

Because the sentence before the pain showed some significant differentiation between ratings of real and control contexts, a form was constructed to pair the before-pain real sentences with control sentences (a sample is in the Appendix to this chapter). The simplicity of the judgment task made it easy to try with varied instructions with many judges. In one version, the judge was to choose the sentence of each pair that was more likely to have preceded a real stomach pain. Subsequently the judge was given the same pairs with new instructions, such as to choose the one of each pair that contained more of a certain quality.

Typical results of these methods were those for Judge AA (see Table 2). First, he was given the form containing 24 pairs of sentences, with no clue about how to make choices. This might be called a free or an intuitive baseline record. He merely was told, "Choose the one in each pair which your intuition tells you came before a stomach pain." With that type of instruction, the judge's choices were almost chance (14 of 24 pairs correct).

TABLE 2
Number of Correct Choices of 24 Matched Pairs of Real Versus Control Sentences

Judge	No clue given	1 clue given: (Concern about Supplies)	2 clues given: (Concern about Supplies & Helplessness)
AA	14	—	20*
JS	15	18*	18*
CF[a]	—	—	19*
PM	14	16	16

Note. Dashes mean no score was given.

[a]This judge had heard a brief discussion on clues for stomach-pain reports, but was uncontaminated on which were real versus control sentences. His score, therefore, is appropriately listed under "2 clues given."

*18 correct yields X^2 of 6.00, $p < .02$

19 correct yields X^2 of 8.16, $p < .01$

Then the judge was given the form with the combined instruction of clue 1, Concern about Supplies, and clue 2, Helplessness: "Make a choice of each pair by applying the combination category: a Concern about Supplies, with a helpless feeling about being able to obtain them." For this task the number of correct choices rose to 20 of 24 ($p < .01$). After doing the baseline forms, Judge JS was provided with each clue in separate stages; his performance was similar to that of Judge AA Judge CF's choices were highly significant, but Judge PM's unaccountably were not.[1]

Method 2B: Rating Symptom Versus Control Contexts

Fifteen stomach pain contexts were selected at random from the 26 reported. Each consisted of 100 words before and 100 words after the report of pain; these 200-word contexts were each paired with one from a control session in which no pain was reported. To further equate the appearance of the symptom and control contexts, the words "There goes my stomach" were inserted in each symptom and in each control context at about the same point it had occurred in the symptom session. Independent ratings were made by five judges on 5-point graphic labeled rating scales. The categories for the rating scales included those that emerged from the just-

---

[1]Actually, the four hit scores of 20, 18, 19, and 16 were remarkably homogenous; $\chi^2(3) = 1.47$, $p = .69$. In addition, Judge PM's nonsignificant hit rate was virtually indistinguishable from Judge CF's significant hit rate (p of difference $= .56$). The message of Table 2: The overall accuracy rate of 76%, which was significant at $p = .00000017$ was based on a meta-analytic approach $E\ Z/(4)^{1/2} = 10.2^{1/2} = Z = 5.105$, and essentially the same result from direct pooling of all four raters' results. These two methods treat judges as fixed and limit generalizability to other sentences judged by the same four raters. Treating judges as random (to be able to generalize to other judges) yields $I(3) = 7.29$, $p = .0027$, with judges having an *average* significance level of .0053! (Robert Rosenthal, personal communication, September 7, 1993).

presented clinical review of stomach pain contexts, along with those that had been used for the study of momentary forgetting (see chap. 3). Judges applied the ratings three times: to the 100 words before, to the 100 words after, and to the sentence immediately before the pain (approximately 30 words).

These 15 variables were rated for the symptom and control stomach pain contexts: (a) degree of direct striving and hoping for fulfillment of his wish; (b) sense of pressure; (c) inability to get his wish; (d) frustration that others can be given things and he cannot; (e) concern that he may have to give in; (f) anxiety about himself, especially somatic; (g) competitive versus noncompetitive; (h) anxiety about showing sexual feelings; (i) anxiety about showing anger; (j) control versus lack of control; (k) guilt and shame; (l) optimistic, elated or euphoric mood; (m) helplessness; (n) concern about supplies; and (o) doubtfulness. Several additional variables were intended to be used, but the raters were unable to find sufficient evidence for them: new attitude or behavior, attention and concentration difficulty, tired and sleepy, and separation concern.

The level of agreement in ratings among five judges was only moderate. The highest correlations were for the sentence just before the stomach pain (about 30 words), with the entire 100 words before and the entire 100 words after being slightly less reliable. For the sentence just before, the most reliable variable was Helplessness, with a mean correlation of judge pairs among the five judges of .63; next was Doubtfulness with a correlation of .60, and the next was Inability to Get His Wish .55. The mean for all 14 variables was .41 with a range from .19 to .63. The two least reliable variables were at .19: Concern that He May Have to Give In, and Control versus Lack of Control. The bases for the unreliability may have been insufficient material from which to judge the variable and possibly the imprecise guidelines for the rater. The quality of the judge apparently made little difference, because for each of the judge pairs the mean reliabilities were all close to .40, which is the overall mean for all judges across all variables.

Differences were taken between the symptom minus control contexts, and t scores were computed from the averaged differences. The one sentence (or 30 words) immediately before the pain yielded more significant differences than did the total 100-word context before the pain or the 100-word context after the pain. This implies that the one sentence before pain contains, in more concentrated form, ingredients that anticipate or help to precipitate the pain. For the two judges who rated the one-sentence samples (in Method 2B), Judge AA obtained five significant differences (see top of Table 3); Judge LL obtained these plus others, but because his ratings might have been contaminated in two or three instances, emphasis will be on those categories for which Judge AA's ratings reached significance. The categories that showed the most significant differences between

TABLE 3
Comparison of Methods for Distinguishing Symptom and Control Contexts in Word Units for Mr. Rycheck

Method	Distinguishing variable or word category	Direction	t	p
2A: Sorting symptom and control contexts in 24 sentence pairs	Concern about Supplies	—	—	—
	Helplessness	—	—	.025
2B: Rating by Judge AA symptom vs. control contexts (30 words)	Oedipal Conflict	Higher	2.38	.010
	Anxiety	Higher	2.37	.013
	Concern about Supplies	Higher	2.09	.023
	Lack of Control	Higher	1.82	.040
	Helplessness	Higher	1.73	.048
Computer scoring with the *Harvard Psychological Dictionary* (100 words before *plus* 100 words after; Spence, 1979)	Technological	Lower		.01
	Possess	Higher		.01
	Family	Higher		.02
	Message form	Higher		.02
	Family theme	Higher		.05
Judge's rating (100 words before *plus* 100 words after; Spence, 1979)	The word *up*	Higher		.02
	The word *down*	Lower		.01

Note. The first two methods were used only for before-symptom versus before-control contexts (one-tailed). The second two were used before *and* after symptom versus control contexts (two-tailed).

symptom and control contexts for Judge AA for the sentence before the pain were Oedipal Conflict ($p < .010$), the next was Anxiety ($p < .013$) and the next was Concern about Supplies, where *supplies* refers to experienced support from others and from the self (significance level $p < .023$). The p values for the second judge were similar.

Intercorrelations of Rated Variables

The highest mean intercorrelation for significantly discriminating variables are Anxiety .48, and Helplessness .48. The level is only moderate for all intercorrelations. What is especially noteworthy about these intercorrelations is that Anxiety and Helplessness appear to be close to the heart of the intercorrelations (see Table 4).

Method 3: Scoring Variables

Dictionaries of psychological words can be useful in distinguishing real versus control contexts. Spence's (1979) reanalysis of our set of 15 symptom-context segments and 15 control-context segments illustrated this. He reported that for 59 word-categories, 5 were significant at or better than the 5% level (chance would expect only 3). The best categories that discriminated the symptom segments from the control segments (see Table 3) were technological (lower), possess (higher), family (higher), message form (lower), and family theme (higher). In addition, an associate of Spence, while scoring the symptom segments and the control segments, perceptively noticed that the word *up* appeared more often in the symptom segments and the word *down* more often in the control segments. For these two words together the multiple correlation was .56, and the correlation with frequency of the symptom was .77. These are valuable new findings about the context of the pain.

Spence (1979), however, attributed his results to the superiority of the computer over the clinician to perform assessments and to focus on words as opposed to themes. Another possible reading is that my clinician

TABLE 4
Intercorrelations of Rated Variables That Significantly Discriminated
Between Symptom and Control Segments

Variable	1	2	3	4	M
1. Anxiety	—	.19	.65	.59	.48
2. Lack of Control		—	.34	.28	.27
3. Helplessness			—	.44	.48
4. Concern about Supplies				—	.44

Note. Based on symptom segments 30 words before stomach pain (Judge AA's ratings).
M = a mean of the correlations for that variable.

judges who used the text of the transcript did not do badly in comparison with Spence, who used the *Harvard Psychological Dictionary* (Stone et al., 1966; see Table 3). The percentage of significantly discriminating rated variables achieved by my clinicians was comparable to the percentage of his significant word categories; in fact, his dictionary approach might have had a greater chance of capitalizing on chance, because 59 word categories were examined!

Another problem with Spence's analysis with this case is that he did not follow enough of the model of the analysis that I had already reported (Luborsky & Auerbach, 1969), in which the symptom segments were examined *separately* for before the symptom versus after the symptom. I had reported that the presymptom segment showed the main significant differences in our study, but Spence lumped the before and the after together into one segment. Taking together as a unit the before *and* after symptoms words means that his analysis had more words (200 words) as compared with my analysis (30 words).

Finally, I believe that Spence's concept of an opposition between the clinician and the computer is not an optimal one. Rather, taking both clinician and computer together provides improved understanding, as the analyses in this chapter suggest. As an example, Spence's speculation that the use of *up* was related to the stomach acting up and that the use of *down* was related to quieting the stomach down, may not have relied sufficiently on the available data. What I discovered through factor analysis was that a highly activated state of surgency—an energized or up factor—may have predisposed the patient to use of the word *up*, whereas the deflated state of desurgency may have predisposed him to use the word *down*. Consequently, although it is a remarkable observation that a person judging the symptom and control segments could find a word that distinguished the two so well, the meaning of that observation is best informed by taking the computer's word counts *together with* the results of the other methods, including the factor analysis and clinical ones presented in this chapter. In fact, as other cases in this book show (see Tables 2 and 3 in chap. 17), under certain conditions clinicians' ratings discriminated symptom from control segments better than did the scoring systems used by a person or as scored by a computer.

Method 4: Evaluating the Broad Background Context

Factors Extracted From the Daily Measurements

Nine factors were found within the intercorrelations of the 46 variables from the daily assessments (see Table 5). Most of the nine factors contained variables from all three levels of assessment—psychological rat-

TABLE 5
The Nine Personality Factors Extracted From Scores on the 46 Daily
Measures for Mr. Rycheck

Variable	Correlation[a]	Direction and name of variable[b]
	Factor 1 F—, or (E+, F—)[c]: Modified desurgency vs. surgency	
39	−.92	Dreams reported to be complete
5	−.70	Low speed of writing and multiplying
36	−.63	Low strength of interest in social activities
18	−.55	Low rating of funniness of jokes
6	−.54	Low disposition rigidity (perseveration) in motor test
40	.51	Long hours of sleep previous night
9	−.44	Large movements in myokinesis (2 in.)
2	−.41	Quick reaction time
	Factor 2 or (E—, G—): Submissiveness, dependence vs. dominance, drive	
39	.72	Dreams reported to be incomplete
22	−.58	*Retiring, submissive, not self-confident*[d]
43	.57	High frequency of laughter in interview
20	.56	*High general emotionality, not calm or steady*
28	−.44	*Low intellectual interest in work and discussion*
45	.42	High lymphocyte count (%)
3	.41	High verbal fluency of association
	Factor 3 or C—; General emotionality vs. emotional stability, maturity	
7	−.67	Ready ability to acquire new mental set
4	.56	High fluency of association in drawing
20	.51	*High general emotionality, not calm or steady*
24	51	*Persistent in desires, insistent, not quitting*
8	.45	Large movements in myokinesis (1 in.)
45	.42	High lymphocyte count (%)
21	.38	*Attention-getting, not self-sufficient*
25	.38	*Sociable interest in people, not shy or cautious*
16	.36	Few words remembered in memorizing
	Factor 4 or H: Adventurous cyclothymia vs. withdrawn schizothymia	
37	.70	Dreams described in many words, long and frequent
15	.68	Large GSR deflection responses
30	−.52	Low glucose concentration in blood
25	.49	*Friendly, interested in people, not shy*
27	.44	*Vigorous, orderly-minded; not languid*
14	.40	High initial resistance on GSR
17	−.38	Brief negative after-image duration
29	−.35	Absorbed, self-sufficient, not distractible or dependent

continues

ings and tests, physiological measures, and free associations. Some of the
factors seemed matchable with factors derived from across-patient (R-
technique; Cattell, 1943) studies as well as those derived from intrapatient
P-technique studies (Luborsky & Mintz, 1972), and a few were unique to
this patient.

TABLE 5 *(Continued)*

Variable	Correlation[a]	Direction and name of variable[b]
	Factor 5 or A: Cyclothymia vs. schizothymia	
37	.69	Dreams described in many words, long and frequent
16	−.58	Few words remembered in memorizing
1	.55	High ratio on warned to unwarned reaction times
45	.48	High lymphocyte count (%)
39	−.39	Dreams described as complete
19	.35	*Cooperative, not obstructive*
29	−.37	Absorbed self-sufficient, not distractible or dependent
8	.30	Small movements in myokinesis (1 in.)
	Factor 6: Relaxation, parathyroidism vs. hypoparathyroidism	
38	−.70	Happy feeling tone at end of dreams
43	.51	High frequency of laughter in interview
1	.47	High ratio on warned to unwarned reaction times
31	.42	High calcium level in blood serum
41	.41	High frequency in urination
14	.40	High initial resistance on GSR
	Factor 7 or F—: Desurgency vs. surgency	
26	−.57	*Poised, quiet vs. lively, jumpy, restless, easily embarrassed*
42	−.54	Low frequency of awareness of stomach pains
37	.48	Dreams described in many words, long and frequent
32	−.46	Low white corpuscle count in blood
7	.42	Low ability to acquire new mental set
38	−.37	Happy feeling tone in dreams
33	.36	High red corpuscle count in blood
2	−.35	Quick reaction time
11	−.33	Acid trend in salivary pH
23	−.32	*Worrying, depressed, anxious, not cheerful*
	Factor 8: Therapeutic trend	
46	.60	Serial order number of session
38	.57	Unhappy feeling tone to dreams
45	.46	High lymphocyte count (%)
39	.45	Dreams reported to be incomplete
29	.44	Distractible, dependent, not absorbed or self-sufficient
3	.42	High verbal fluency of association
31	.37	High level of calcium in blood serum
	Factor 9: Fatigue or vagotonia	
34	−.81	Low strength of interest in food
35	−.64	Low strength of interest in sex
32	−.47	Low white corpuscle count
29	.44	Distractible, dependent, not absorbed or self-sufficient
44	−.42	Low neutrophil count (%)
41	.41	High frequency of urination

[a]Correlation of each variable with the factor.
[b]These names of the variables take account of signs and are directly interpretable.
[c]Capital letters refer to the most similar factors in cross-sectional studies. Capital letters in parentheses refer to greater tentativeness of the matching. (See Cattell & Luborsky, 1950)
[d]The combined psychological ratings of Luborsky and the patient's friends are identified by italics.

Time Trends Revealed by Factors

Once the nine factors were identified, the patient's status on the day of each session could be portrayed by a profile of these factors. The curves of these factors over the time of Mr. Rycheck's 54 sessions showed different sorts of time trends: Factor 1, a large rise in "modified desurgency"; Factor 3, a slight rise in "emotionality"; Factor 7, a slight rise in "surgency"; and Factor 8, a rise in "therapeutic trend." Several shorter-term trends also appeared: Factors 3 and 7 dropped over the weekend, and Factor 9 showed weekend rises in fatigue.

A variable related to the therapeutic trend factor, the patient's rated interest in social activities, decreased with time ($-.78$), implying that he became less concerned about being with people. Perhaps he was also less concerned about doing well on the tasks the assessor presented to him and more withdrawn, as was suggested by longer sleep. The "therapeutic trend" factor itself correlated highest of the factors with the session number (.60). It may be inferred that the therapy gradually aroused resistance. For example, "dreams reported to be incomplete" correlated highly (.64) with the session number—the higher the session number the less complete was the dream. The trends in increased emotionality and resistance could well have had to do with Mr. Rycheck's reaction to the nearing of the time when he felt he would get feedback about the results of the daily assessments; he seemed to have become more upset and negative about the waiting, as he also did about his increased need to make plans.

These therapeutic trends from the daily assessments have to be taken together with the fact that he was getting his life together and actually making reasonable plans for his future; these changes appear to have reflected some of the benefits from the treatment. However, the treatment did involve a few sessions beyond the endpoint of the daily assessments, so the end of the assessments was not exactly the same as the endpoint of the treatment.

The Relation Between Recurrent Stomach Pain and Surgency Factor 7

Only one of the nine factors, surgency, appeared in reports of stomach pain; only in the context of the ups and downs of surgency did stomach pains appear (Table 5). The stomach pain was associated with the highest factor score (the factor loading of stomach pain was .54).

In the factor called *Desurgency versus Surgency*, Surgency had the highest loadings on six variables: (a) lively, jumpy, restless, easily embarrassed (daily rating by three friends and the therapist); (b) high frequency of reports of stomach pain; (c) infrequent dreams, described in few words; (d) high white-corpuscle count; (e) high ability to acquire new mental sets (e.g., substitution multiplication); and (f) frustrated, fearful, sad tone at end of dreams.

The core of this broad background surgency state, therefore, seems to be a psychophysiological state of disequilibrium based on the patient's increased feeling of pressure and of pushing himself. For example, the highest single correlation with reports of stomach pain was the Galvanic Skin Response (GSR) measure of percentage of deflections (loss in resistance, gain in conductance) in four learning tasks, such as learning words (.48).

The surgency state is also broad temporally: It exists in the session for more than the brief period of the stomach pain, and the state is active not only in the entire session in which the stomach pains are reported, but also before and after it, and this state may remain for several days. The evidence of surgency's temporal breadth is that most of the measures composing the surgency factor were obtained in the 1-hr assessment period before each session, and the high factor scores came in bunches, with a series of high scores on successive days.

THE CONTRIBUTIONS OF SYMPTOM-CONTEXT RESEARCH ON STOMACH ULCER PAIN

1. *The immediate background conditions contribute to the appearance of the symptom.* "Condition 1" is the immediate state just before each report of stomach pain; it is followed by the broad background state of "Condition 2." Both conditions contain qualities that remain present in the patient's verbalizations from occasion to occasion, that is, a wish for supplies along with an anxious and helpless feeling about being able to obtain them.

2. *The discovery of the surgent state has contributed to the understanding of the onset conditions.* I have shown that Condition 2's larger background state is a pressured disequilibrium, termed a *surgent* state from the P-technique-derived Factor 7. Some of the physiological parts of this state are known (Table 5), for example, GSR liability associated with increased skin conductance.

3. *The P-technique allows for extracting factors from intra-individual fluctuations in measures over time and for discerning longitudinal trends in the treatment of individual patients.* Measures may be derived from psychotherapy as well as from repeated psychological and physiological tests. As in the case of Mr. Rycheck, some of the factors that emerge will be recognized as like those that appear from the usual cross-sectional aggregates-of-people studies (R-technique), and some are unique for the individual. Mr. Rycheck's factors included only 4 that overlapped with the then-known 11 factors from the usual P-technique studies.

The P-technique method has special power to extract the factors that capture the sometimes unique changes within each patient over time during the treatment (Cattell, 1963). These factors provide just the kind of information that helps to explain the patient's changes in psychotherapy.

For Mr. Rycheck's treatment, for example, the trends included changes in the five factors reflecting both lowered stress and increased resistance. Symptom contexts that are examined in combination with P-techniques are now much more practical to use in the sense that they take much less time than they did in the 1946–1947 era when this study was done. At that time, for example, to do the factor analysis alone took a full-time assistant 2 months!

Mintz and I (1970) thought of the P-technique's power as being still in the good idea stage. With the reevaluation by Nesselroade and Ford (1985) and the larger review by Jones and Nesselroade (1990), the quality of the findings has become even more substantial. The number of applications of the P-technique to psychotherapy are increasing. The earliest group of them were those of Cattell and Luborsky (1950), Luborsky (1953), Mintz and Luborsky (1970), Zimmer and Hakstian (1972), and Dahl (1972). The more modern studies that have been undertaken in the last two decades have been sampled in a special section of the *Journal of Consulting and Clinical Psychology* (Russell, 1995).

However, one of P-technique's possible limitations, first pointed out by Holtzman (1962), is that the method may violate the statistical assumption of independence of the observations: A person's score may depend on (i.e., correlated with) a score from neighboring days. Fortunately there are now methods available to cope with this possibility, such as Molenaar's (1982). His method is to have a correlation matrix that also includes observations with a lag of 1, 2, or 3 days, at least, so that the correlation matrices can be examined for the degree to which they show or do not show serial dependence. An informative study using this "dynamic factor analysis" is illustrated by Jones, Wood, Ahern and Nesselroade (1988).

4. *The symptom-context method and the P-technique's factors can be used together to locate within the contexts the immediate and background conditions for recurrent symptoms.* It can be helpful to include in the intercorrelation matrix measures of important recurrent symptoms, as is illustrated by reports of stomach pain in the course of the session that were found to be part of the surgency factor. Such studies can be valuable for psychosomatic research on theories of symptom formation and can help in focusing on the conditions in this patient's typical immediate and background symptom-contexts.

HOW THE DISCOVERY OF *HELICOBACTER PYLORI* SHOULD CHANGE THE FIELD'S PERSPECTIVE

Research in the past decade has demonstrated that for many patients with peptic ulcers, a bacterium, *helicobacter pylori*, is a basic contributory condition for the stomach ulcer because it sets up an inflammation of the pylorus (Graham & Go, 1993). The inflammation, the hydrochloric acid secretion, and the contractions are together all responsible for the pain from time to time. The immediate conditions certainly include the patient's perception of the pain, but the broad background conditions also include the damaging effects of the bacterium. The broad background context is not only biopsychological in terms of the patient's surgency (Factor 7) but also is associated with the underlying physical condition set up by the bacterium that contributes to the state.

Sometimes very big discoveries seem to require us to revise or even to wipe away what were thought to be the usual psychological causative factors, because they point to causative physical factors that had been missed. Such a big shift in understanding the conditions associated with peptic ulcer recently astonished researchers on gastrointestinal disorders. This shift was begun in the early 1980s by J. Robin Warren of Perth, Australia, who found in the stomach the common bacterium, helicobacter pylori. Then in 1984 Barry J. Marshall, from the same hospital staff as Warren, began to show that this bacterium was a basic cause of the damage from peptic ulcer. The damage appears to come from the inflammatory response set up by this bacterium. By now this new causation is well established as a primary cause of ulcers. Graham and Go (1993) confirmed the causation by this bacterium of such diverse diseases as gastritis, gastric ulcer, duodenal ulcer, and even gastric carcinoma. Now the new appropriate treatment is relatively rapid and inexpensive: combined bismuth-and-antibiotic therapy with a 12-day course of the antibiotics amoxicillin and metronidazole. The treatment takes the place of the older usual treatment with antacids, such as Zantac.

But this new leap in knowledge does not mean that all of the studies over the last 50 years about the role of psychological factors in formation of ulcers were completely wrong. For example, among these studies were those by Grace and Graham (1952) reviewed in Weiner (1977), and many others who reported observations with implications that psychological stress increases the secretion of gastric juice and that sets off the duodenal or stomach ulcer. Moving closer to home, does the new knowledge about helicobacter pylori also imply that our observations were wrong about the role of psychological factors in the ulcer-related stomach pain of our patient? Probably not. Even though this newly recognized bacterium was probably involved in Mr. Rycheck's ulcer, and the role of this bacterium could have been far greater as a factor than any of the other factors, the most fitting overarching explanation is that *the bacterium and related physiological factors plus the psychological factors must have interacted.* In time, we should expect the inevitable eventual discovery of even more basic preconditions for each symptom and often, as with this symptom, the discovery will be on the biological level.

SUMMARY AND CONCLUSIONS ABOUT THE CONTEXT FOR MR. RYCHECK'S STOMACH PAIN

By Clinical Review

A set of conditions were inferred by the clinical review of Mr. Rycheck (Method 1):

- strivings to fulfill his wish to attain high public position, such as the presidency of the YMCA (see the example from Session 8), to win his girlfriend (see the examples from Sessions 14 and 19), to get appreciation from others, to get ahead in school, and to acquire a lot of money
- the consequences of his striving to attain his wishes: a fear of using up his energy, money, power, and to be left weak and vulnerable to be taken advantage of
- a renewed effort to convince himself of his strength, power, energy, optimism, worth, and moral standing
- a tendency to express to father figures wishes to please them and convince them about the goodness of his motives, but also to express to them competitive and resentful feelings
- a giving in to submissive feelings that he was only partially aware of.

The clinical review suggests that before the pain, Mr. Rycheck was stewing in the aftermath of the intruding anxious thought that he was weak, that he might not win in his manifest striving. Then the stomach pain was usually reported with a mixture of feeling hurt, and complaining, with a reference to the pain as "kicking me," that is, as if he were the passive object kicked around by the stomach (his perception of weakness was stated or clearly inferable in 17 of the 26 instances of reports of stomach pain).

By Ratings

Ratings of the immediate context led to further focus on the set of qualities that distinguished the symptom versus the control contexts. My initial free method was compared with guided choice by clues of sentence pairs from before the pain versus before the controls. Judges were typically unable to distinguish symptom from control sentence pairs when they were not given any clues about what to look for. But most judges were able to make the distinction accurately when given the combined clues of attending to Concern about Supplies and Helplessness. With rating scales the qualities that were most differentiating were (for the sentence before the pain) Concern about Supplies, Anxiety, Helplessness, and Striving and Hoping for Wish Fulfillment.

By Scorings

Scoring systems also showed some success in revealing distinctions for the symptom and control segments. For example, the Helplessness manual (see description in chap. 8) distinguished significantly ($p < .02$) as scored by one judge and as scored by another.

In terms of the broad background, several methods were used to distinguish symptom and control segments.

By Dictionaries

Dictionaries of psychological words showed significant differences between symptom and control segments (Spence, 1979), and these differences were almost as large as those based on rating methods (Table 3).

By the Surgency Factor

Another broad background factor was revealed by the presence of the recurrent stomach pain within the P-technique-derived psychophysiological surgency factor.

Final Familiar Findings

Several other familiar findings are evident in this chapter and in the data analyses:

- There is a parallel between findings in the immediate context of the symptom and in the background context symptom.
- There was a special set of qualities for the onset conditions for Mr. Rycheck, and among these qualities was Helplessness and a factor that has appeared repeatedly for other patients in this book along with other familiar qualities: Concern about Supplies and Anxiety.
- As powerful as the symptom-context method and the P-technique are, clinical skill is still needed at several points: (a) in selecting the variables to be included in the ratings and in the other measures, (b) in understanding the factors that emerge in relation to the content of the session, and (c) in deciphering the context of the recurrent symptoms that relate to the factors.

SAMPLE OF EIGHT PAIRS OF REAL AND CONTROL
SENTENCES BEFORE STOMACH PAIN

I'd see more of the harshness of it (of life), the reality, you might say. I never will if I live over here (in U.S., as opposed to Europe)—we haven't been able to see the realities of our lives over here.

(I'm) kind of wondering in my mind whether I'll go to school or whether I'll take some kind of trip to Europe or something of that sort—

I just try to get the committees to be in the fore most of the time and right down to business—I find that this psychology works best.

I'll be pretty darned busy until this pressure gets off of it—until I get back, you might say, to normal—if I ever was normal (laughs) normal for me.

When it came time to go to sleep I didn't feel like going to sleep at all—come normal time to go to bed, some darned committee to pester me—

I just happened to think of Easter Sunday and how I should be in the Presbyterian Church and also how that conflicts with an invitation to go home with this fellow, a friend of mine in Decatur—not Decatur, excuse me . . . gosh, I can't think right now.

I do it at the expense of my own health, vigor, and so what I shall build won't amount to anything—so I figure on paying a little more attention to Jose (a pet name for himself).

Something that I worry about occasionally. Oh, I don't worry about it—it is just something to be guarded against that some political leader or someone who could sway them the wrong way.

Couldn't get to sleep right away—there are things I've got to straighten around, at least part way, to halfway meet the situation—it will cost me $4.17 more than to go the regular way.

I've been running in a contest for a long time. I just begin to wonder how the darned thing is going to work out—

I've got various contacts on campus but don't have time to see them—that ought to be going on at the same time that the subject is being taught—that relatedness and relationship—

She knew the score pretty well—perhaps even better than I did at the time—yet she was going in another direction than I thought I was going—

I never thought of the word *go-giver* or its relation to *go-getter*, but the principle I thought of a long time ago—

I guess I didn't quite realize I was burning the candle a little too fiercely. I realize my old principle, what this fellow says as "go-giver," giving all you got, then everything comes back in the same proportions—it's still a good principle, but I can't do it—I have to rest.

It will be nice for her, as she was in Europe before—she speaks four other languages besides English—

I'm looking forward to next week—get working on these results (of the experiment with T.) all right. That will be all right, yes sir. Looking forward to getting the house painted.

REFERENCES

American Psychiatric Association. (1994). *Diagnostic and statistical manual of mental disorders* (4th ed). Washington, DC: Author.

Cattell, R. B. (1943). The description of personality: Foundations of trait measurement. *Psychological Review, 50,* 559–592.

Cattell, R. B., & Luborsky, L. B. (1950). P-technique demonstrated as a new clinical method for determining personality structure. *Journal of General Psychology, 42,* 3–24.

Cattell, R. (1963). The structuring of change by P and incremental R-technique. In C. Harris (Ed.), *Problems in measuring change* (pp. 98–103). Madison: University of Wisconsin Press.

Dahl, H. (1972). A quantitative study of a psychoanalysis. *Psychoanalysis and Contemporary Science, 1,* 237–257.

Grace, W. J., & Graham, D. (1952). Relationship of specific attitudes and emotions to certain bodily disease. *Psychosomatic Medicine, 14,* 243–251.

Graham, D., & Go, M. (1993). Helicobacter pylori: Current status. *Gastroenterology, 105,* 279–282.

Holtzman, W. (1962). Methodological issues in P-technique. *Psychological Bulletin, 59,* 248–256.

Jones, C., & Nesselroade, J. (1990). Multivariate, replicated, single-subject measures designs and P-technique factor analysis: A review of intra-individual change studies. *Experimental Aging Research, 16,* 171–183.

Jones, C., Wood, P., Ahern, F., & Nesselroade, J. (1988). *Simultaneous and time-developed relationships between vital statistics and short-term memory: A multivariate time series investigation of three elderly individuals.* Paper presented at the annual meeting of the Gerontological Society of America, San Francisco, CA.

Luborsky, L. (1953). Intra-individual repetitive measurements (P-technique) in understanding symptom structure and psychotherapeutic change. In O. H. Mowrer (Ed.), *Psychotherapy: Theory and research* (pp. 389–413). New York: Ronald Press.

Luborsky, L. (1993). Documenting symptom formation during psychotherapy: The conditions for momentary forgetting. In N. Miller, L. Luborsky, J. P. Barber, & J. P. Docherty (Eds.), *Handbook of dynamic psychotherapy research and practice* (pp. 3–13). New York: Basic Books.

Luborsky, L. (1995). The first trial of P-technique in psychotherapy research—A still-lively legacy. *Journal of Consulting and Clinical Psychology, 63,* 6–140.

Luborsky, L., & Auerbach, A. H. (1969). The symptom-context method: Quantitative studies of symptom formation in psychotherapy. *Journal of the American Psychoanalytic Association, 17,* 68–99.

Luborsky, L., & Mintz, J. (1972). The contribution of P-technique to personality, psychotherapy, and psychosomatic research. In R. M. Dreger (Ed.), *Multivariate analysis: Essays in honor of Raymond B. Cattell* (pp. 387–410). Baton Rouge: Claitor's Publishing Division.

Mintz, J., & Luborsky, L. (1970). P-technique factor analysis in psychotherapy research: An illustration of a method. *Psychotherapy: Theory, Research and Practice, 6,* 13–18.

Molenaar, P. C. (1982). A dynamic factor model for the analysis of multivariate time series. *Psychometrika, 50,* 181–202.

Murray, J. B. (1982). The psyche and stomach ulcers. *Genetic Psychology Monographs, 105,* 181–212.

Nesselroade, J., & Ford, E. (1985). P-technique comes of age. *Research in Aging, 7,* 46–80.

Netter, F. (1959). The upper digestive tract. [Figure]. *The CIBA Collection of Medical Illustrations, 3,* 85.

Russell, R. L. (1995). Introduction to the special section on multivariate psychotherapy research: Structure and change in the talking cure. *Journal of Consulting and Clinical Psychology, 63,* 28–36.

Spence, D. (1979). Human and computer attempts to decode symptom language. *Psychosomatic Medicine, 32,* 615–625.

Stone, P. J., Dunphy, D. C., Smith, M. S., et al. (1966). *The General Inquirer: A computer approach to content analysis.* Cambridge, MA MIT Press.

Weiner, H. M. (1977). *Psychology and human disease.* New York: Elsevier.

Zimmer, J. M., & Hakstian, A. R. (1972). Dimensions of counselee responses over several therapy sessions. *Journal of Counseling Psychology, 19,* 448–454.

8

THE CONTEXT FOR MIGRAINE-LIKE HEADACHES

LESTER LUBORSKY, ARTHUR AUERBACH, and
A. THOMAS MCLELLAN

A pain in the head is likely to have a different physical source than a pain in the stomach, yet one might still find that the psychological context for both is similar. I began the search for sources by examining the psychological context for the headaches of 3 patients as the headaches erupted during sessions; 2 of these patients were in psychoanalysis and 1 was in psychoanalytic psychotherapy. The 2 patients in psychoanalysis had only minor, occasional headaches. The patient in psychotherapy, Peter Berger, discussed here, had frequent, painful, migraine-like headaches that sometimes were experienced by him as near-catastrophic. At such times, he even had the thought that it was better to end his life to escape the pain. Because of the frequency and severity of his headaches and because the available data about the location of the headaches for the other two patients were incomplete, only Mr. Berger's data were included in a symptom-context study; this report of results is much more extensive than the one in Luborsky and Auerbach (1969).

An earlier version of this chapter appeared in Luborsky, L., & Auerbach, A. H. (1969). The symptom-context method: Quantitative studies of symptom formation in psychotherapy. *Journal of the American Psychoanalytic Association, 17,* 68–99. It has been adapted, revised, and expanded by the author with permission of the publisher.

MR. BERGER'S HEADACHE SYMPTOMS

The headaches first started when Mr. Berger was 20 years old, shortly after he moved from his hometown to another city to begin graduate work. At age 27, while still in graduate school, he began psychotherapy with the hope that it could help with his very severe and debilitating headaches. He had already seen many doctors about the headaches, which had become recurrent and violent in the past 3 years, although minor ones had been infrequently present most of his life. He had tended to look at these as largely physical and at times as entirely physical, although he could see threads of evidence that psychological conditions played some part. The agreement made between the patient and therapist at the start of psychotherapy was that he would continue to see a physician whose specialty was treating headaches concurrently with the psychotherapy.

Physical examinations to find the cause of his headaches had been negative. His headaches were described as left-sided, beginning in the left frontal area, radiating into the left jaw, and back to the left occiput. They frequently occurred at night, principally on awakening, and at times they would awaken him from a sound sleep. The pain was excruciating and might last form 30 min to several hours. Many of the characteristics of these headaches were described in the section on histaminic cephalgia by Steinhilber, Pearson, and Rushton (1960). They described such headaches as "unilateral, of short duration, sudden and severe, with the majority occurring at night, with incessant and excruciating pain. The pain does not follow the distribution of any cranial nerve. The neural pathways are not known" (Steinhilber et al., 1960, p. 691). Such cluster headaches have sometimes been called *migraine headaches* or *Horton's headache*, and they are thought to be a form of vascular headache.

This is a report from one of the headache specialists Mr. Berger consulted, and it was typical of such examinations:

> He has had occasional mild headaches all of his life and the present type began four years ago. They occur nearly every day, but he has enjoyed intervals of freedom as long as one month in duration. They occur primarily on awakening in the morning, but they frequently awaken him from a sound sleep. It begins with a faint, dull feeling in the head followed by pain which develops within five to thirty minutes. The pain starts over either eye and radiates down into the teeth and neck. The eye becomes red, but the nose does not get stuffed up. His face may become slightly swollen. The pain is excruciating and may last from two to forty-eight hours. It is not accompanied by nausea, vomiting, or diplopia. There are no scotoma. The pain is pounding in nature. The father suffered from a similar type of headache and his brother has allergies. I believe this is a rather typical vascular headache of the so-called histamine type. It is my personal impression that most

of these are due to food allergies and we have started him on a simple elimination program in an effort to identify these specific allergens. Also, Cafergot and prednisone were prescribed.

The headache specialist's recommended treatments, the elimination diet and the drugs, were found to be ineffective.

MR. BERGER'S BACKGROUND AND PERSONALITY

When he started graduate school, his teachers thought highly of him. By the time he started psychotherapy, he had passed his preliminary examinations and had only his thesis left in order to complete his PhD requirements. He was working slowly on his thesis while teaching courses.

About 3 years before beginning psychotherapy, he began to engage in overtly homosexual behavior. He did not see his headaches as being in any way connected to his homosexuality, although he had consulted with a psychologist within the past year before his current psychotherapy.

The patient continued to be highly concerned about his parents and wanted very much to please them, especially his mother. He seemed to be scared and frightened of his father, who was easily angered. The patient had a married younger brother with whom he was somewhat distant. The patient volunteered that he was not sure how much sibling rivalry there was, by which he meant that he was not aware that there was much if any.

The patient tended not to pay much attention to his own feelings. Instead, he often looked for cues outside himself for impressions about what he was like. He tended to decide on responses by telling something to someone and then hearing how they responded.

He had few memories of his childhood. His earliest memory, possibly from around age 3, may have been a memory based on what was told to him by his parents. The "memory" was about wanting something and clenching his fists with anger and frustration. He added that his mother would say, "Isn't he cute the way he does that when he wants something?" Another memory was from around age 13, when he remembered fighting with a boy in the neighborhood. When he told his father, his father teased him for being cowardly. The patient had wanted to fight the boy by wrestling, at which he was skillful, but his father insisted that he box, which he could not do very well. A much later memory, from around age 24, was of a verbal fight between his parents when they were flying in an airplane; his father had turned on his mother with anger because she had concealed her age when they had gotten married (she was 1 year older than her husband). In all three early memories, anger appeared to be a consistent element.

Diagnostically, Mr. Berger had psychological symptoms that could have been associated with his headaches, but his symptoms did not warrant a specific Axis I mood or anxiety disorder or an Axis II diagnosis. In criteria from the fourth edition of the *Diagnostic and Statistical Manual of Mental Disorders*, he could be coded as "316: Stress-Related Physiological Response Affecting Migraine-Like Headaches."

METHOD 1: CLINICAL REVIEW OF CONTEXTS WITH HEADACHES

The buildup and decline of these headaches in the course of sessions were not as closely demarcated as was the stomach pain (in chap. 7), which had a more rapid onset and disappearance. The patient's reports of headache were therefore not as precisely linked to the beginning of pain. This observation was partially confirmed by the typical description of onset for each of the two types of pain: for the stomach pain, "There goes my stomach again"; for the headache, "I am *starting* to build up a headache."

Whenever a headache developed during the session, it always was reported by the patient and was obvious to the therapist. Its start was typically mild, although, as the patient knew, it almost always became severe. In a total of 130 sessions, there were 7 in which a headache developed during the session; in 8 other sessions, he had come to the session with a headache. In the majority of other sessions, the patient reported that headaches had occurred either on the day of the session or on the intervening days. For the original sample of sessions, the 6[1] with headaches that developed in the sessions were Sessions 104, 107, 128, 86*, 92*, and 95*; the 6 selected as controls with no headaches appearing in the sessions were Sessions 112, 114, 115, 123, 93*, and 95* (those with asterisks were based on concurrently written notes by the therapist). Most analyses were based on this original sample. In the past year, we created a new sample by replacing those few based on concurrent notes by the therapist with those based on tape recordings. The 6 with headaches were Sessions 104-4, 107-18, 128-34, 153-12, 169-17, and 169-19; the 6 controls were Sessions 112-4, 114, 115-3, 115-6, 123-5, and 123-10.

The context for headaches that appeared during the course of sessions can be understood most easily by a clinical review. Just before the headache's onset in seven of such headaches, the clinical review revealed that the patient was feeling more pressured, blocked, frustrated, squeezed, depleted, or about to be depleted. A similar set of feelings was uncovered in the session as a whole. At least two main sources seemed to be creating the pressure bind: a wish for a particular form of gratification that he felt would be denied him and a feeling of being in a state of hopelessness and

---

[1]No recording was made for the 7th of these sessions, and the process notes were not complete enough to warrant its use, although it seemed to conform to the pattern in the other 6 sessions in the analysis of the original sample.

helplessness to do anything about the situation of wanting something and being denied. In each instance of a headache that appeared in a session, that bind was specifically experienced within the relationship with the therapist.

The three verbatim examples I present were the first three taped sessions in which a headache developed during a session. They illustrate the presence of the main contextual ingredients; these revolved around Mr. Berger's feeling of lack of control in getting the response he needed from the therapist (T). In Session 104, the patient (P) was slightly depressed; he had wanted to go South to help with the vote registration of Blacks but felt stuck by having to come to sessions with the therapist. When that feeling became acute, a headache started (underlined in text). In Session 107 he felt "dried out"; he labored at talking, but felt "tongue-tied" in relation to the therapist and forced to be silent. At that point a headache started (underlined in text). In Session 128, he again felt caught—he wanted the therapist to recognize his willingness to try, but he did not feel that he could get his wish across. At that point a headache started (underlined in text).

Session 104: Before a Headache

P: I can't|[100] say it is, uh (pause) unbearable. I mean it's bearable. It's just not too pleasant (pause of 2 min). I always had some thoughts of going down South for a while and working in one of the registration drives. Frankly, one of the things that stopped me was coming here twice a week (pause).

T: Going down there and working on the registration would give you more of a feeling of--

P: (interrupting)|[50] involvement.

T: Involvement.

P: Of some meaning.

T: Yeah, would fill you up more.

P: Uh-hum.

T: Coming here prevents you from being filled up, from that point of view.

P: Yeah, Yeah.

T: Prevents you from doing something that would--

P: Yeah, this is the only--

T: --fill you up more, hum?

P: Yeah. Of course, my work would prevent my, you know, my--any prolonged stay, too. Well, but I mean, that was the thought that made me dismiss it, was, I realized that I would be coming here (pause of 3½ min). <u>I'm starting to get a little minor headache.</u>

Session 107: Before a Headache

T: It's funny; a little while ago you were saying it's funny that everything you say pointed to your feeling in a bind, but you don't feel in a bind. And right now you're saying, "I <u>do</u> feel in a bind."

P: Yes, right now I do, yeah (long pause). And now I'm not even thinking clearly (long pause).

T: You said that a part of the bind is that you want to go on and talk about a different subject.

P: [100]|Um-hum.

T: The idea must be that somewhere you feel that I am binding you, like the guy in the dream, to talk about certain subjects. You want to go off and talk about some other subjects.

P: Well, that, and the fact that I think the other subject's so dried out; I have nothing to say about it, you know. Uh, I don't know what uh, how to, uh, respond, uh,

T: Uuhm.

P: (long pause of 20 s) This, you know, this never happened anyplace else but here. I usually don't get in the, into the|--[50] in the, in these binds (pause of 10 s).

T: You didn't get into a bind about registration?

P: Well, not to the extent that I'm tongue-tied. You know, I can't think.

T: You were in a bind with the Alka-Seltzer, in a bind in relation to the bar, or in a bind in any other area?

P: No, I mean now I'm just tongue-tied, can't even think straight.

T: In a bind in your dream?

P: Well, in the dream, yeah. No, I mean I-I, I'm not forced to lapse into these total silences and uuuhuh, you know (long pause of 55 s). |Now, I think I'm starting to get a headache. Uh--|

Session 128: Before a Headache

T: But you still feel maybe I'm still dissatisfied with you, though, about how you've been able to do.

P: [44]|Yeah, yeah. You're becoming a dissatisfied mother again--

T: (laughs).

P: (continues)—uh, Z's (a pet name the patient made up for himself at that moment) not coming through. But the feeling has that quality. I'm not that uneasy. I just thought that I would put it on the table, you know.

T: OK, Z, you did put it on the table.

P: [100]|Yeah. Um, I don't know; maybe I just don't understand what I should do in these sessions as much as I think I understand. I think by this time, I know. But maybe I am-- (pause).

T: I think you do understand. But I think you--what I sense, mainly, is that you're wondering whether I'm satisfied with your ability to go back over it. OK? Whether I'm still mad at you.

P: Not so much my ability--my willingness. Maybe I'm taking it for granted, but I[50] take it for granted that you think I am able to do it. Um, but I still sense that you think I am unwilling to do it. And I don't think I am. Maybe I'm fooling myself. But I don't think I am. And I think that I'm trying, too.

T: Yes, you are. I know you are.

P: ↓I, I, I, when I go out, I assess the meetings. When I leave here, I'm usually getting a mild headache. ↓ (The patient started to look like he was starting a headache.)

T: Are you getting one now?

P: Yeah, just a mild one. It's not going to be anything.

The patient's involvement with the therapist and sense of lack of control of getting the response he needed also was the main focus during other sessions in which a headache was reported during the session and in which the therapist took verbatim notes (part of the original sample). Two examples are described briefly here. The first time the patient developed a headache during a session (Session 73), he had looked forward to talking about a book with the therapist and began the session by speaking about it for 5 or 10 min. As soon as the therapist stopped responding by talking about the book and the patient's ideas about the book and began to refer to the patient's feelings, the patient's headache started. When discussion about the book resumed a few minutes later, his headache disappeared. (This on–off sequence of appearance then disappearance of the headache has the quality of a controlled experiment.) The patient similarly explained the ins and outs of the headache's appearance: When the therapist put aside talking about the book, Mr. Berger felt he had no power to ask the therapist to resume the discussion. If the therapist wanted to change the subject, he, the patient, could do nothing about that. When the therapist asked what had pleased him in speaking about the book, the patient revealed that he wanted a particular kind of closeness with the therapist—the feeling of two men, two professionals, talking about something they have in common.

When a headache developed in Session 92, before the headache started the patient began to say what he keenly felt, that he was dull and would not be able to get a positive response from the therapist because the patient himself knew that what he had presented was dull. At that point, a headache began.

The headaches occurring outside the session seemed, from his accounts, to have had similar contexts to those occurring in the session, with two important differences: (a) The relationship with the therapist was less explicit and (b) the amount of obvious anger and rage was far greater. Therefore, it seems likely that the patient had been suppressing or avoiding direct expressions of anger when headaches developed in the therapist's presence. He said, for example, in Session 130, "I know when I have headaches; the more anger, the worse the headache."

Because medical treatments for his headaches had been largely unhelpful, he hoped that through psychotherapy he would come to enough understanding of their context to control them. He had made some gains in this goal, in general adjustment, and in work performance, but he prematurely interrupted treatment because of a later episode of a similar disappointment in his level of satisfaction of his wish for understanding with his therapist, and there was no follow-up on his status.

According to Adler and Adler (1988), the psychodynamic pattern in patients with this type of headache appears to be similar to the pattern found in Mr. Berger. Adler and Adler (1988) described as part of the usual pattern that "the patient frantically tries to become intimate with a father figure (although with an underlying competitiveness). When this is frustrated, tremendous anger builds up, especially at the point where the effort at reunion breaks down and the effort at closeness fails" (p. 6). This pattern has considerable generality to other psychosomatic symptoms, but in these patients the physical conditions are conducive to a cluster-migraine pattern. The pain is typically reported to be excruciating, although it usually lasts less than an hour. It "rapidly reaches a crescendo unaffected by anything but occasional prompt pharmachotherapy. . . . Typically it awakens the patient bolt upright from his sleep" (Adler and Adler, 1988, p. 6).

METHOD 2: RATING SYMPTOM AND CONTROL CONTEXTS

Independent ratings were made for a before-symptom 50-word unit and then for the entire 250-word unit of the context before the symptom on most of the same categories used for the stomach pain contexts. For this symptom, only the before-symptom period was analyzed after the headache began because he tended to be preoccupied with it and talked of not much else. Several headache-related categories were added to the usual set of variables: Anger to Therapist, Anger to Others, Hopelessness, Receptiveness, Dependency, Experiencing Warmth to Therapist, Empathy for Therapist, Activity, Feeling Blocked and Frustrated by Therapist, Heterosexuality, and Homosexuality. Several categories were dropped because of difficulty in achieving reliability of ratings: Competitiveness, Inability to Get Wish, and Striving for Wish Fulfillment.

Significance levels (by one-tailed tests) of the differences between the six symptom and six control contexts tended to be high in the original sample (see Table 1). For the 50-word contexts, the categories achieving significance for Judge AA, whose variables were completely uncontaminated (with the most differentiating variables listed first), were as follows: Feeling of being Blocked and Frustrated (by therapist), Lack of Control, Hopelessness, Helplessness, Dependency, Hostility to Therapist, Anxiety, and Doubt. The two judges had about the same number of variables significant for the 50-word unit before the headache; for the 250-word unit before the headache, AA had more variables significant than did the other judge.

The intercorrelations ranged from low to moderate (see Table 2). The highest of the mean intercorrelations were for Hopelessness (.48) and Helplessness (.38). A few of these were negative correlations of Dependency with the other variables; for some reason, here dependency tended to be negatively related to the other variables.

TABLE 1
Significant Differences Between Ratings of Segments Before Headaches
(*n* = 6) Versus Before Controls (*n* = 6; Original Sample)

Word unit	Judge LL				Judge AA			
	50-0		250-0		50-0		250-0	
	t	*p*	*t*	*p*	*t*	*p*	*t*	*p*
Lack of Control	4.45	.001	1.85	.047	3.86	.002	4.26	.001
Blocked by Therapist	7.79	.000	8.62	.000	4.07	.003	3.53	.005
Hopelessness	4.79	.001	1.12	.145	3.51	.003	2.36	.020
Dependency	2.89	.008	1.55	.085	3.08	.006	2.89	.015
Helplessness	4.41	.002	1.51	.081	2.79	.010	2.28	.023
Hostility to Therapist	1.81	.065	1.63	.083	2.39	.019	2.45	.017
Anxiety	2.22	.026	0.82	.215	2.14	.029	1.63	.066
Doubt	1.58	.088	0.25	.402	2.07	.033	2.01	.036
Pressure	6.36	.000	1.09	.150	0.62	.275	0.41	.345
Supplies	2.30	.022	2.12	.030	0.45	.332	0.62	.277

Note. AA was a completely independent judge and therefore was the primary judge; his 50 words before were ranked by a probability value (one-tailed).

TABLE 2
Intercorrelations of Rated Variables That Significantly Discriminated Between Migraine Headaches and Control Segments

Variable	1	2	3	4	5	6	7	8	M^a	M^b
1. Anxiety	—	-.38	.76	.62	.66	-.09	-.18	-.23	.16	.42
2. Anger to Therapist		—	-.09	-.18	.05	.29	.45	-.23	-.01	.24
3. Lack of Control			—	.83	.91	.25	.33	-.53	.35	.53
4. Helplessness				—	.89	.31	.60	-.38	.38	.55
5. Hopelessness					—	.56	.58	-.28	.48	.56
6. Doubt						—	.67	.40	.34	.37
7. Blocked							—	-.19	.32	.43
8. Dependency								—	-.21	.32

Note. Data are based on symptom segments 50 words before migraine headache (AA's ratings).
[a]Correlations of that variable with the other variables.
[b]Mean of the absolute value of each correlation for that variable.

METHOD 3: SCORING SYSTEMS FOR SYMPTOM VERSUS CONTROL CONTEXTS

Usual Scoring Systems

The results based on the new sample are summarized in Table 3: Reference to Therapist, Cognitive Disturbance, Speech Disturbance, and Helplessness manual. For the 50-word unit before the headache, Cognitive Disturbance was significant at the .04 level. Speech Disturbance was significant at the .03 level for the 250-word unit before the headache. The

TABLE 3
Significant Differences Between Scorings of Segments Before Headaches (*n* = 6) Versus Before Controls (*n* = 6; New Sample)

	Word unit			
	50-0		250-0	
Variable used	*t*	p^a	*t*	p^a
Reference to Therapist	1.63	.089	1.47	.108
Cognitive Disturbance	1.80	.041	2.21	.018
Speech Disturbance	1.14	.146	2.13	.036
Helplessness manual (Difference score)	1.41	.093	1.86	.046

[a]Tests were one-tailed.

Helplessness manual as used here and in most of these studies[2] was not significant for the 50 words before the headache but it was for the 250 words before the headache.

Other Speech Behaviors

Coding methods were tried by another independent judge (SH) for speech-related behaviors such as stuttering, pauses, and positive and negative affect. Although almost all the differences between the six symptom and the six control contexts were in the expected direction, only a few achieved marginal significance (even by one-tailed tests). This low level of significance appeared despite the fact that comparison of the contexts, pair by pair, would favor the hypothesis (in six out of six or five out of six pairs). Apparently, the low significance level was the result of the variability of the scores, the small sample size, and the atomistic nature of the codes.

In four of six pairs, more long pauses and stuttering occurred in the symptom than in the control contexts. In the other two pairs, no long pauses or stuttering were noted, but this was expected because these pairs were not transcribed from tape but were taken from the therapist's notes (as part of the original sample).

An active exchange between the patient and the therapist seemed to be going on in the symptom contexts compared with the control contexts; both the patient and the therapist tended to make numerous brief statements. This was true for six of the six pairs ($p < .05$, one-tailed). In the symptom contexts, the patient tended to make more statements referring to the here and now in the session than to outside the treatment. All six pairs of real contexts had more negative than positive affect statements; four of the six control contexts had more positive than negative affect statements. In all six of the symptom segments, the patient was talking about the therapist; this was not true in any of the control contexts.

In summary, relevant measures were created with little dependence on raters' inferences. The results suggest that the patient felt anxious, helpless, and caught in a bind in the immediate relationship with the therapist. These findings based on scorings were similar to those from the ratings.

---

[2]I also tried another form of Helplessness manual consisting of a dictionary of helplessness-related words, including *in a bind, inadequate, ineffectual, victimized, manipulated, bogged down, adrift,* and so on. More of these words were found in the symptom segments than in the control segments (in five of the six comparisons). The trends were in the predicted direction both in the transcripts as well as in the dictated notes, but they were usually stronger in the transcripts.

METHOD 4: EVALUATING THE BACKGROUND STATE IN THE SESSIONS

These varied background variables were associated with the increase or decrease in his headache frequency over time.

A Headache-Prone Background State (Increase)

The headaches developed in the context of a broader headache-prone state. This state showed itself on the psychological level as a Feeling of Pressure and of a Lack of Control because the patient felt unable to get his needs for support and affirmation met and felt depleted, about to be depleted, or made to submit. At such times he reported, and one could observe, that his headaches were more readily set off both within and outside the session.

The headaches generally occurred in clusters, with a slow buildup over the course of several days. Each cluster lasted several days to several weeks and then declined for several days or several weeks. Although this was the overall pattern, it was not regular. For example, there were occasional moderate headaches beginning around 9/1/64 and lasting through 10/19/64; there was then a gradual increase in the frequency of headaches lasting until 11/24/64 and then just a few headaches for a week, with an increase in frequency and severity from 12/1/64 through 12/13/64. The patient observed that if he had one headache, he was likely to have more. His observation fit with our observation that the headaches occurred in clusters and were probably precipitated by a headache-prone state.

A large-scale study of variables that could precipitate or relieve headaches supported the view that cluster headaches are a distinct entity (Drummond, 1985). More neurovascular involvement was apparent in this study for patients whose headaches were toward the migraine end of the headache spectrum; psychological factors and symptoms of muscular contraction were more often associated with constant rather than episodic headaches. Mr. Berger's symptoms, however, did not easily fit the category of constant headaches; they were cluster headaches that were associated with physical, probably neurovascular symptoms, as well as with psychological factors (see the extensive classification system in Oleson, 1994).

Interruption of Contact With the Therapist (Increase)

The effects of interruptions of treatment seemed to play a part in the pattern of headaches. For example, at the beginning of treatment there was a slow buildup of headaches. On resuming treatment at the end of the therapist's vacation (9/1/64), headaches started to occur but gradually increased in frequency for the next 2 weeks. The same happened when the therapist returned from vacation on 9/12/65: There was a gradual worsening of the headaches. That trend toward a worsening of headaches was diminished when the patient proposed and the therapist agreed to change the frequency of sessions from twice a week to once a week. The headache frequency decreased, although later bunches of headaches eventually reappeared.

Frustration of Wish for Response From Others (Increase)

Among the reasons for the pattern was the buildup of an involvement in the conflictual relationship patterns. The pattern involved the gradual buildup of the wish for immediate response from the therapist, which led to impotent frustration and covert rage that his wish would not be satisfied. Those feelings played a part in setting off the headaches, as the examples in the clinical review section illustrate.

Receipt of Satisfactions in Relationships (Decrease)

Among the qualities that had a good effect on the frequency of his headaches was his occasional experiencing of a positive relationship with the therapist. For example, a relatively long period of being headache-free occurred following Session 31 (9/1/64) after the treatment resumed after the therapist's vacation. The patient reported many headaches during the vacation interval, but it was unusual for him that his awareness of depression was related to therapist's absence. It was novel for him, he said, to be aware of his depression being a result of missing someone. In the next 2 weeks, the headaches continued and got worse (9/15/64). In that session, the patient revealed that he felt in a bind:

> I am too dependent on you and I can do nothing about it. . . . I am in a brick prison. I can count the bricks but I cannot move them. As soon as I leave here, I cannot do anything. I am all alone except for the two hours I see you.

At this point, the therapist emphasized that what started as feeling like a natural dependence began to feel like a feeling he could do nothing about. For this reason, it made him uncomfortable to feel a "we-ness feeling" with the therapist; the therapist went on to say that it was hard for Mr. Berger to hold on to the closeness and with it all that he had gained when the therapist was out of sight, as had been true during that vacation. This interpretation may have had a part in the beginning of the headache-free period.

Receiving satisfactions of other kinds also might have reduced his headaches. When he started a new drug, the headaches briefly improved no matter what the drug was, although, as we noted earlier, that was not always true. When he was able to phone his mother, his headaches improved. On one occasion, reported in Session 65, he was visited by a homosexual partner and then his headaches improved.

The patient also had noticed that other satisfactions, such as smoking, masturbation, or a bowel movement, all could shorten or stop the development of the headaches.

A Different Recurrent Symptom: Momentary Forgetting

Along with recurrent headaches, another recurrent symptom, momentary forgetting, occasionally occurred, so we examined the comparative conditions for each symptom in the same patient.

Momentary forgetting tended to occur during periods when he had no headaches and at times when his mood was good or elated. A small clump of forgettings occurred during a period in which he was headache-free: from Sessions 35 to 43. These momentary forgettings tended to clump together toward the end of the headache-free period and then no longer occurred when the headache-free period ended. This association of good or even elated moods with forgetting has been noted for some other patients (Luborsky, 1967).

With this patient and other patients, during periods of more elated mood the patient tends to be trying a new attitude, but the intent to try this new attitude begins to frighten him. After expressing thoughts that are reflective of the new attitude, his contact with his own thoughts and with the therapist appear to become disturbed. Session 69 is a good example. He expressed interest in a girlfriend—a new attitude for him. In recounting this event he was anxious, pressured, and showed momentary forgetting.

The themes for the momentary forgettings appeared to be similar to the themes of the headaches, that is, the anxiety about getting a response to what the patient wanted from the therapist. An example of this occurred at the end of a session in which there nevertheless was a headache (Session 128). It was much like a momentary forgetting, but it did not exactly meet the usual criterion for a momentary forgetting because he did not have the thought clearly in mind before he forgot it: "I thought I wanted to say something ... but I didn't know [what] I wanted, I had the feeling of wanting to say something. ... I had the feeling I would get a response from you." So the main theme in this example is the issue of whether he would get a response from the therapist. It was a very special moment when he captured the thought that he intended to say, "I think you [meaning himself] should be satisfied that is very true and that is exactly what I was getting at."

SUMMARY AND CONCLUSIONS

Following are the main conclusions about the contexts for Mr. Berger's headaches:

- For the conditions in the immediate context, significant qualities distinguished headache segments from control segments in ratings of 50-word units before the headache: Blocked, Lack of Control, Hopelessness, Dependent, Helplessness, Hostility to Therapist, Anxiety, and Doubt. These qualities were mostly evident in the clinical review. It is noteworthy that the hostility appeared in the clinical review and in the ratings of the headaches that appeared in the sessions, but very likely it was even more evident in the headaches that appeared outside the sessions.

- For the conditions in the larger background state, some of the same qualities were evident in terms of the feeling of lessened control. These also were shown in terms of long pauses, stuttering, negative affect, and the helplessness manual.

- The two classes of conditions, that is, the immediate context conditions and the broad background context conditions, appeared to interact and contributed to the migraine-like headaches in this patient.

REFERENCES

Adler, C., & Adler, S. (1988). Psychodynamic findings in patients with cluster headaches. *Academy Forum, 32,* 6–8.

Drummond, P. (1985). Predisposing, precipitating and relieving factors in different categories of headache. *Headache, 25,* 16–22.

Luborsky, L., & Auerbach, A. H. (1969). The symptom–context method: Quantitative studies of symptom formation in psychotherapy. *Journal of the American Psychoanalytic Association, 17,* 68–99.

Luborsky, L. (1967). Momentary forgetting during psychotherapy and psychoanalysis: A theory and research method. In R. R. Holt (Ed.), *Motives and thought: Psychoanalytic essays in honor of David Rapaport* (pp. 177–217). Madison, CT: International Universities Press.

Olesen, J. (Ed.). (1994). *Headache classification and epidemiology.* New York: Raven Press.

Steinhilber, R., Pearson, J., & Rushton, J. (1960). Some psychological considerations of histaminic cephalgia. *Proceedings of the Staff Meetings of the Mayo Clinic, 35,* 691–699.

9

THE CONTEXT FOR ABSENCE EPILEPSY EPISODES (PETIT MAL)

LESTER LUBORSKY, JOHN P. DOCHERTY, LOUIS A. GOTTSCHALK,
THOMAS C. TODD, PETER H. KNAPP, ALLAN F. MIRSKY,
ANDREA WAGNER, ARMAND SIEGEL, and STUART ROSENTHAL

After a series of symptom-context studies of self-reported symptoms, I realized that I also had to re-search in a new direction: to find recurrent physical symptoms that could be measured without requiring the patient's self-reports. It could be that the usual psychological antecedents of symptoms may appear only before those that are self-reported; those that I have studied so far by the symptom-context method relied on the patient's reports to identify the symptom. Thus, the possibility existed that the patients sometimes chose not to report a symptom, that they did not faithfully report it at the moment it occurred, or even that the appearance of the antecedent qualities is somehow linked to self-reports.

Fortunately, we found 3 patients with absence epilepsy (Commission on Classification, 1981) who could be monitored by an electroencephalograph (EEG) while they were being interviewed. The well-known marker for an "absence" episode (formerly called *petit mal*) was used in all three patients: symmetrical and synchronous 3-cycle per second (cps) spike and wave activity in the EEG.

An earlier version of this chapter appeared in Luborsky, L., Docherty, J. P., Todd, T. C., Knapp, P. H., Mirsky, A. F., & Gottschalk, L. A. (1975). A context analysis of psychological states prior to petit mal EEG paroxysms. *Journal of Nervous and Mental Disease, 160,* 282–298. It has been adapted, revised, and expanded by the author with permission of the publisher.

I begin this chapter, which expands on Luborsky et al. (1975), with the first of the 3 patients, Ernest Schull. I discuss this patient more than the other 2 patients because he was the only one who was a patient in psychotherapy, and it might be more likely that his seizures were associated with his antecedent psychological state.

Diagnostically, all 3 patients did not have any apparent Axis I or Axis II diagnoses other than the obvious adjustments and concerns about their neurological disorder. With the first patient, however, there were extremes of depression and self-blame, perhaps secondary to the adjustment to his diagnosis of epilepsy.

ERNEST SCHULL

We relied on data from psychotherapy sessions with Mr. Schull; some of the data have been reported previously (Gottschalk, 1955). His first seizure occurred at age 23, when he was an army private. He was studied at age 24, when he had a seizure on returning to his military post after a 3-day leave of absence. The patient's absence seizures, but not his grand mal attacks, showed up on the EEG but not clinically (as in this example in Figure 1). For this reason, these absence events are referred to as *EEG paroxysmal states*. The main data used for my analyses were the tape-recorded psychotherapy sessions with concurrent EEG recordings.

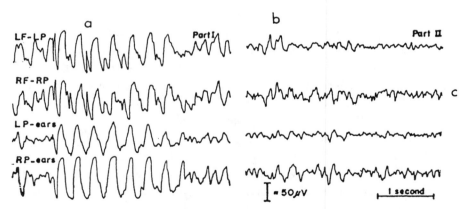

Figure 1. Electroencephalographic paroxysmal brain wave activity (ES). *Part I.* Pt. resting with eyes closed. *Part II.* Eyes closed. Pt. counting silently. *a.* This is indubitably 3/s spike and wave activity. *b.* This is theta activity (about 5 cps). *c.* This is, in general, compatible with a right-sided slow wave predominance, but from this sample one could not argue that there was a right *temporal* predominance. LF = Left front; LP = Left posterior; RF = Right front; RP = Right posterior.

Method 1: Clinical Review of the Symptom Contexts

My review of these data suggested that the EEG paroxysmal states occurred during periods of heightened negative affect, especially hostility set off by criticism of himself or by others. In fact, this state appeared to lead to severe separation anxiety. When he was in this state, it eliminated transiently the suppressing effect of speaking on his abnormal EEG slow-wave bursts.

Additional clues about the onset conditions were suggested by the patient's description of a severe "spell," which suggested that when he got "excited" or angry at others and at himself, he might have been more prone to the attacks:

> Recently I bit my tongue something terrible. When I wake up from a spell I have a headache and my arms hurt. Most of the spells occur when I'm asleep. It seems that if I get excited or worked up, one or two days later I get a spell. I notice I'm very irritable lately. I make scenes of little things. I catch myself doing this and I wonder why. I get sorry for hollering at people.

Study of tape-recorded interviews, which were synchronized with the EEG record, indicated that slow-wave paroxysms occurred roughly within 30 s after the patient expressed a fear of being criticized adversely or repudiated or after he criticized and repudiated himself. The thought of repudiation of himself by his mother and father, God, the army, doctors, nurses, or the investigator appeared to be just as commonly followed by a slow-wave paroxysm. Consistent with this, actual adverse criticisms of the patient by the investigator or another person were found to be followed by the slow paroxysmal cerebral electrical activity during certain recording sessions; no such paroxysmal activity occurred for 20 min of blander interviewing before and after such criticism.

Without any changes in anticonvulsant medication, the total frequency of this patient's paroxysms of cerebral dysrhythmia decreased over a period of 2 months, during which the investigator attempted to help him feel acceptable and likable. Yet when the patient's self-criticism was not lowered but stimulated, the paroxysmal rate tended to increase. When there was a decrease in the brief seizure patterns observed in the EEG, the patient's clinical status improved. No changes in seizure frequency were observed after he was taken off of anticonvulsant medication during the 3rd month of hospitalization.

The analyses were based on verbatim transcripts of four interviews with concurrent recordings of the EEG from which 19 before-symptom segments and 19 before-control segments were extracted. Most symptom segments contained about 30 patient-words preceding EEG paroxysmal activity; each control segment contained 30 words preceding a randomly selected control point when no such activity was present. The following is a sample of the first four symptom segments containing a sufficient number of patient-words for the analyses. The depressive content is obvious by inspection of these samples.

No. 1 (No. 13)

ES: I cried and cried and cried. In fact, I cried most of the time. Some nurses are so irritable, they make everybody want to hate them.

No. 2 (No. 14)

T: You get so mad at people, you could almost kill them.

ES: I guess I don't appreciate life; I guess I just want it to be a basket of roses.

No. 3 (No. 16)

ES: Mother is looking forward to my getting well. I do, but it hurts to read the letters of my mother and my sister. It's hard to read sister's letters.

No. 4 (No. 17)

ES: She was sick before I came home.

T: How do you feel about sister?

ES: Sister and I were always close. I know she is always sincere in what she says.

Method 2: Sortings and Ratings

Method 2A: Sortings. Free or Intuitive Judgments of Symptom Segments Versus Control Segments

The set of 38 segments was first given to each of five independent judges with a "free" instruction: "The patient whose interview is included in these segments was subject to short EEG paroxysmal episodes lasting from 1 s to a few seconds. His interview was conducted while EEG leads were attached, so that the EEG paroxysmal activity could be recorded. Decide for each segment whether it is one that came before a symptom segment or before a control point when no such activity was present on the EEG (control segment). Half of these 38 segments are symptom segments and half are control segments. Please proceed by first dividing the 38 into 19 symptom and 19 control segments, and then rank all 38, with the top one the most certain to have come before a symptom and the 38th the most certain to be a control segment."

Because the presence of affect is the most common hypothesis in the literature and commonly reported by judges, and by Gottschalk (1955), the judge was then given the same set of segments with the "affect-clue" instruction: "Please do the same ranking, but this time rank it in terms of the following clue—the presence of high negative affect, especially involving anger or criticism to others or self."

Finally, the judges were given the complete transcripts of the four interviews with a small blank at the end of each of the 38 segments for judgments "in context of sessions." The instructions were the same as the "affect" instructions.

These procedural variations were aimed at learning the factors governing the judgment process. I could then compare (a) the basic global free instruction; (b) the affect-clue instruction; (c) the same affect instruction applied after the judges read the entire session (to learn whether knowing the entire session would offer any advantage over knowing only the segment); and (d) the variations in (a), (b), and (c), but using only the judges' two-category judgments of symptom versus control (to check my assumption that ranking all segments would be better than a two-category judgment).

The accuracy of judgments (based on discriminating symptom from control segments) for all three conditions combined was significant at the .01 level (see Table 1). The affect instruction and affect instruction with entire sessions were each significant at the .01 level. It is noteworthy that knowing the whole session did not significantly improve their judgments. The free-instruction ratings by themselves were not significant, as I found

TABLE 1
Number of Correct Choices From Sorting 19 Preparoxysmal (Symptom Segments) Versus 19 Control Segments for Ernest Schull

Judge	"Free" instructions	"Affect" instructions	In context of session "affect" instructions
GK	22/38	24/38	22/38
DS	14/37	23/37	28/38
PK	20/37	24/37	16/38
WM	24/38	28/38	24/38
MT	24/38	22/38	28/38
Mean for five judges	20.8/37.6	24.2/37.6	23.6/38
Mean difference from chance[a]	ns	p < .01	p < .01

[a]Chance expectation = 19/38.

in chapter 7 for the stomach pain symptoms; there was no significant difference among conditions. When questioned after the free-instruction ranking, most judges seemed to have relied on the amount of negative affect in making their ratings. Finally, the two-category judgments involved some loss of information (as compared with ranking all segments), a finding that has been reported in other research.

Method 2B: Ratings

Three bases were important in the selection of variables: (a) Some were precursors of the other symptoms studied so far by the symptom–context method; (b) others were from a review of studies of the immediate antecedents of a variety of symptoms (Luborsky, Docherty, & Penick, 1973); and (c) several were from a review of studies of the patient's state immediately before petit mal attacks.

Each of the 38 segments was rated on 18 variables by two judges independently on a 5-point scale ranging from 1 *(little)* to 5 *(much)*. A high percentage of these variables differentiated symptom from control segments at the .05 level or better (see Table 2), despite difficulties of rating such short segments and despite the consequently low reliabilities on some variables such as Separation Anxiety, Feeling Blocked by Therapist, Lack of Control, New Attitude, Tiredness, Attention Difficulty). These variables with low reliability were mainly ones in which both raters saw little evidence of the variable. The most differentiating variables (starting with the most) were Depression, Involvement with Therapist, Feeling Blocked, Hostility, and Anxiety.

The 13 variables that significantly discriminated between absence epilepsy episodes and control segments were intercorrelated and listed in Table 2. The highest of these were Anxiety, Helplessness, Hopelessness, and Concern about Supplies. What is especially noteworthy about these intercorrelations is that although they tended to be low, they could be thought of as being at the heart of the conditions that contributed to the setting off of the symptom.

Method 3: Scoring Systems

A precise scoring of the type of affect preceding EEG paroxysmal activity was offered by Gottschalk and Gleser's (1969) measures of negative affect and was described further by Gottschalk (1995). These measures were based on independent judges' objective scoring of the patient's words. Table 3 includes results of a comparison of 16 preparoxysmal and 16 nonpreparoxysmal verbal samples. The most discriminating scored variable was Hostility-Inward, a Gottschalk-Gleser variable that has much in common with Depression. The next most discriminating was Reference to Therapist, a

TABLE 2
Intercorrelations of Rated Variables That Significantly Discriminated Between Absence Epilepsy Episodes (Petit Mal) and Control Segments (Ernest Schull)

Variable	1	2	3	4	5	6	7	8	9	10	11	12	13	Mᵃ	Mᵇ
1. Concern about Supplies	—	.53	.36	.66	.34	.28	-.02	.65	-.01	.01	-.11	.27	-.19	.23	.29
2. Anxiety		—	.63	.35	.30	.23	.17	.27	.31	-.03	.06	.09	.24	.26	.27
3. Separation Concern			—	.21	.11	.38	.04	.15	.01	-.08	-.13	-.06	.12	.15	.19
4. Helplessness				—	.72	.41	-.40	.75	.19	.21	-.30	.62	-.41	.25	.44
5. Hopelessness					—	.24	-.30	.60	.37	.20	-.23	.76	-.29	.24	.37
6. Blocked						—	-.21	.63	-.23	.50	-.34	.24	-.36	.15	.34
7. Blocked by Therapist							—	-.38	-.37	-.47	.66	-.53	.73	-.09	.36
8. Lack of Control								—	.02	.30	-.37	.56	-.50	.22	.43
9. Guilt									—	-.13	-.34	.48	-.16	.01	.22
10. Hostility										—	.03	.31	-.33	.04	.22
11. Hostility to Therapist											—	-.40	.59	-.07	.30
12. Depression												—	-.50	.15	.40
13. Involvement with Therapist													—	-.09	.37

Note. Mean ratings are based on symptom segments 30 words before absence epilepsy episodes (petit mal).
ᵃMean of the correlations for that variable.
ᵇMean of the absolute value of each correlation for that variable.

TABLE 3
Reliability and Discrimination Between 30 Words Before
Preparoxysmal EEG Segments Versus Control Segments
(19 Real and 19 Control) for Ernest Schull

Variable	Pooled reliability (two judges)	t	p	Rank
Rated				
Concern about Supplies	.77	1.77	.042	
Anxiety	.53	2.55	.008	9
Separation Concern	−.29	1.92	.032	
Helplessness	.75	2.41	.010	10
Hopelessness	.36	2.71	.006	6
Blocked	.61	3.90	.000	2
Blocked by Therapist	—	2.61	.007	8
Lack of Control	−.02	2.11	.021	
Guilt	.60	3.21	.002	5
Hostility	.38	3.42	.001	4
Hostility to Therapist	.56	2.69	.007	7
Depression	.55	4.90	.000	1
Tired	—	0.94	.176	
Reflective	.31	0.77	.224	
Involvement with Therapist	.69	3.70	.000	3
Attention Difficulty	—	0.59	.280	
Scored				
Reference to Therapist (LL)	.91	0.92	.205	
Anxiety (G-G)	—	2.32	.025	4
Hostility-Outward (G-G)	—	1.32	.100	
Hostility-Inward (G-G)	—	2.99	.003	1
Ambivalent hostility (G-G)	—	0.21	.420	
Total Affect (G-G)	—	2.40	.025	3
"Schizophrenic" (G-G)	—	2.59	.010	2
Cognitive Disturbance (LL)	—	0.90	.187	
Speech Disturbance (GM)	—	−1.53	.085	
Helplessness manual (Difference score; LL)	—	1.84	.042	5

Note. All positive t values indicate more of the variable found in symptom segments than in control segments. The most discriminating rating was depression; for scorings it was Hostility-Inward (depression). All probability values are one-tailed. All t and p values are based on the sentence before petit mal (about 30 words). EEG = electroencephalograph.

scored variable that has much in common with Involvement with Therapist. (Three of 19 samples had to be dropped because of insufficient number of words.)

I learned from these analyses that total Negative Affect, Anxiety, and Hostility-Inward were significant at the .05 level. Hostility-Outward and Ambivalent Hostility did not reach significant levels. Discrimination between preparoxysmal verbal samples were improved by including Positive Affects (from the Gottschalk Human Relations Scale) and Negative Affect ($p < .01$). Positive Affect by itself showed a slight trend ($p < .10$). This supported the hypothesis that high Affect, positive or negative, tends to be associated with EEG paroxysmal activity. In conclusion, the Gottschalk measures provided a more precise statement than we had—a confirmation that high Negative Affect was indeed distinguishing, but specifically it was Anxiety and Hostility-Inward that were the most relevant.

Conclusions: Antecedents for Symptoms for Ernest Schull

- By rating and scoring methods, the differentiation was large between before-symptom versus before-control segments, mainly on the types of Negative Affect variables preceding the symptom. It is informative to compare my findings with those from the clinical analysis. Gottschalk (1955) had concluded that "slow wave paroxysms occurred within 30 seconds after he [the patient] expressed a fear of being criticized adversely or repudiated, or after he criticized and repudiated himself" (p. 658). Furthermore, Gottschalk (1955) noted that "adverse criticism of the patient by the investigator or another person was found to be followed by paroxysmal cerebral electrical activity" (p. 658). My independent symptom-context analyses confirmed that increased affect precedes the paroxysmal EEG activity. Negative Affect generally, especially anger at or criticism of others or the self, was significantly associated with EEG paroxysms. Specifically, in terms of the Gottschalk-Gleser measures, high Negative Affect was relevant, but especially high Anxiety and Hostility-Inward. High Positive Affect also tended to be associated with the onset of EEG paroxysms. In summary, Gottschalk's (1955) clinical impression, which was based on paying attention to the content of patients' verbalizations immediately before the abnormal EEG activity, was corroborated and precisely specified in kind and amount, but it was also expanded by virtue of the current method.
- On these variables, judgments made from the contents of the entire interviews were not significantly better than those made from the segments alone. This was of interest in terms of the amount of information helpful in making clinical judgments of interview data.
- Ranking according to the degree of certainty yielded somewhat greater differentiation than simple, dichotomous judgments of the segments, but only when the judge had ample information on which to base his judgment (as provided by the total session context). This appears to be a methodological finding of interest.

- Judges could quickly and easily evaluate the context preceding the onset of an attack with highly significant differentiation of these contexts from control contexts. This differentiation could be achieved by providing the judges with the affect-clue instruction, but could not be done when they were using only free or intuitive judgment.

CLAIRE NORTON

Two other patients, Claire Norton and Scott Thompson, also were studied. There were two differences from Ernest Schull that might make comparisons difficult: (a) Although they were both patients, they were not patients in psychotherapy, as was Mr. Schull; and (b) both of these patients also might have had some physiological differences from Mr. Schull in the nature of their convulsive disorder.

Both Ms. Norton and Mr. Thompson were studied at Boston University Medical Center with interviews scheduled for the same time of day each day. The patients made no changes in their medical routines and appeared to follow instructions about not eating breakfast. During the interviews, they were recumbent or semirecumbent, with the interviewer seated at about a 45° angle to the left and front. Patients could move their extremities provided that no contact was made with the EEG electrodes. After a preliminary period in their first interview, they were instructed to close their eyes in order to decrease the amount of artifacts in the EEG record.

One channel of a four-channel Harvard Instrument Company write-out recorded the EEG, using amplifiers from the Lexington Instrument Company. A pair of electrodes on the opposite side served as a backup channel that could be switched on in case of failure of the primary pair. Placements were frontocentral. The patients' previous participation in absence epilepsy studies using multichannel recordings provided extensive EEG data against which to compare our own records. Two investigators each read the EEG independently and subsequently went over the records together, identifying as definite paroxysmal activity those EEG bursts to which both had given a high confidence rating (almost all were 0.5 s or longer). In most of the "experimental" sessions, only the single channel was used. The single-channel recording was rarely ambiguous in identifying such activity, and review of the multichannel recordings usually resolved such ambiguities.

To establish the correspondence between the EEG and the voice recorder, a time marker delivered auditory signals into the tape recorder and visual signals into the polygraph at 1-min intervals. One investigator synchronized the record of attacks from the EEG tracing with the typescript, using a stopwatch to pinpoint the exact words being uttered by the patient as the spike and wave burst occurred. (The matching accuracy was approximately 2 s from the initiation of the spike and wave burst.)

The diagnostic evaluation of Ms. Norton clearly indicated absencelike bursts of spike and wave activity. Before discussing further the data analytic procedures, I provide a brief introduction to Ms. Norton.

Method 1: Clinical Review

Claire Norton was a 16-year-old girl who had had absence episodes (petit mal) epilepsy since the age of 10. The patient was the oldest of three children. The other children were healthy. She was described as being the brightest of the three children, having maintained an 88% grade point average up until the eighth grade of parochial school. Her grades deteriorated after she was transferred, for financial reasons, to a public school. Her parents were 39 years old. At one time the father was treated for a peptic ulcer. A maternal aunt suffered from grand mal seizures subsequent to a head injury during pregnancy. She gradually deteriorated to the point where commitment to a hospital was necessary. The patient's mother feared a similar outcome for her. The parents were described as happily married. The father was unemployed for a while, and the mother supported the family as a seamstress in a clothing factory. The family was closely knit, and both parents were cooperative in any venture that could help their daughter. They encouraged her to participate in activities with her peers and take pride in her social success.

The epilepsy was first noticed by a teacher at school when she had a spell subsequent to being asked to climb a ladder. She had only one single grand mal, which occurred in school 4 years earlier. She was under fair drug control; bursts were noted by her mother in the early morning. These spells were characterized by brief periods of staring; no automatism or myoclonic components had appeared. She was presently under the care of a neurologist, receiving Zarontin (ethosuximide) and Valium (diazepam) three times a day. The patient tended to forget her midday dosage. Her parents felt that her condition was aggravated "if something important is coming up" and just before her menses, when they described her as being moody.

To evaluate the interview samples, I selected the first four sessions of Peter Knapp's interviews with Claire Norton. Within these, 75 segments (each on a separate page) of 50 words each were selected for rating by judges. One third of these were segments that came before 3-cps paroxysmal EEG activity (symptom segments). The remaining two thirds were segments chosen by an arbitrary randomization procedure from the remaining parts of the interview, where no such paroxysmal activity was present (control segments). These control segments were selected so that they were at least 200 words away from the point of paroxysmal activity. A sample of two symptom segments is presented to help in understanding of the results.

No. 1

CN: Um, we used to go walking a lot down to Lincoln Park of y-know, places of amusement, on to the beach.

T: Uh-huh. And what else?

CN: Those are the main places we used to go. Or else we used to go fishing or bicycle riding. There weren't too many dances in the summertime 'cause it was so warm. We jus' go ridin' around.

No. 2

CN: . . . all the subjects that you have to take. And you take business, commercial college course, general, agriculture. There was this man that came to school one day after English class; this girl came and got me, and his name is Mr. Russo--he wanted to talk to me about-um.

Method 2: Sorting and Rating

Method 2A: Sortings. Free or Intuitive Judgment of Symptom Versus Controls

I began with judges' sorting of seventy-five 50-word segments, 25 preparoxysmal segments, and 50 control segments; because I had so many more for Ms. Norton (see Tables 4 and 5), I doubled the number of control segments. Also, because there were now 75 segments, they were judged using a sorting of the segments with 11 piles (instead of rankings). The

TABLE 4
Mean Ratings of Preparoxysmal Segments for Claire Norton

Judge	"Free" instructions	"Affect" instructions	In context of interview and "affect" instructions
HB	5.24	5.36	5.76
AT	4.76	5.08	5.08
RH	5.24	5.76	—
TT	—	5.40	5.24
SP	5.64	—	—
M	5.22	5.40	5.36

Note. Chance expectation rating = 5.0; perfect discrimination = 2.04.

TABLE 5
Reliability and Discrimination Between Preparoxysmal EEG Segments Versus Control Segments for Claire Norton

Variable	Pooled reliability (two judges)	t
Rated		
Concern about Supplies	.73	−0.84
Anxiety	.80	0.00
Separation Anxiety	.12	0.26
Helplessness	.79	−0.98
Hopelessness	.87	−0.73
Blocked	.78	−1.37
Blocked by Therapist	.83	1.17
Lack of Control	.69	−1.27
New Attitude	−.07	−0.65
Guilt	.74	−0.97
Hostility	.77	−2.02*
Hostility to Therapist	.89	0.34
Depression	.77	−1.01
Tired	−.11	−1.13
Reflective	.61	−0.06
Involvement with Therapist	.67	0.72
Attention Difficulty	.49	−0.23
Scored		
Reference to Therapist (LL)	.80	1.05
Anxiety (G-G)	—	0.49
Hostility-Outward (G-G)	—	−1.79**
Hostility-Inward (G-G)	—	−0.40
Ambivalent Hostility (G-G)	—	−0.94
"Schizophrenic" (G-G)	—	1.27
Cognitive Disturbance (LL)	—	0.92
Speech Disturbance (GM)	—	−2.11*

Note. All positive t values indicate more of the variable in symptom segments than in control segments. EEG = electroencephalograph.
*$p < .05$. **$p < .01$.

sortings were done three times, just as before, according to free instruction, affect instruction, and affect instruction in the context of the entire interview session.

Although the mean ratings were close to the chance expectation of 5.00 (the free-instruction mean was 5.22, affect instruction 5.40, and in-context instruction 5.36), the results were consistently in the opposite direction of that which was predicted (see Table 4). If high-affect instructions were associated with seizures, the means should have been lower than 5.00. For 10 of the 11 judgments for the three combined conditions, discrimination was in the "wrong" direction. When the data were scored on a dichotomous basis, there was the same tendency for results to be in the opposite direction, although the tendency was less marked.

Method 2B: Ratings of 18 Variables

For the second type of analysis, I used ratings by two independent judges of all 75 segments. The variables and the method were the same as for Mr. Schull. The two judges' ratings were highly concordant with one another, except for Separation Anxiety, emergence of New Attitudes, and Tired, probably because there were almost no occurrences to be scored for those. Several other variables also had moderately low rates of occurrence. Table 5 shows the results using the pooled ratings of the two judges. Hostility was the only one of the 18 variables that was significant at the .05 level, but, again, it was in the wrong direction—the control segments had more hostility than did the symptom segments.

Method 3: Scoring Systems

I went on with content analyses by scoring systems of sixty-one 200-word segments, 19 symptom segments and 42 control segments for seven variables. (Six of the 25 symptom segments and eight of the 50 comparison segments were not included because they would have overlapped with other segments.) Only one judge made these scorings, but the reliability of these scoring systems was reported to be high (Gottschalk & Gleser, 1969). The scales were Gottschalk and Gleser's Hostility-Outward, Hostility-Inward, Ambivalent Hostility, Anxiety, Schizophrenia, a Speech Disturbance scale (Mahl, 1956), and a Cognitive Disturbance scale (Luborsky, 1966).

One of these scales, Speech Disturbance gave significant differentiation at the .05 level, and another scale, Hostility-Outward, gave significant differentiation at the .10 level, but both of these were in the wrong direction (see Table 5). Furthermore, the 200-word segments were divided into first and second 100-word units to determine whether there would be a trend toward an increase in the variables when the words were closer to the symptom, as had been found in all other similar analyses of symptom onset (Luborsky & Auerbach, 1969). No such trend occurred.

Conclusion: Antecedents for Symptoms for Claire Norton

The clinical judgment systems were not significant, and both the ratings and scorings yielded little, that is, only two significant differentiations at the .05 level (out of 25 variables)—the preparoxysmal segments had less rated Hostility and Speech Disturbance. These two were not atypical in direction for this patient. All those that approached significance were consistent with these. The direction of the differences was opposite from those for the previous patient, Mr. Schull, a matter I evaluate after the results are given for the next patient.

SCOTT THOMPSON

The procedures and analyses essentially were the same as those applied to the other 2 patients. A sample of the EEG evaluation clearly was consistent with the diagnosis of absence epilepsy. Stuart Rosenthal, then of Boston University, conducted the free-association interviews. The following history is from the original evaluation.

Mr. Thompson was a 25-year-old man who had had absence epilepsy since he was 10 years old. His aunt noticed his frequent "stares" at this time and told his parents about them. A year after that, the patient had his first grand mal attack. These invariably followed a bout of nearly continuous absence attacks, and they occurred approximately three times a month until his sophomore year of high school, when medication decreased their frequency to once every 3–6 months. His last grand mal attack was 5 years ago. At the time of study, he was having one to three absences on a "good" day, going from one every 2 days to dozens daily. Much of this variability depended on his ability to adhere to his medical regimen, although this regimen was only partially effective. Mr. Thompson was supposed to take half a tablet of Mysoline (primidone) three times a day and two capsules of Dilantin (phenytoin) twice daily. An earlier experience with barbiturates revealed that they made him lethargic. This patient's seizures were characterized by several seconds of staring, accompanied by myoclonic movements of the left lower lip and the fingers of the left upper extremity. There was an associated amnesia for immediately preceding events. Automatisms were not present. He believed that anxiety and a lack of sleep predisposed him to more bursts. Although there was no aura, Mr. Thompson stated that he could predict a "bad" day by vague tenseness and "not feeling like myself." On the other hand, he believed that seizures were infrequent when he was mentally and physically active and that seizure duration was inversely related to frequency. He attempted to abort grand mal attacks by counting and claimed success for this tactic.

There was no history of prenatal, neonatal, or developmental abnormalities for this patient other than epilepsy. He was the second oldest of five children. His siblings were in good health, and there was no history of epilepsy in the family. His father was a manufacturer who was successful, affable, and in good health. The mother, who was sensitive, warm, and active, was employed and disliked the role of housewife. The parents were happily married, financially comfortable, and religious, but they tolerated their son's more "liberal" behavior. The patient moved to Massachusetts from another eastern state in his early adolescence and came under the care of a specialist. He later attended a small college for three semesters, where he majored in art, but found the milieu stultifying and transferred to a school in Boston on the advice of his instructor. His progress there was considerable; he won an art scholarship for study abroad. He intended to use this after a year. After some hesitation because of religious differences, he married and had two small children, both of whom were healthy.

Method 1: Clinical Review

The first four preparoxysmal segments are presented to show this patient's manner of expressing himself.

No. 21

> ST: ... anyway this was a bone of contention between us as far as getting married and everything and this postponed the whole business and we just kind of-you know-put it out of our minds-you know-thinking-you know-not even thinking-you know just going on-you know ...

No. 27

> ST: ... the marriage-you know-you know-they should really be notified about the marriage-you know-about being married. As a matter of fact, I had sent M-[wife] back to -y-y-you still want me y- are still interested in all this business? Um-okay-so anyway, as a matter of fact ...

No. 20

> ST: ... way, whose name is C—, but everyone calls her Peach.
>
> T: Is she?
>
> ST: Is she a peach? Yes, she is. Uh, and she-uh-ma-sh-cousin and I were very good friends. We were the same age and apparently she just noticed it one day when I was coming down from sch-when I was home.

No. 101

> ST: ... though they didn't have the money-they would have-they just didn't know any better, and the doctor felt that he could handle it himself, until it got to the point where-uh-I don't know-they sent me to (hospital) and-you know-gave me the-you know-diagnostic thing ...

These segments do not appear to have the level of negative affect that was easily observed with Mr. Schull.

Method 2: Sorting and Rating

Method 2A: Free or Intuitive Judgments of Real and Control Segments

Five clinical judges were asked to try to discriminate between the 55 real segments and the 55 control segments. As with Claire Norton, 11 scale points were used, but the Q-sort procedure was abandoned because it was too cumbersome. The mean rating for symptom segments was 6.06, compared with 6.26 for the control segments. This difference was in the expected direction for four of the five judges; however, this difference was far from statistically significant.

Method 2B: Ratings of 18 Variables

The same 18 variables were rated by two judges on the 110 segments. None of these variables showed significant differences, or even trends, at the .10 level (see Table 6).

Method 3: Scoring Systems

From among seven variables, two were significant discriminators: Gottschalk and Gleser's (1969) Ambivalent Hostility scale was lower (.025) before a paroxysmal activity and the Cognitive Disturbance scale was higher (.01) before paroxysmal activity (see Table 6).

Method 4: Slightly Expanded Immediate Context as a Sample of the Background Context

The studies so far have concentrated on 50-word units prior to EEG paroxysms versus prior to control segments, that is, segments just before EEG paroxysms, commonly defined as 3-cps spike and wave. Yet, the 50-word segment was so short that it would have missed the possible buildup of disturbance several minutes before the EEG paroxysmal activity.

We therefore examined one patient's (Scott Thompson's) verbalizations during an expanded immediate context of about 5 min before and 5 min after EEG paroxysmal activity. I particularly examined Speech Disturbances and Cognitive Disturbances in the patient's verbalizations.

The data consisted of five tape-recorded, quasi-therapeutic, free-association sessions with concurrent EEG. Two of these were filmed and three were not filmed (the three older sessions that were not filmed were part of the earlier report, described earlier).

Within these five sessions, there were 10 "seizures" that were usable for the current analyses. A *seizure* was defined as a period of bursts of symmetrical and synchronous 3-cps spike and wave on the EEG lasting

TABLE 6
Reliability and Discrimination Between Preparoxysmal EEG Segments Versus Control Segments for Scott Thompson

Variable	Pooled reliability (two judges)	t
Rated		
Concern about Supplies	.71	−1.05
Anxiety	.30	1.38
Separation Anxiety	.77	−1.41
Helplessness	.67	−0.07
Hopelessness	.34	−1.14
Blocked	.57	0.87
Blocked by Therapist	—	0.89
Lack of Control	.58	1.33
New Attitude	.69	−1.49
Guilt	—	−1.58
Hostility	.49	−1.15
Hostility to Therapist	—	0.21
Depression	.65	1.56
Tired	.89	0.85
Reflective	.19	0.58
Involvement with Therapist	.53	0.55
Attention Difficulty	.42	0.90
Scored		
Reference to Therapist (LL)	.72	−0.15
Anxiety (G-G)	—	0.00
Hostility-Outward (G-G)	—	0.10
Hostility-Inward (G-G)	—	−1.37
Ambivalent Hostility (G-G)	—	−2.38**
"Schizophrenic" (G-G)	—	−0.50
Cognitive Disturbance (LL)	—	2.88*
Speech Disturbance (GM)	—	−0.63

Note. EEG = electroencephalograph.
*$p < .01$. **$p < .025$.

more than 1 s and surrounded by symptom-free 600 words before and 600 words after. Most of these 10 seizures in the five usable sessions were 4–6 s long. The analyses were the typical ones used for the symptom-context method (given in chap. 2). The same qualities were scored for the same word units before and after two kinds of control segments: Control 1 was nonseizure material from other parts of sessions that contained actual seizures; Control 2 used segments taken from sessions that had no seizures. For both symptom segments and control segments, the words before and after each seizure were divided into 100-word units. The twelve 100-word units before and after totaled 1,200 words. Mean time elapsed was 9.6 min. Identifying when a seizure was present could be done highly reliably.

Cognitive Disturbance and Speech Disturbance before and after EEG paroxysmal activity. The curve in Figure 2 for Cognitive Disturbance showed

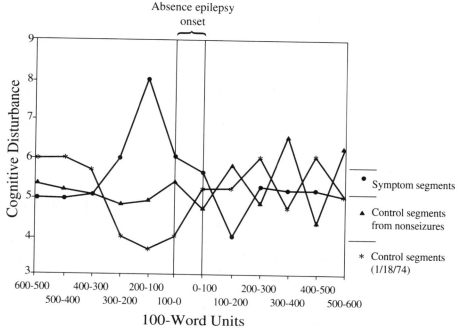

Figure 2. Cognitive Disturbance in relation to EEG paroxysmal activity. Means for symptoms versus control for Scott Thompson.

a rise between 100 and 300 words before the seizure, with the peak at 200 words. Two kinds of nonseizure controls are shown; the main difference in the seizure versus the two nonseizure times was in this 100- to 300-word preseizure time.

The curve for Speech Disturbance is similar to that for the Cognitive Disturbance curve. The main increase also occurred between the 100- to 400- word points, with the peak around 200–300 words before the seizure. The nonseizure controls did not show such a peak and provided a baseline for the frequencies of Speech Disturbance; the baseline was not much different, whether we used the segments from nonseizure sessions or nonseizure material from the same session. It is impressive that the Cognitive Disturbance and Speech Disturbance scales, which do not contain the same items and which correlate with each other only moderately, both showed the same preseizure shape, with a peak around 200–300 words before the seizure (approximately 3 min before the seizure). The curves for Cognitive and Speech Disturbance for the symptom segments represent the mean of 10 instances. They *both* showed a hump around 200–300 words before the seizure. In essence, the same event may occur in the 3 min before the seizure, which is reflected in Speech and Cognitive Disturbance, but it would strengthen the understanding of the process to trace other facets of this event in three other modalities:

Facial tension cues. Facial movements were seen before the spike and wave activity. For the eye, it included a double blink, triple blinks, rubbing eyes, eye flutter, and the hand touching the eye. For the brow, it included tension in brow, wrinkle, and the hand on the brow. For the mouth, it included tension in the mouth, pulling on the mouth, hand on the mouth, and licking one's lips. The two main measures used were the mean length and number of these facial tension cues. Most of these cues were around 200 words prior to spike and wave activity. These data support my impression of a special psychological event around the 200- to 300-word point prior to EEG spike and wave activity.

EEG analysis. Allan F. Mirsky and Armand Siegal's comparison of the EEGs for the symptom and control segments was difficult because slow voltages were an obstacle to ordinary computer analysis. There were some differences for the segments, probably from brief bursts of high voltage and high frequency set off by the patient's movements. They might, however, have been associated with the Cognitive and Speech Disturbances that were found to be special for the symptom segments.

Rate of speaking. The rate of speech per 100 word units was almost unchanged until the point of the seizure. In fact, the rate of speaking gradually became slightly more rapid starting around the 400-word point and continued to get slightly more rapid until the seizure appeared. After that, there was a marked slowing of speech for the next 100 words.

In summary, the antecedent conditions showed disturbances in the expression of thoughts, facial tension, and rate of speech. The four types of disturbance covered the period from 300 words to the onset, which would be about 4 min before the onset. The four disturbances were Cognitive Disturbance, Speech Disturbance, length of facial tension, and number of signs of facial tension. The rate of speech showed a buildup, but only in the 100 words after the onset.

In conclusion, these four measures suggested a clear disturbance within the 4 min before the onset. The interpretation of the disturbance involved a dilemma about which came first: (a) The antecedent disturbance might have been part of the triggering of the seizure or (b) the antecedent disturbance might have been merely one offshoot of the slowly building-up, underlying brain disturbance that culminated in the seizure.

COMPARISONS OF THE 3 PATIENTS

The psychological preconditions for Mr. Thompson appeared to be more similar to those for Ms. Norton than to those for Mr. Schull. The EEG characteristics also were more similar to Ms. Norton than to Mr.

Schull. In contrast to Mr. Schull, only a few variables reached significant levels of discrimination. Ambivalent Hostility was less prominent before paroxysmal activity. An increase in Cognitive Disturbance before paroxysmal activity was the most discriminating for Mr. Thompson; the reader can easily see these in the examples. For example, there was a buildup of many vague circumlocutions such as "you know" and "I don't know."

In the EEG paroxysms during speech versus during silence, at least two sets of investigators have shown that bursts of spike and wave activity are more likely to occur in silence than during speaking (Gottschalk, 1955; Zegans, Kooi, Waggoner, & Kemph, 1964). In both studies, the findings were based on a comparison of EEG paroxysmal activity frequency during a 30-min or longer period of silence with that during a comparable period of an interview. To my knowledge, our own analysis was the first that exactly inspected the location of EEG paroxysmal activity within an interview; it compared the frequency of EEG paroxysmal activity during the patient's speech, the therapist's speech, the silence after the patient's speech, and the silence after the therapist's speech. The attack frequency could be compared with the actual amount of speech versus silence in each of the four interviews. Two of the 3 patients showed a deviation from the expected proportions. Both Mr. Schull and Ms. Norton showed more than the expected proportion of episodes in the silence after the patient's speech (as compared with the actual proportion of the interview containing silence after the patient's speech). Similarly, both showed fewer episodes during the patient's speech than would be expected on the basis of the proportion of interview time devoted to the patient's speech. For Mr. Thompson, there was essentially no deviation from the expected proportions.

As a final review, 2 of the 3 patients showed more bursts of EEG paroxysmal activity when they stopped talking than when they were talking, a finding that is consistent with that reported by other investigators using a slightly different method. The effect seemed to be function of focused versus unfocused attention, as Gottschalk (1955) showed by presenting a variety of tasks to Mr. Schull. Gottschalk found that counting by 3s was even more potent than speaking in reducing episodes; in fact, it abolished them. Talking usually entails greater focusing of attention than does silence. Gottschalk therefore logically suggested that EEG paroxysms that appear during a patient's talking should have stronger psychological antecedents than those that appear during silence. I had enough data to test this possibility only for Mr. Schull, but I found no tendency for psychological antecedents to be greater for episodes that occurred while Mr. Schull was talking.

In relation to the duration of EEG paroxysms if psychological factors are involved in their onset, it seems reasonable to expect that there would be more of them before longer bursts. No prior research has been reported on this, although some other investigators must have considered the importance of the factor because they dropped episodes of 1 s or less, for example, Gottschalk (1955) and Zegans et al. (1964).

Dropping attacks that were less than 1 s in duration had virtually no effect on the results for Ms. Norton or Mr. Thompson. Data on the duration of attacks were not available for a sufficient number of Mr. Schull's episodes to justify this type of analysis.

For Ms. Norton, however, there were available data on the duration of 18 of the 25 episodes. For these 18, the correlation of length of the episodes with the 18 clinical variables was generally positive and higher than similar correlations with symptom versus comparison segments. No clear tendency was shown by the seven scored variables. Hopelessness was the only variable that reached statistical significance for this small sample ($r = .57$, $p < .05$); that is, the longer the episode, the more Hopelessness.

To examine this issue for Mr. Thompson, I correlated the duration of the paroxysmal activity for each of the 55 symptom segments with the 25 variables previously used. When two episodes occurred in close proximity (three instances), I used an average duration. No significant relationships were obtained. The two largest correlations were Hostility-Outward ($r = .25$) and Hopelessness ($r = .22$) scores. (Neither of these variables had shown any discrimination between symptom and control segments. Their correlations with symptom versus control segments scored 1 and 0, were .02 and −.03, respectively.) Neither Cognitive Disturbance nor Ambivalent Hostility scores showed significant correlations with the duration of the episode. Cognitive Disturbance scores were in the same direction ($r = .14$); Ambivalent Hostility scores were not rated as occurring in any of the symptom segments.

In conclusion, correlations of the contents before an EEG paroxysm with its duration did not usually reveal substantial relationships, although there was more of a relationship for Ms. Norton than for Mr. Thompson.

SUMMARY AND CONCLUSIONS

- *Our purpose was to more fully report the first use of the symptom–context method to evaluate the psychological antecedents in patients who have absence epilepsy. The significant antecedents of 3-cps spike and wave activity for three patients are summarized in Table 7. If one's expectations were that all such patients would be like Mr. Schull, then the results represent a failure of replication. If, however, one's expectations had been that patients differ in the amount and type of psychological antecedents, then the results are a confirmation. Strong psychological antecedents were found for Mr. Schull.*

TABLE 7
Summary of Significant Differences Between Before-Symptom and Before-Control Segments for Three Patients

More Before EEG Paroxysmal Activity	p	More Before EEG Nonparoxysmal Activity	p
Ernest Schull		Claire Norton	
Blocked	.000	Hostility	.05
Depression	.000	Hostility-Outward (GG)	.10
Involvement with Therapist	.000	Speech disturbance (GM)	.05
Hostility	.001		
Concern about Supplies	.042		
Anxiety	.008	Scott Thompson	
Helplessness	.010	Ambivalent hostility (GG)	.025
Hopelessness	.006		
Blocked by Therapist	.007		
Lack of Control	.021		
Separation Concern	.032		
Guilt	.002		
Hostility to Therapist	.007		
Anxiety (G-G)	.025		
Hostility-Inward (G-G)	.003		
Schizophrenic (G-G)	.010		
Total Affect (G-G)	.025		
Helplessness manual (LL)	.042		
Scott Thompson			
Cognitive Disturbance (LL)	.01		

These consisted of the types of negative affects typically reported before many psychosomatic symptoms, for example, feeling depressed, blocked, or hostile (Luborsky et al., 1973). For Ms. Norton and Mr. Thompson, there were a few significant differences and these were difficult to interpret. My findings of marked individual differences in psychological antecedents for the 3 patients, because of the method by which they were established, have a unique place in the literature on antecedents of bursts of spike and wave activity in absence epilepsy.

- Although the 3 patients had no clearly consistent psychological antecedents, *the nearest possibility of a consistent antecedent was some form of hostility,* but the particular hostility variable differed for each patient. For Ms. Norton and Mr. Thompson, the relationship was inverse: Hostility was greatest before EEG nonparoxysmal periods.
- *The difference in magnitude of the findings for Mr. Schull versus for Ms. Norton and Mr. Thompson is impressive.* However, in view of the small sample size, the answers must be speculative.

The psychological differences in the patients may reflect physiological differences in the nature of their convulsive disorder. For both Ms. Norton and Mr. Thompson, the onset of disorder was in childhood and was characterized by typical absence attacks with clinically manifest episodes. These indicators, as well as the EEG pattern, would characterize these patients as having "classical" or "typical" absence attacks. For Mr. Schull, however, the disorder apparently began in adulthood, which statistically would make it a relatively rare type of petit mal. The EEG paroxysmal activity was not associated with clinically manifest episodes. The EEG also was suggestive of a right temporal lobe focus, which is perhaps compatible with a diagnosis of secondary bilateral synchrony subsequent to a cortical focus of abnormality. Inspection of the tracings suggested abnormally slow background activity in Mr. Schull's record, which also may be compatible with the diagnosis of cortical damage or dysfunction. The data are insufficient to establish that the behavioral differences between Mr. Schull and the other 2 patients were a function of these clinical–diagnostic differences. However, the presence of temporal lobe abnormality in Mr. Schull may provide some clue that bears watching in future studies of such patients. Of particular interest might be patients who have a mixed diagnosis of generalized epilepsy (absence) in the presence of localizing or focal features.

Our results with this small sample tend to agree with the view of many clinical neurologists and some neurophysiologists that the psychological antecedents are minimal with absence patients. At least 2 of the 3 cases partly agree with this view (Merrit, 1963; Small, Stevens, & Milstein, 1964; Stevens, 1959), although there were still some differences between the seizure and control periods even for 2 of the 3 cases that were the least discriminating.

On the physiological level, in the past 10 years there has been clarity about this disorder as involving the thalamocortical circuitry (Snead, 1995). There is a basic cellular mechanism within the tension between excitation and inhibition that involves the T-type calcium current. There may, then, be bilaterally synchronous spike–wave discharges.

Ms. Norton and Mr. Thompson might have been more inhibited than Mr. Schull about putting their feelings into words. This could make a lot of difference because the patients' words determine the ratings and scores on the personality variables. However, this point is more speculative than the preceding one because we have no estimate of the amount of experienced freedom to express feelings. Nevertheless, it is true that Mr. Schull was in a form of combined psychotherapy and absence epilepsy exploration, but Ms. Norton and Mr. Thompson were only in exploration of absence epilepsy.

Another basis for a difference may apply to Ms. Norton because of her regimen of Valium, which could have had some effect in the direction of a numbing of her affect.

The differences were probably not related to the average length of the episodes of EEG bursts of spike and wave activity, because we have shown that the relationships with duration were slight and uneven: They were insignificant for Mr. Thompson and only slightly related for Ms. Norton.

- A finding emerged about the operation of the various types of evaluations of the onset conditions for symptoms: *The free or intuitive judgments by themselves did not reach significance levels for any of the patients,* not even for Mr. Schull, who had such large differences by the rating and scoring methods. Apparently, symptom versus nonsymptom distinctions are difficult for judges to make, unless they are focused on a specific variable (as also has been shown in chap. 6 for similarly analyzed data before patients' reports of stomach ulcer pain).
- Finally, *the EEG paroxysmal activity occurred more often during the patients' silence than during the patients' speech* (for 2 of the 3 patients). Talking probably reflects more focused attention than silence; more focused attention or activity tended to reduce the frequency of attacks.

REFERENCES

Commission on Classification and Terminology of the International League against Epilepsy. (1981). Proposal for revised clinical and electroencephalograph classification of epileptic seizures. *Epilepsia, 22,* 489–501.

Gottschalk, L. A. (1955). Psychologic conflict and electro-encephalographic patterns. *Archives of Neurological Psychiatry, 73,* 656–662.

Gottschalk, L. A. (1995). *Content analysis of verbal behavior: New findings and clinical applications.* Hillsdale, NJ: Erlbaum.

Gottschalk, L., & Gleser, G. (1969). *The measurement of psychological states through the content analysis of verbal bahavior.* Berkeley: University of California Press.

Luborsky, L. (1966). *A cognitive disturbance scale.* Unpublished manuscript.

Luborsky, L., & Auerbach, A. H. (1969). The symptom-context method: Quantitative studies of symptom formation in psychotherapy. *Journal of the American Psychoanalytical Association, 17,* 68–99.

Luborsky, L., Docherty, J. P., & Penick, S. (1973). The onset conditions for psychosomatic symptoms: A review of quantitative studies. *Psychosomatic Medicine, 35*, 187–204.

Luborsky, L., Docherty, J., Todd, T., Knapp, P., Mirsky, A., & Gottschalk, L. (1975). A context analysis of psychological states prior to petit-mal seizures. *Journal of Nervous and Mental Disease, 160*, 282–298.

Mahl, G. (1956). Disturbances and silences in the patient's speech in psychotherapy. *Journal of Abnormal Social Psychology, 53*, 1–15.

Merritt, H. (1963). *Neurology*. Philadelphia: Lea & Fibiger.

Small, J. D., Stevens, J. R., & Milstein, V. (1964). Electroclinical correlates of emotional activation of the EEG. *Journal of Nervous and Mental Disease, 138*, 146–155.

Snead, D. C. (1995). Basic mechanisms of generalized absence seizures. *Annals of Neurology, 37*, 146–157.

Stevens, J. R. (1959). Emotional activation of the EEG in patients with convulsive disorders. *Journal of Nervous and Mental Disease, 28*, 339–351.

Zegans, L., Kooi, K., Waggoner, R., & Kemph, J. (1964). Effects of psychiatric interview upon paroxysmal cerebral activity and autonomic measures in a disturbed child with petit mal epilepsy. *Psychosomatic Medicine, 26*, 151–161.

10

THE CONTEXT FOR PREMATURE VENTRICULAR CONTRACTIONS OF THE HEART

JOHN P. DOCHERTY, HOYLE LEIGH, PAUL DAVID,
LESTER LUBORSKY, LOUIS DIGUER,
RACHEL KASABAKALIAN-MCKAY, SCOTT FRIEDMAN,
SUZANNE JOHNSON, and LOUIS A. GOTTSCHALK

In the current study, I wanted to extend the range of dysfunctions studied by the symptom-context method, help highlight symptom-specific differences, and bring important commonalities across symptoms into sharper focus.

However, there was another, more powerful motive emerging from the current state of the art of symptom-context studies. The symptom-context method provides a powerful research strategy that helps to trace the concurrent flow of physiological and psychological activity leading to the emergence of a symptom or dysfunction; in that sense, it places us at the psychosomatic interface of data derived in a psychological frame, with data derived in a biological frame. If one remembers the criteria for symptom-context studies and reviews the symptoms previously studied by this method, it is clear that there are methodological concerns with them. Depressive shifts, stomach ulcer pains, and migraine headaches all have relied on subjective reports for knowledge of onset, which may open them to difficulties: (a) The relationship between the time of onset and the time of report is unclear. This might mean, then, that although I think I am studying the psychological context antecedent to the appearance of the symptom, I might actually be studying a state consequent to it. (b) Because I am relying on subjective reports, what I am studying might be more reflective of and characteristic of the intention to report the psychological

243

symptom than the conditions for the appearance of the symptom. (c) I cannot be certain of what symptomatic periods I might have missed or where they might lie in the stream of data; therefore, control periods cannot be chosen with full confidence.

When Luborsky et al. (1975) and Docherty, Berger, & Oradei (1977) decided to investigate the immediate psychological context of bursts of electroencephalographic (EEG) paroxysmal activity in absence episodes, discussed in chapter 9, it seemed as though these difficulties could be overcome successfully. But, three problems became apparent. First, there was not complete agreement among EEG raters on the occurrence of bursts of paroxysmal activity (absence episodes) in the EEG record, although interrater reliability was high. Second, because of the reliance on scalp recordings, one cannot be certain of recording all relevant seizure activity. Finally, the issue has been raised repeatedly that the seizure dysfunction itself is one that might be expected to exert significant cognitive effects.

I thus reviewed other dysfunctions for possible study, and this led to the consideration of cardiac dysrhythmias. They seemed ideally suited to study by this method. Premature contractions in particular attracted my attention because they can be recorded easily with clarity and precision, monitored continuously, and intrude minimally into the stream of verbal material.

I then reviewed the literature to see whether there would be any basis to assume that psychological factors play some role in the appearance of cardiac premature contractions (Docherty, Leigh, & David, 1974). I discovered several lines of evidence pointing in that direction: clinical, conditioning, experimental animal, and brain stimulation studies.

In terms of clinical studies, M. L. Miller and McLean (1940) reported on their observations of 4 patients who episodically developed palpitations during the course of psychoanalysis. They thought that there was a clear relationship between one's emotional state and the onset of these episodes. Stevenson, Duncan, S. Wolf, Ripley, and H. G. Wolff (1949) investigated a series of 12 patients who had extrasystoles. These patients were occasionally interviewed while their heart was monitored via electrocardiograph (EKG), and notes were made on the interview material. Stevenson et al. thought that the incidence of extrasystoles was unequivocally associated with the patient's emotional state. Wolf (1969) reported on a large group of patients followed for years with periodic EKGs and correlated psychosocial assessments in patients in whom he found a clear correlation between troublesome life situations and the occurrence of premature ventricular contractions (PVCs). Leigh, Hofer, Cooper, and Reiser (1972) compared "open" and "closed" coronary care units and found that certain affective states seemed to be associated with a significantly higher risk of developing cardiac arrhythmia.

A second major line of evidence for the role of psychological factors in the occurrence of PVCs came from conditioning studies demonstrating this possibility for both classical and instrumental conditioning of PVCs. Peimer (1953), working in Russia, demonstrated that it is surprisingly easy to classically condition the occurrence of PVCs and reported success in conditioning their appearance to verbal stimuli within three to five trials. Perez-Cruet (1962), working at Walter Reed Army Hospital, demonstrated the classical conditioning of PVCs to visual stimuli. Finally, Weiss and Engel (1971) used biofeedback in an instrumental conditioning paradigm and were able to help some patients achieve control over the frequency of occurrence of PVCs via control of heart rate.

Working with dogs, Lown, Verrier, and Corbalan (1973) studied factors influencing electrical instability of the heart. They found that the threshold for inducing repetitive ventricular response (which consistently anticipates ventricular fibrillation) was markedly lower in dogs tested in a psychologically stressful setting than one in which they previously had experienced shock.

The data just presented suggests that cortical activity may be involved in the genesis of PVCs, and Lown et al. (1973) concluded that a major trigger of such heart rhythms is not the heart but the brain and the central nervous system. There is some direct evidence for this. There is voluminous literature that attests to the influence of the hypothalamus on cardiovascular functioning and the results of diencephalic stimulation on the production of dysrhythmia. Hockman, Mauck, and Hoff (1966) concluded that there is strong evidence for the influence of telencephalic stimulation and that stimulation of cortical loci seemed to exert a more specific autonomic control than lower levels of the brain.

With this review as background, I undertook a study of the immediate psychological context of PVCs.

METHOD AND PROCEDURE

Participant

The participant, John Green, was a 29-year-old professional man who had benign PVCs that he first noticed about 6 years earlier. He had no other cardiac disease, and his PVCs were the sole disturbance of cardiac rhythm. Mr. Green had never received anti-arrhythmic medication and was on no other medication at the time of the study. Unlike the participants in other chapters in this book, he was not a patient in psychotherapy, but he did take part in 12 psychotherapy-like, free-association sessions. He gave his informed consent to participate and was told that the purpose of the study was to investigate the relationships, if any, between psychological state and the occurrence of PVCs.

Diagnostically, there was nothing in his free-association sessions that would suggest an anxiety disorder, even though his responses to anxiety and other affects appeared to have physical effects. He did not reveal any clinically significant symptoms and certainly not enough to warrant a *DSM-IV* psychiatric diagnosis.

Procedure and Apparatus

The essential procedure in this study consisted of the concurrent recording of an interview along with continuous EKG. Mr. Green reclined on a couch and had three chest leads attached in a standard position to minimize movement artifacts. His EKG was continuously monitored and recorded on a Beckman polygraph. The tape-recorded free-association interview of about an hour's duration was conducted concomitantly. Mr. Green was urged to report as fully as possible whatever thoughts and feelings came to mind. The interviewer made only minimal comments, and those were to encourage a full report by Mr. Green.

ANALYSIS OF THE DATA AND RESULTS

Selection of Data for Analysis

Mr. Green's EKG showed a continuous stream of PVCs occurring at a rate of about 10 per minute, but there were both marked increases and decreases in PVC activity. I therefore studied these categories of PVC activity in 30-s segments: (a) activation or high PVC activity (PVCs are markedly increased [8–11 PVCs per 30-s segment]); (b) base rate or midrange PVC activity (PVCs are at their usual level [4–6 PVCs per 30-s segment; these segments were used for control comparison]); and (c) suppression or low PVC activity (PVC activity is markedly decreased [0–2 PVCs per 30-s segment]).

The high- and low-activity segments were chosen by dividing the entire recorded session into 30-s segments and rank ordering these segments according to the density of PVC activity. All segments within the top 10% were considered high-activity segments, and all those in the bottom 10% were considered low-activity segments. In fact, all high-activity segments fell within the upper 5.7% of their sessions and all low-activity segments fell within the lower 5.4% of their sessions.

The occurrence of the suppression phenomenon in these data was surprising. To my knowledge, it has not been investigated previously, nor am I aware of prior work on the immediate psychological antecedents of the suppression of physiological dysfunction. The appearance of this phenomenon in these data led to a modification in the application of the symptom-context method. Thus, as illustrated in Figure 1, in this design I dealt with three categories of "symptomatic" activity instead of the usual two.

Each of the periods under the time zone marked *target* represented a segment of 30 s. Thus, the target zone of study was a 30-s period of activation of PVC activity, continued base rate activity, or suppression of PVC activity. Moreover, these segments were chosen from the beginning of a period of activation or suppression and were chosen randomly from base rate periods. I chose 10 of each type of target segment.

For each target I also extracted from the interview material the antecedent 60 s. For most of the analyses, I divided this minute into two 30-s periods. The segment from 60 to 30 s was called *Antecedent A*. The 30 s immediately preceding the target segment was called *Antecedent B*. This yielded a total of 90 segments for analysis.

METHOD 1: CLINICAL REVIEW OF SEGMENTS OF ACTIVATION, BASE RATE, AND SUPPRESSION OF PVCS

As I noted earlier, Mr. Green's PVC abnormality had been recognized about 6 years earlier but was "silent," in that little was known to the patient or to his physicians about the relation of the symptom to the patient's psychological state. One of the patient's beliefs was that his PVCs would increase after exercise when he followed the exercise by an attempt to relax by deep breathing.

Clinical Review of Sample Symptom Segments Before Activation

These four segments were selected from the 30-s periods just before activation. The mean number of words in the 30-s intervals was about 80. (Slashes mark off thought units; ellipses indicate pauses.)

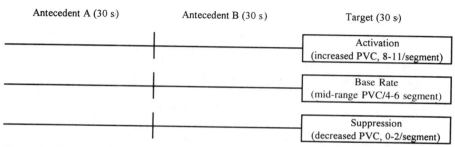

Antecedent A (30 s)   Antecedent B (30 s)   Target (30 s)

Activation (increased PVC, 8-11/segment)

Base Rate (mid-range PVC/4-6 segment)

Suppression (decreased PVC, 0-2/segment)

Figure 1. Nature of three types of segments. PVC = premature ventricular contraction.

Antecedent B 30-s Segment 6. I measure conflict material now by the many number of PVCs /... that become externally dependent ... (laughter) on external assessment./ I-I don't know what kind of .../ .I, I ... think that this is somewhat less conflictual for me than it was last week,/ or than it was earlier this week/ because um ... a couple of things .../ . it's interesting what they are. ... I haven't really verbalized them/ but they flashed into my mind .../ .one is, I am reading this book which I find so overwhelmingly fascinating .../

Note that in this segment the patient was talking about the degree to which his conflicts were related to the number of PVCs. Conflicts were obviously present, but "somewhat less conflictual for me than it was last week." The implication is that high anxiety was evident now.

Antecedent Segment B 30-s Segment 9. .... at the end of a seminar/ or at the end of a lifetime you will have tried and tried and tried to have understood it/ and basically you won't know a damn thing more than a three-year old kid/. ... you know what I mean?/ (laughter). .... That's where ... that's where I think M's faith,/ the things he was saying and my faith really disagrees./ He was saying "well, C (participant's name) that's pretty pessimistic,/ maybe you're wrong. ...."/

The participant was speaking in the segment about the idea of trying and not understanding, a discouraging idea. The patient was talking about failure and keeping up one's morale to cope with failure.

Antecedent Segment 6. /That was definitely very high on the list of most tense moments in my career as shrink./ And the other thing that I found that was really tense was that,/ unlike something that is tense in the emergency room,/ a patient that's psychotic and they yell at you,/ oh it's "well, who are you" you know,/ "I don't know you, I'm not concerned about your fate,/ I really don't have much feeling for you except in a very generalized way/ and I am going to hospitalize you because you are crazy,"/ but with a patient that you know you think "oh my God, poor you,"/ you know,/ "oh gee, is this what it is that you've been telling me about/ ... oh no ... no wonder you complain so much. ...."

The participant was talking about the upset that comes from taking seriously what he was saying and fully understanding that this patient had a lot to complain about.

Antecedent Segment 20B. /... and it's kind of functional in America,/ because nobody is that bad off that your identification is so painful, you know,/ your identification is kind of functionally helping you to get in there and help them./ But in India it's overwhelming,/ you just feel shattered,/ "holy shit if I'm like these people,/ holy fuck it's horrible,/ I can't take it, you know,/ I'm gonna starve or they're gonna starve."/ That's the experience, you know, why ... how did I get food .../ I don't see exactly the connection there is a good one/ ... Okay, I ...

The affects in this segment were anxiety and revulsion at being near discouragement and depression.

For these four examples, the main affects were anxiety and trying to maintain a good level of morale and not getting discouraged and depressed.

METHOD 2

Method 2A: Sorting of Verbal Segments Into Probable Levels of PVC Activity

As an initial screening of the data to see how the symptom would relate to the psychological state, five independent experienced clinician judges sorted the categories of verbal segments. They were given two groups of segments: all the antecedent segments in one group and all the target segments in a second group. They were asked to sort the antecedent segments according to the category of PVC activity the segments preceded (low, mid, or high) and to sort the target segments according to the PVC activity that they thought was concurrent with each segment (low, mid, or high).

In Trial 1 of the sorting, they were asked to carry out this sorting on the basis of clinical intuition. In Trial 2, they were asked to carry out a second sorting to account for a practice effect. As indicated in Exhibit 1,

EXHIBIT 1
Instructions Given to the Judges for the Sorting Task

Here are your clues: The clues give characteristics of antecedent symptom-activation segments and target symptom activation and symptom suppression segments:

Antecedent symptom activation
1. Strong and immediate personal involvement of the participant
2. An overt statement of anxiety or other index of strong affective arousal
3. Participant seems to feel or be vulnerable

Target symptom activation
1. Increased self-involvement (compared with base rate and suppression segments)
2. Confusion (this may be subtle)

Target symptom suppression
1. An attitude of "noblesse oblige." This is expressed as a feeling of superiority manifested in mild or benign derision of others or a feeling of resignation and being somehow above things.
2. Warmly related to interviewer
3. Elation in association with intellectualization

they were asked in Trial 3 to carry out a third sorting using clues that the experimenters felt differentiated the segment categories.

In Trial 1, the judges' sorting was not significant. In Trial 2, after practice, their scores improved only slightly. However, on Trial 3, after the clues, their accuracy was much improved. As can be seen in Figure 2, antecedents to activation were selected with high accuracy, $p < .001$.

No other individual category was selected with significant accuracy. However, as can be seen, all the scores were better than chance, and, according to a chi-square test, their total accuracy was significant ($p < .01$).

Method 2B: Ratings of Verbal Segments of Antecedents to Activation Versus Antecedents to Base Rate

In light of these findings on judges' ability to sort verbal segments into the different PVC categories, we then carried the examination further by ratings of segments antecedent to activation (symptoms) versus segments antecedent to base rate (controls). Two experienced clinical judges did the ratings independently on 5-point graphic and defined scales (see

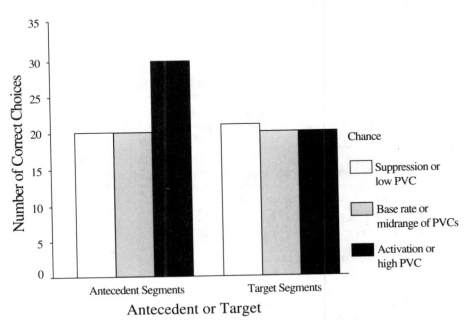

Figure 2. Judges' sorting (Trial 3: with clues) of three types of segments. PVC = premature ventricular contraction.

the Appendix to this chapter) for 11 variables that had also been used for other symptom-context studies.

Agreement of Judges

The two judges agreed moderately well (see Table 1) in terms of percentage of agreement. But there was a wide range of agreement in terms of correlations, and some of the variables had low correlations. With some variables, however, the correlations might have been an underestimate because the variance was sometimes small.

Results

For these 11 variables, significance of difference between symptoms and controls was high for five variables (see Tables 2 and 3; in order of probability values starting with the largest). For Anxiety it was .0005, for Lack of Control it was .01, for Depression it was .01, for Hostility to Therapist it was .02, and for Hopelessness it was .04.

The main surprise in these results was that Helplessness did not reach the usual significance level that it did for the other symptoms in this book, but it is noteworthy that an almost-synonymous variable, Lack of Control, was highly significant.

In terms of time trends, Lack of Control also showed a significant time trend: The 60–30 s before was not significantly different, but the 30–0

TABLE 1

Agreement of Two Judges (RKM and SF) by Percentage Agreement and by Pearson Correlations for Ratings of Antecedents to Activation (Symptoms) Versus Antecedents to Base Rate (Controls)

Variable	% Agreement (−1, 0, 1)	r	p
Helplessness	60	.40	.08
Hopelessness	85	.77	.0001
Anxiety	80	.46	.04
Hostility to Others	100	.60	.005
Hostility to Therapist	100	.47	.04
Involvement with Therapist	85	.16	.50
Guilt and Shame	90	.29	.21
Blocked	85	.36	.12
Depression	90	.04	.88
Lack of Control	85	.35	.13
Feeling Pressure	95	.70	.0006
M	86.8	.38	

Note. The percentage agreement was based on agreement together with a latitude of one more or one less.

TABLE 2
Means, Differences (*t* Values), and Significance of Differences in Ratings
Between Symptoms (Antecedent to Activation) and Controls (Antecedent
to Base Rate) for Two Judges Combined: RKM and SF)

Variable	Control mean	Symptom mean	*t*(18)	*p*	Rank
Helplessness	4.4	5.1	1.05	.150	
Hopelessness	2.7	4.2	1.87	.040	5
Anxiety	4.4	6.3	4.19	.000	1
Hostility to Others	3.5	3.8	0.49	.320	
Hostility to Therapist	2.0	2.7	2.33	.020	4
Involvement with Therapist	3.1	4.1	1.43	.090	
Guilt and Shame	3.0	3.5	0.96	.180	
Blocked	4.6	5.1	0.68	.260	
Depression	2.2	3.1	2.93	.010	3
Lack of Control	5.6	7.0	2.94	.005	2
Feeling Pressure	4.2	5.0	1.10	.150	

Note. All probability values are one-tailed.

segment was highly significant ($p = .005$). Depression also showed a similar time trend.

We also tried ratings for an unusual comparison for the symptom-context studies of the period within the symptom itself: the target activation versus the target base rate segments. By contrast, however, the ratings were not significantly different for these two categories of segments. The period within the symptom was unusual as a focus in the symptom-context studies because for other symptoms, we did not have available scores for the within-symptom data. It was confirmatory, however, that these negative results for the within-symptom period were somewhat consistent with the sorting results when significant results were found for the

TABLE 3
Intercorrelations of Rated Variables That Significantly Discriminated
Between PVC and Control Segments

Variable	1	2	3	4	5	*M*[a]	*M*[b]
1. Hopelessness	—	.02	−.02	.74	.53	.31	.33
2. Anxiety		—	.29	−.25	.27	.08	.21
3. Hostility to Therapist			—	−.23	−.11	−.02	.16
4. Depression				—	.24	.13	.36
5. Lack of Control					—	.23	.29

Note. Data are based on increase in PVC segments during 60 s before PVC. PVC = premature ventricular contraction.
[a]Mean of the correlations for that variable.
[b]Mean of the absolute value of each correlation for that variable.

category of antecedents to activation but other categories were not judged with significant accuracy.

The main variables were not highly correlated with each other (see Table 3), which implies that they were measuring somewhat different qualities in the antecedent conditions—except for Hopelessness and Depression.

METHOD 3: SCORING SYSTEMS

Reference to Therapist

The trend was present, as it was usually present, for more References to Therapist before symptoms, but it was not significant.

Cognitive Disturbance

I also applied a Cognitive Disturbance measure for speech samples (Luborsky, 1966) that was based on the frequency of occurrence in the verbal sample of varieties of forgetting and near-forgetting, uncertainty, and unclarity. Although absolute values showed no difference for the total score among the activation categories, a "sign" test revealed a significant increase in the activation series from Antecedent A to Antecedent B (the 30 s immediately before; $p < .04$, two-tailed). Note that an increase in certain qualities, such as Cognitive Disturbance, was usual for other symptoms

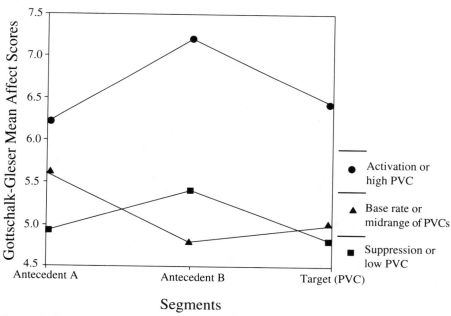

Figure 3. Total Gottschalk-Gleser Affect Scores during three types of segments. PVC = premature ventricular contraction.

described in this book the closer the sample was to the emergence of the symptom.

Gottschalk-Gleser Content Analysis Affect Scales

Gottschalk-Gleser Affect scale (Gottschalk & Gleser, 1969; Gottschalk, Winget, & Gleser, 1969) scoring was done for 88 of the segments. (Two segments were dropped from this analysis because their word count was below 75 words, which would have decreased the reliability of the scoring of these segments (one was an Antecedent A to activation and the other was an Antecedent B to activation). These scales have well-established validity and reliability for five affect scales: Anxiety, Hostility-Inward, Overt Hostility-Outward, Covert Hostility-Outward, and Ambivalent Hostility. I also summed these measures to derive a Total Affect score.

This analysis showed that, as can be seen in Figure 3, overall affect was clearly the highest for the activation series (two-tailed t test, $p < .04$ vs. base rate and $p < .01$ vs. suppression). However, the pattern of rise and fall for Total Affect was similar for both activation and suppression.

If one looks at the individual affect scores, it can be seen that the difference by two-tailed t test between activation and base rate was most marked and significant for Anxiety ($p < .05$; see Figure 4) and for Hostil-

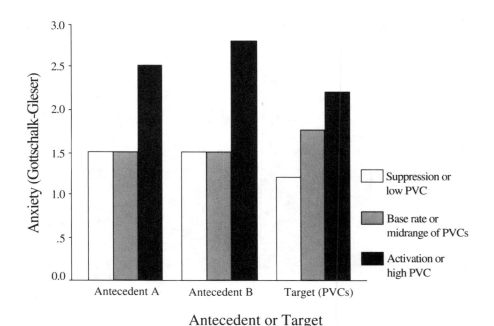

Figure 4. Anxiety by Gottschalk-Gleser scores during three types of segments. PVC = premature ventricular contraction.

ity-Inward ($p < .02$; see Figure 5). (As discussed earlier, by the rating method Anxiety also was significant; if one accepts Hostility-Inward as being equivalent to Depression, it also was significant.)

The activation and suppression series showed the greatest difference for Anxiety ($p < .003$) and Ambivalent Hostility ($p < .04$).

Suppression showed no overall difference from base rate segments for level of affective arousal. Yet, when I looked at the pattern of change in the affect scores from Antecedents A to B and from Antecedent B to the target segment for the three categories, I discovered that the pattern of change in the affect scores was exactly the same for the activation segments and suppression segments, but the pattern was different from the control segments (see Figure 6). Both showed increasing scores on Anxiety, Overt Hostility, Hostility-Inward, Ambivalent Hostility, and Total Affect and a decreasing score on Covert Hostility. The exact probability of this was less than .02.

When I examined the change from Antecedent B (30 s immediately before) to the target segment, I found that those segments that showed the opposite change in PVC activity (that is, activation vs. suppression) also showed the opposite change in the hostility measures. As shown in Figure 7, both demonstrated decreased Anxiety and decreased Total Affect scores. At the same time, activation had a general attenuation of clearly directed Hostility-Outward and increased Hostility-Inward; the suppression segments revealed a mirror image of this, with a generally freer expression of Hostility-Outward and decreased Hostility-Inward.[1]

Pronoun Counts

My inspection of the data and review of the judges' sorting suggested that one of the best discriminators of the activation segments was high involvement of the "self." I then tried to objectify this impression by using a scoring system. I considered how I would pick up high involvement when listening to a patient and thought that one simple way was by the frequency with which the patient referred to himself or herself. I tried a count of the pronoun "I" and found that indeed the "I's" had it. As one can see in Figure 8, "I" occurred significantly more frequently in the activation segments than in the other segments (by one-tailed t test, $p < .025$) and also had a stepwise increase into the moment of activation.

Emboldened by this finding and bearing in mind previous findings suggested that involvement with the experimenter or therapist increases just prior to the onset of a symptom or physiological activation (chaps. 3 and 6), I counted the second-person references: the occurrence of the pro-

---

[1]Antecedents A and B before activation versus Antecedents A and B before base rate for the Gottschalk computer scoring system indicated a probability value of .015 for shame depression.

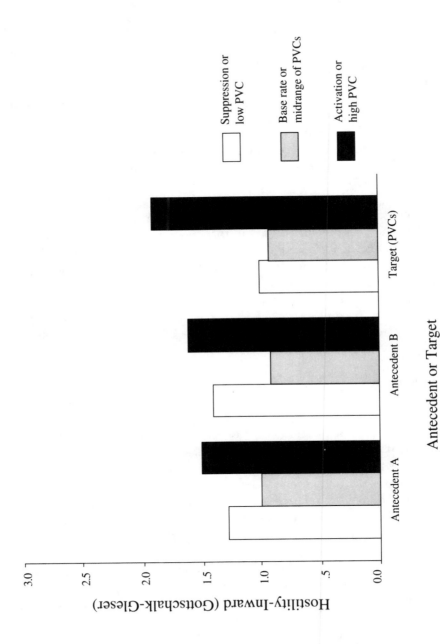

Figure 5. Hostility-Inward Gottschalk-Gleser scores during three types of segments. PVC = premature ventricular contraction.

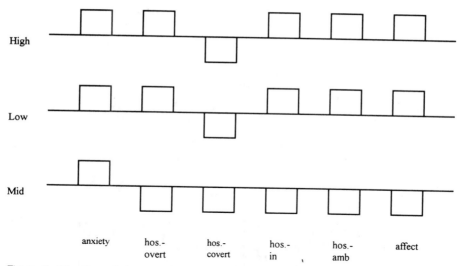

Figure 6. Direction of change of Gottschalk-Gleser affect scores from Antecedents A to B. Hos. = hostility; amb = ambivalent.

noun "you." As illustrated in Figure 9, I found that "you" occurred the most frequently in the 30 s immediately prior to PVC activation (one-tailed t test, $p < .01$).

I also counted occurrences of the pronoun "we." As shown in Figure 10, I found that it occurred most frequently in the suppression segments,

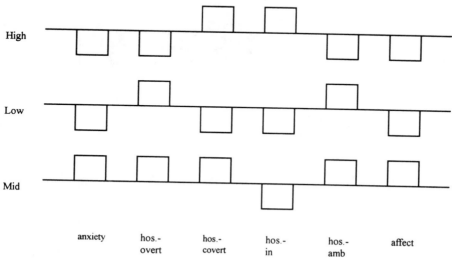

Figure 7. Direction of change of Gottschalk-Gleser affect scores from the Antecedent B to target. Hos. = hostility; amb = ambivalent.

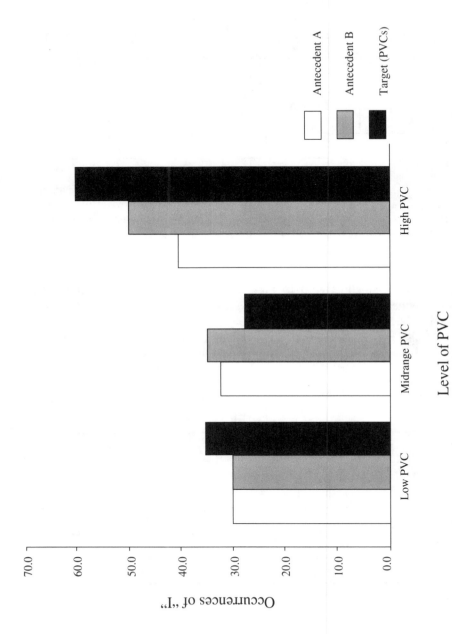

Figure 8. Occurrences of "I" during three types of segments. PVC = premature ventricular contraction.

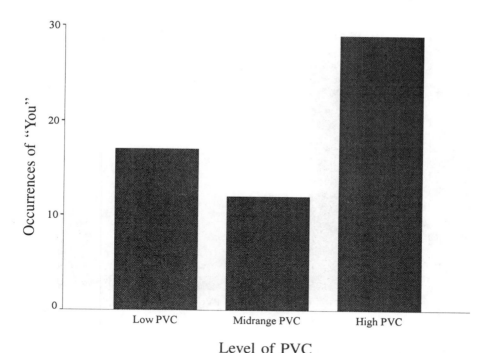

Level of PVC

Figure 9. Occurrences of "you" in Antecedent B before PVCs. PVC = premature ventricular contraction.

$p < .01$. This was particularly interesting because it fit with my impression that the suppression segments were characterized by an attitude of noblesse oblige and a feeling of expansiveness.

Word Fluency

The mean number of words was less for the 60 s before activation (158 words) than the 60 s before base rate (165 words). Similarly, the mean for the 30 s of target activation was 79 words versus 86 words for the target baseline.

It is possible that the reduced number of words reflects the impact of depression. I reported earlier that one of the antecedents to activation was greater depression. I know from other studies (as in chap. 5 on depression) that the more depressed a person is, the fewer words he or she utters.

Number of Laughs

The number of laughs was clearly greater for the antecedents to activation ($M = 1.3$) than the antecedents to baseline ($M = 0.3$). The same

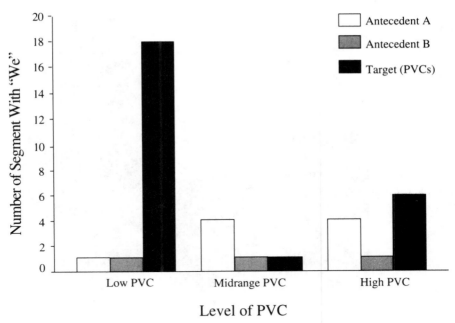

Figure 10. Occurrences of "we" during three types of segments. Numbers are estimated, not exact. PVC = premature ventricular contraction.

direction was found for the comparison of target activation ($M = 0.4$) versus target baseline ($M = 0$).

Assessment of Heart Rate

Mean Heart Rates for Each Segment Group

Figure 11, which summarizes the heart rate data for each of the major segments groups, shows that in every instance of suppression, the heart rate increased from Antecedent B to the target. This yielded a highly significant "sign" test ($p < .002$, two-tailed). However, the increase was relatively small and there were numerous instances when the same changes occurred without suppression. Thus, some increase in heart rate appears to be, for this patient, a necessary but not sufficient feature of the suppression phenomenon. I also found that the change in heart rate from Antecedent B to the target segment for the activation or high activity series also yielded a significant sign test based on the individual segment changes ($p < .04$, two-tailed).

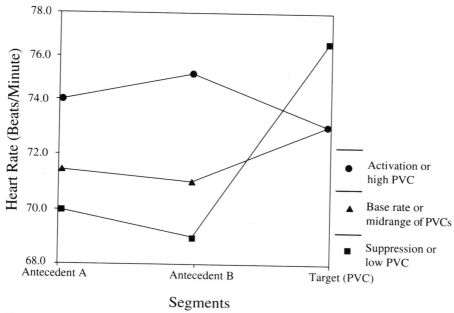

Figure 11. Heart rate for three types of segments. PVC = premature ventricular contraction.

Correlation of Heart Rate With Number of PVCs

For the range of heart rate represented in the data, tests for correlations yielded no significant association between absolute heart rate and number of PVCs.

SUMMARY OF FINDINGS AND CONCLUSIONS

In my review of the state of research on the immediate psychological context of "symptom activation," I found that a methodologically more exact study was needed. I therefore selected for study the immediate psychological context of PVCs using the symptom-context method.

Continuous recording of the participant's EKG and concurrent interview revealed three categories of PVC activity: increased PVC activity (activation), decreased activity (suppression), and a predominant PVC rate of about 8–10 per minute (midrange). Ten 30-s segments were selected for each of these three categories of PVC activity (target segments). In addition, the minute preceding this target segment also was extracted and divided into two 30-s segments: 60–30 s prior to the target (Antecedent A) and 30–0 s prior to the target (Antecedent B). The verbal segments for each of the time periods was studied by multilevel methods such as those presented in other chapters.

In the discussion, I review the findings, compare the results with those of previous studies on PVCs, speculate about the meaning of the physiological data and its implications for processes possibly mediating the psychological state and the level of PVC activity, discuss questions raised about the bearing of the findings on treatment, compare the findings with those of immediate-context studies of other symptoms, and note further work I have begun along with a useful causal model from the review of the literature and my own work with PVCs.

Our main findings are summarized in Table 4, but mainly for the usual comparison in this book: antecedents to symptoms (activation) versus antecedents to controls (base rate).

Sortings of the Three PVC Categories

Five independent judges sorted the segments according to the category of PVC activity that the segments preceded (antecedents) or represented (targets). Antecedent B to activation was selected with highly significant accuracy ($p < .001$) using the clues for negative affect and self-involvement.

Ratings

For antecedents to activation versus those to baseline (controls), five significant variables are listed in rank order with the most listed first: Anxiety, Lack of Control, Depression, Hostility to Therapist, and Hopelessness. (For the 30-s target segment, the rated variables did not show significant differences from the base rate.)

Scorings

Cognitive Disturbance

There was no difference among segments in absolute Cognitive Disturbance scores, but a sign test revealed a significant increase in Cognitive Disturbance from Antecedent A to Antecedent B in the activation series ($p < .04$, two-tailed).

The Gottschalk-Gleser Affect Scales

These scores revealed the highest overall affect in the activation series of segments (activation vs. midrange, $p < .04$; activation vs. suppression, $p < .01$). For individual affects, the difference between activation and midrange was most marked for Anxiety ($p < .05$) and Hostility-Inward ($p < .02$).

TABLE 4
Summary of Psychological Findings From the Context of PVCs by Probability Values

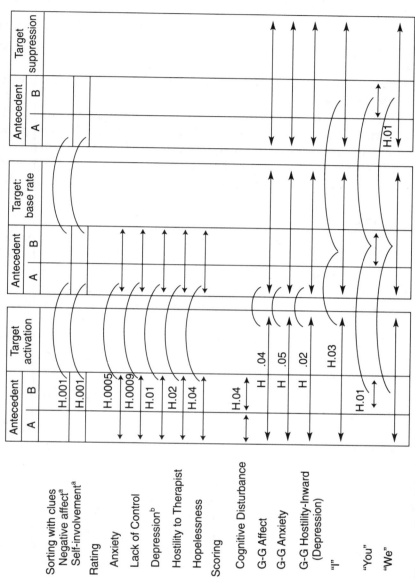

	Target activation		Target: base rate		Target suppression	
	Antecedent A	Antecedent B	Antecedent A	Antecedent B	Antecedent A	Antecedent B
Sorting with clues						
Negative affect[a]		H.001				
Self-involvement[a]		H.001				
Rating						
Anxiety		H.0005				
Lack of Control		H.0009				
Depression[b]		H.01				
Hostility to Therapist		H.02				
Hopelessness		H.04				
Scoring						
Cognitive Disturbance		H.04				
G-G Affect	H .04					
G-G Anxiety	H .05					
G-G Hostility-Inward (Depression)	H .02					
"I"		H.03				
"You"						
"We"		H.01				H.01

Note. ⟷ = The length of each period compared; ⌒ = the periods compared, for example, for the ratings of anxiety: The Antecedents A and B before activation were significantly higher than the Antecedents A and B before base rate; PVCs = premature ventricular contractions; G-G = Gottschalk-Gleser; H = higher for antecedents to the symptoms than the antecedents to the controls.
[a]The three PVC antecedent segments were correctly sorted, with these two clues, into activation, base rate, and suppression.
[b]Shame depression by the Gottschalk and Bechtel (1995) computer scoring system also was significant at the .01 level.

The differences between activation and suppression were significant for Anxiety ($p < .003$) and Ambivalent Hostility ($p < .04$). Suppression showed no significant difference from midrange for level of affective arousal.

The pattern of change of the Gottschalk-Gleser scores from Antecedents A to B was exactly the same for the activation and suppression series ($p < .01$). Both showed increasing Anxiety, Overt Hostility, Hostility-Inward, Ambivalent Hostility, and Total Affect scores and a decreasing Covert Hostility score.

However, from Antecedent B to the target segment, the pattern of activation and suppression was a mirror image in the hostility measures, with activation demonstrating an attenuation of clearly directed Hostility-Outward and Increased Hostility-Inward and suppression demonstrating a freer expression of Hostility-Outward and decreased Hostility-Inward.

Pronoun Counts

To aid in quantifying an aspect of engagement–involvement, I counted the occurrence of pronouns in each segment: (a) "I" occurred significantly more frequently ($p < .025$) in the activation segments. Furthermore, there was a stepwise increase from Antecedent A to the target segment. (b) "You" tended to occur most frequently (*ns*) in the 30 s prior to activation. (c) "We" occurred with significantly greatest frequency ($p < .01$) in the target suppression segment. This appeared to be consistent with our impression that the suppression segments were characterized by a feeling of expansiveness and an attitude of noblesse oblige.

Heart Rate

For every instance of suppression, there was an increase in heart rate from Antecedent B to the target segment. This yielded a significant difference in mean heart rates ($p < .1$) and a highly significant sign test ($p < .002$). However, there were numerous other instances in which heart rate changes of similar magnitude and direction occurred without suppression. Thus, for this participant, this appeared to be a necessary but not sufficient feature of the suppression phenomenon.

Heart rate showed a decrease from Antecedent B to the target activation segment ($p < .04$, two-tailed sign test). There was no overall correlation between heart rate and number of PVCs for the range of heart rate represented in the data.

Comparison With Studies of PVCs

In 1940 M. L. Miller and McLean reported on 4 patients they had observed during the course of psychoanalysis with episodically exacerbating extrasystoles that were accompanied by the subjective sensation of palpitation. It was their impression that during the period of activation, the patients all demonstrated clearly manifest increased levels of anxiety. They then wanted to locate the source of this anxiety. Anxiety appeared to be aroused by the urge to express hostility along with an inhibition in the expression of competitive hostility. Stevenson et al. (1949) examined the phenomenon of PVC activation more closely, observing 12 patients, as I mentioned earlier, while EKG was being recorded. Without the benefit of more objective and time-focused methods of assessing affective state, they also were impressed with the clearly manifest anxiety that characterized the onset of PVC activation. They observed that anxiety was the most frequent emotion associated with extrasystoles and was shown in speech and other behavior (Stevenson, 1949). However, they mentioned an observation that reflected another curious feature of these patients: their timidity and their dependence.

Finally, Leigh et al. (1972), in their study of patients in coronary care units, found that patients at the highest risk for developing PVCs were those who demonstrated the highest levels of Separation Anxiety and Hostility-Inward and the lowest levels of overt Hostility-Outward, as measured by the Gottschalk-Gleser scales.

There is thus a remarkable concurrence in the findings in these few studies. This concurrence is even more remarkable here because of the apparent heterogeneity of PVCs and the vast differences in their physiological contingencies. Furthermore, I found, as in Luborsky, Docherty, and Penick's (1973) review of the onset conditions of psychosomatic disorders, that more recent carefully controlled studies generally have tended to confirm the earlier impressionistic studies. What more carefully controlled studies have added lies along the dimension of what I have added: a more highly developed assessment of the several components of the immediate psychological state and a more specific delineation of the nature of the affective arousal and the process of its unfolding.

Mediation of the Physiological Effects

This study bears out several emerging facts about the relation of heart rate and PVCs: (a) In the naturally occurring setting, there is overall a poor correlation between absolute heart rate and PVCs. This was borne out in my study by an overall lack of correlation; it was further underlined by the fact, as shown in Figure 11, that the heart rate associated with the onset of the period of suppression was just about the same as that of the period antecedent to activation, which was associated with base rate activity. (b) A change in PVC rate (either an increase or a decrease) tends to be associated with a change in heart rate (either an increase or a decrease). This also was true in this study. What was surprising was that such a small change in heart rate was associated with such a dramatic change in PVC activity.

Furthermore, two other facts are consonant with the findings and helped us to understand why it may not only be the quantity of arousal but the pattern and type of physiological arousal that is important in producing PVCs. First, it is not only a change in heart rate that is important in precipitating or suppressing PVCs but also the way in which that change is produced. For example, in some patients, isoproterenol leads to a stimulation of beta receptors leading to increased heart rate and brings about a decrease in PVCs. However, in these same patients, atropine leading to vagal blockage and subsequent increased heart rate of similar magnitude brings about no change in PVC activity and actually causes an increase in some cases (Weiss & Engel, 1971; Weiss, Lattin, & Engelman, 1975). Second, the action of excitation at any time depends on the currently prevailing state of the organism, as concluded by Wolf (1969) that there is an interaction in the central nervous system rather than effects of single variables on each other.

With these considerations as background I can speculate about the mediation for this participant of the activation of PVCs and the suppression of PVCs.

Activation

The period of activation was preceded by a period of high anxiety and moderately high anger. This could thus be seen as a period of high sympathetic tone with some predominance of epinephrine secretion. The moment of activation showed some diminished Anxiety and Hostility-Outward but increased Hostility-Inward and this was correlated with a fall in the heart rate and increased PVC activity. The mechanism of this decreasing rate and, therefore, the more proximate mediation of the activation of PVCs was not clear. However, there are two possibilities. It may be due simply to a reduction in sympathetic tone, allowing for a kind of "release phenomenon"; on the other hand, it may be due to an increased parasympathetic tone that, according to much speculation and some study is associated with depression and Hostility-Inward. That the addition of vagal stimulation to an already-hyperstimulated sympathetic state could underlie ectopic beat exacerbation has some experimental support. Scharf, Blumenfeld, and Yildiz (1973) demonstrated that increased rate is particularly enhanced by the simultaneous stimulation of the vagus and sympathetic nerves, and this is consistent with the work of Wolf (1969).

Finally, a report by Mr. Green adds credence to the latter hypothesis. He reported that his PVCs were the most frequent if he followed a period of vigorous physical activity with attempted relaxation, especially if the relaxation entailed deep breathing. This exactly recapitulated my hypothesis of exacerbation, namely, a period of high sympathetic tone, primarily epinephrine-mediated followed by a sudden increase in parasympathetic tone.

Suppression

I do not have sufficient information to make any definite assertion about the suppression of PVCs, but I can speculate. The antecedent period before suppression was characterized by low anxiety and a relatively low heart rate. The target segment in the data was characterized by high Overt Hostility and an increased heart rate. Previous work has shown that anger is differentially associated with norepinephrine secretion (Adsett, Schottstaedt, & Wolf, 1962; Ax, 1953; Bogdonoff, 1959). One might suppose, then, that what I observed was a norepinephrine-induced suppression of PVCs. This could have important clinical implications if it were more generally true, for the exercise test is heavily relied on clinically to assess the suppressibility of PVCs. However, exercise primarily stimulates epinephrine secretion and thus might not disclose heart rate-increased suppression of PVCs via norepinephrine stimulation.

Therapeutic Implications

Possible therapeutic implications of my work involve four main areas: brief psychotherapy, minor tranquilizers, antidepressants, and antiarrhythmics.

Brief Psychotherapy

C. K. Miller (1965) demonstrated that patients with myocardial infarctions had significantly higher Anxiety and Hostility-Inward scores than did a matched control group of medical patients without coronary disease. These two scales also were the two that most clearly differentiated the activation from base rate series in Mr. Green. Furthermore, Gottschalk, Mayerson, and Gottlieb (1967), in a study of changes after brief psychotherapy, found that immediately after and then again at 3 months and 6 months follow-up, patients showed a significant decrease in Anxiety and Hostility-Inward scores. This would lead one to wonder whether in patients in whom one might expect ectopic beats to pose a continued life threat, a brief psychotherapy contact might enhance survival and avoid the risks of medication (Knoblauch, 1993).

There are no controlled studies of the value of brief psychotherapy for patients with cardiac arrhythmias, but there continue to be reports of single-patient treatments in which emotional factors were found to be related to ventricular arrhythmias and in which the assessment and treatment were helpful (Baker, Dorian, Newman, & Cancelliere, 1994).

Drug Treatment

Minor tranquilizers. Tranquilizers are widely used in patients with PVCs, and their usage seemed to have received some support from this study because of the potentially priming role played by high Anxiety. However, with regard to the effect of these drugs on hostility, the picture is not clear. There are conflicting reports about the hostility-suppressive or - excitatory properties of these drugs, although accumulating data indicate that by and large these drugs help to release hostility.

Antidepressants. The consideration of these drugs arises because of the considerable overlap of the Hostility-Inward scale with other clinical rating scales of depression and the possible importance of Hostility-Inward in the precipitation of PVCs. Antidepressants can be beneficial, such as nortriptyline for depression (Madakasira, 1986). In any case, this class of drug may cause problems. The first problem would be to decide whether the patient can safely be given an atropinic drug because there is a group of PVC patients who clearly worsen with vagal blockade. A second problem is the anxiety-evoking property of these drugs, which would be an unwanted effect.

It also is known that depression correlates with a poor prognosis in coronary patients (Bruhn, Chandler, & Wolf, 1969; Kornfel, 1965). Therefore, one would want a pharmacological agent that produced a quick response with minimal or no side effects, such as had happened with trazodone (Aronson & Hisham, 1986). This led me to wonder about the possibility of using DOPA along with a peripheral blocker in these patients as a short-term intervention.

Anti-arrhythmics. It would be very interesting to investigate the effects of anti-arrhythmics on the process I began to explore in the current study (Reiffel, Estes, Waldo, Prystowsky, & DiBianco, 1994); they may change the picture entirely.

Management

If one takes the findings of Leigh et al. (1972) into account, it would seem reasonable to explore which type of person develops these "high-risk affects" in which type of setting. It is increasingly clear that from a psychosocial perspective, different environments are more suitable for different people (Schmidt, Dembroski, & Blumchen, 1986). Because these arrhythmias do represent the major life-threatening complication in the postmyocardial infarction period (Desilva, 1978), this might prove a useful way for deciding who, for example, should be placed in an open unit and who should be placed in a closed unit. One study restated the clinical point that Engel made eloquently: Outward hostility seems to be a positive prognostic sign in medical illness and ought not to be construed by the hospital staff as a target symptom for double-barreled psychiatric intervention. For patients who are undergoing programmed electrical stimulation for cardiac arrhythmias, it is worth knowing which ones show depression and cognitive impairment because it is those patients who show increased morbidity and mortality (Kennedy, Hofer, Cohen, & Shindledecker, 1987).

There are no reports of an attempt to directly condition a diminished rate of PVCs. It is my view, however, that the isolation of the suppression period, which I have shown in this study, presents the possibility for a simple technique. The patient need only be informed each time a period of suppression begins.

It is interesting that repeated monitoring in itself was associated with a significant decrease in PVC frequency but that relaxation practice did not produce a clear effect (Weiss, 1985).

Comparison With Other Immediate-Context Studies

A literature review demonstrated a close concordance of the findings on the role of affect with those reported for all immediate-context studies. Hostility, frustration, anxiety, and helplessness–hopelessness each accounted for about 20% of the reported immediate antecedents to symptom exacerbation or about 80% together. (This included studies of absence epilepsy [petit mal], nasal dysfunction, high blood pressure, asthma, headaches, backache, Raynaud's disease, colon dysfunction, diabetes, and momentary forgetting.) This is highly consistent with my findings. If one looks at the well-controlled studies of symptom exacerbation, one again sees some highly similar antecedent conditions (as in the meta-analysis in chap. 17).

It is on the basis of a close inspection of these findings, the studies I have reviewed, and my own study that I developed the working model described in this discussion. One of the major values of the model has been the template it provides for establishing the correspondences between the psychological and physiological data (Reiser, 1980). However, its most exciting impact has been in generating potentially testable hypotheses about the nature and property of the immediate psychological context of symptom activation.

In conclusion, in the course of the examination of the findings for this PVC-prone patient, I have contributed the following:

- knowledge of the psychological antecedents to PVCs
- some commonalties of the antecedents to PVCs with the onset conditions for the variety of other symptoms analyzed in this book
- a novel discovery of the existence of a suppression phenomenon for PVCs
- a proposed scheme for the physiological mediation of PVCs
- several therapeutic implications
- the development of model for the immediate psychological context of the activation of PVCs

RATING SCALES AND DEFINITIONS
(USED FOR REANALYSES)

Helplessness

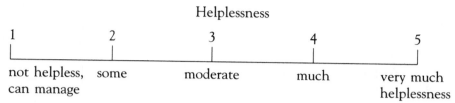

1	2	3	4	5
not helpless, can manage	some	moderate	much	very much helplessness

Definition: Giving up, feeling weak, inadequate, not handling interaction well, overpowered.

Hopelessness

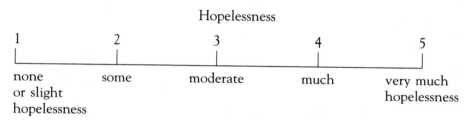

1	2	3	4	5
none or slight hopelessness	some	moderate	much	very much hopelessness

Definition: Feels there is no hope, no way to cope, has given up trying.

Anxiety

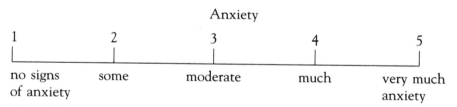

1	2	3	4	5
no signs of anxiety	some	moderate	much	very much anxiety

Definition: Anxiety, fearful, apprehensive about the future, tension; also anxious about physical symptoms, such as breathing disorders. These may be expressed verbally or nonverbally.

Hostility to Others

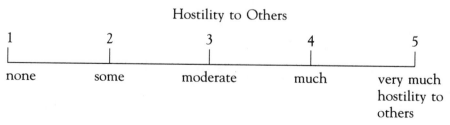

1	2	3	4	5
none	some	moderate	much	very much hostility to others

Definition: Hostility, anger, rage, annoyance to others.

Hostility to Therapist

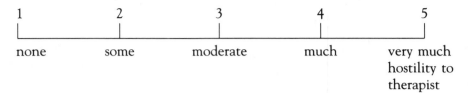

Definition: Hostility, anger, rage, annoyance at therapist.

Involvement with Therapist

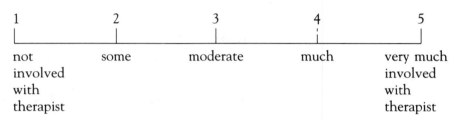

Definition: One's thoughts and feelings are occupied with and focused on the therapist.

Guilt and Shame

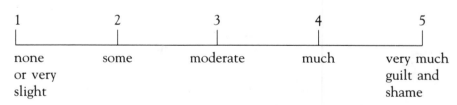

Definition: Guilt, shame, embarrassment, self-criticality.

Blocked

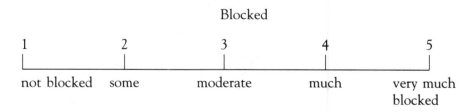

Definition: Blocked, hindered, prevented from getting what one wants.

Depression

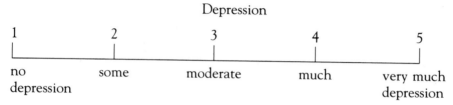

1	2	3	4	5
no depression	some	moderate	much	very much depression

Definition: Depressed mood and thinking; feeling blue or down.

Lack of Control

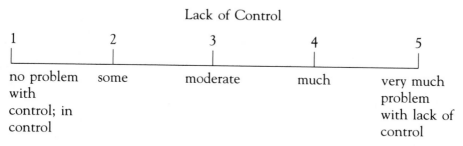

1	2	3	4	5
no problem with control; in control	some	moderate	much	very much problem with lack of control

Definition: Feeling or acting out of control, without a sense of direction; overcompulsive.

Feeling Pressure

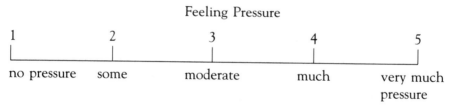

1	2	3	4	5
no pressure	some	moderate	much	very much pressure

Definition: A sense of being weighted down with pressures, demands, obligations.

REFERENCES

Adsett, C. A., Schottstaedt, W. W., & Wolf, S. (1962). Changes in coronary blood flow and other hemodynamic indicators induced by stressful interviews. *Psychosomatic Medicine, 24*, 331–336.

Aronson, M., & Hisham, H. (1986). A case of trazodone-induced ventricular tachycardia. *Journal of Clinical Psychiatry, 47*, 388–389.

Ax, A. F. (1953). Physiologic differentiation between fear and anger in humans. *Psychosomatic Medicine, 15*, 433.

Baker, B., Dorian, P., Newman, L., & Cancelliere, A. (1994). Psychological resolution of a supraventricular tachycardia. *Psychosomatics, 35*, 87–91.

Bogdonoff, M. D. (1959). Cardiovascular response to affect changes. *Circulation*, *20*, 353.

Bruhn, J. G., Chandler, M. A., & Wolf, S. (1969). A psychological study of survivors and nonsurvivors of myocardial infarction. *Psychosomatic Medicine*, *26*, 8–19.

Desilva, R. A. (1978). Ventricular premature beats, stress, and death. *Psychosomatics*, *19*, 649–653.

Docherty, J. P., Leigh, H., & David, P. (1974). The immediate psychological context of premature ventricular contractions. *Psychosomatic Medicine*, *36*, 461–462.

Docherty, J. P., Berger, F. K., Oradei, D. (1977). Psychological factors associated with premature ventricular contractions: A controlled study. *Proceedings of the Fourth Congress of the International College of Psychosomatic Medicine* (pp. 375–378). Kyoto, Japan.

Gottschalk, L., & Bechtel, R. (1995). Computerized measurement of the content analysis of natural language for use in biomedical and neuropsychiatric research. *Computer Methods and Programs in Biomedicine*, *47*, 123–130.

Gottschalk, L., & Gleser, G. (1969). *The measurement of psychological states through the content analysis of verbal behavior*. Berkeley: University of California Press.

Gottschalk, L., Mayerson, P., & Gottleib, A. (1967). The prediction and evaluation of outcome in an emergency brief psychotherapy clinic. *Journal of Nervous Mental Disorder*, *144*, 77–96.

Gottschalk, L., Winget, C., & Gleser, G. (1969). *Manual of instructions for using the Gottschalk-Gleser content analysis scales: Anxiety, hostility, and social alienation-personal disorganization*. Berkeley: University of California Press.

Hockman, C. H., Mauck, H. P., Jr., & Hoff, E. C. (1966). ECG changes from cerebral stimulation. II. A spectrum of ventricular arrhythmias of sympathetic origin. *American Heart Journal*, *71*(5), 695–700.

Kennedy, G., Hofer, M., Cohen, D., & Shindledecker, R. (1987). Significance of depression and cognitive impairment in patients undergoing programmed stimulation of cardiac arrhythmias. *Psychosomatic Medicine*, *49*, 410–421.

Knoblauch, D. (1993). A psychological treatment approach for persons who have premature ventricular contractions of the heart. *Journal of College Student Psychotherapy*, *7*, 5–22.

Kornfeld, D. (1965). Psychiatric complications of open heart surgery. *New England Journal of Medicine*, *273*, 287–292.

Leigh, H., Hofer, M., Cooper, J., & Reiser, M. (1972). A psychological comparison of patients in "open" and "closed" coronary care units. *Journal of Psychosomatic Research*, *16*, 449–457.

Lown, B., Verrier, R., & Corbalan, R. (1973). Psychologic stress and threshold for repetitive ventricular response. *Science*, *182*, 834–836.

Luborsky, L. (1966). *A cognitive disturbance measure for speech samples: The sum of forgetting, uncertainty, and unclarity of communication*. Unpublished manuscript.

Luborsky, L., Docherty, J. P., & Penick, S. (1973). Onset conditions for psychosomatic symptoms: A comparative review of immediate observation with retrospective research. *Psychosomatic Medicine, 35,* 187–204.

Luborsky, L., Docherty, J., Todd, T., Knapp, P., Mirsky, A., & Gottschalk, L. (1975). A context analysis of psychological states prior to petit-mal seizures. *Journal of Nervous and Mental Disease, 160,* 282–298.

Madakasira, S. (1986). Cardiac antiarrhythmic effect of nortriptyline. *General Hospital Psychiatry, 8,* 123–125.

Miller, C. K. (1965). Psychological correlates of coronary artery disease. *Psychosomatic Medicine, 27,* 257–265.

Miller, M. L., & McLean, H. V. (1940). The status of the emotions in palpitation and extrasystole with a note on "effort syndrome." *Psychoanalytic Quarterly, 10,* 545.

Peimer, I. A. (1953). Conditioned-reflex extrasystole in man (tr. NIH) Fiziologicheski Zhurnal *SSSR imeni I. M. Sechnova 39,* 286–292.

Perez-Cruet, J. (1962). Conditioning of extrasystoles in humans with respiratory maneuvers as unconditional stimulus. *Science, 137,* 1060–1061.

Reiffel, J., Estes, N., Waldo, A., Prystowsky, E., & DiBianco, R. (1994). A consensus report on antiarrhythmic drug use. *Clinical Cardiology, 17,* 103–106.

Reiser, M. F. (1980). Implications of a biopsychosocial model for research in psychiatry. *Psychosomatic Medicine, 42,* 141–151.

Scharf, D., Blumenfeld, S., & Yildiz, M. (1973). Experimental study on ventricular extrasystoles produced by vagal stimulation. *Circulation, 47,* 291.

Schmidt, T. H., Dembroski, T. M., & Blumchen, G. (Eds.). (1986). *Biological and psychological factors in cardiovascular disease.* New York: Springer-Verlag.

Stevenson, I. P., Duncan, C. H., Wolf, S., Ripley, H. S., & Wolff, H. G. (1949). Life situations, emotions and extrasystoles. *Psychosomatic Medicine, 11,* 257–272.

Weiss, T. (1985). Effects of repeated ambulatory ECG monitoring and relaxation on premature ventricular contractions. *Psychosomatic Medicine, 47,* 446–450.

Weiss, T., & Engel, B. (1971). Operant conditioning of heart rate in patients with premature ventricular contractions. *Psychosomatic Medicine, 33,* 301–321.

Weiss, T., Lattin, G., & Engelman, K. (1975). Vagally medicated suppression of premature ventricular contractions in man. *American Heart Journal, 89,* 700–707.

Wolf, S. (1969). Central autonomic influences on cardiac rate and rhythm. *Modern Concepts of Cardiovascular Disease, 38,* 29–34.

IV

THE ONSET CONDITIONS FOR NONSYMPTOMATIC BEHAVIORS

11

LAUGHING MATTERS IN PSYCHOTHERAPY: HOW TO READ THEIR CONTEXT

LESTER LUBORSKY, LOUIS DIGUER,
RACHEL KASABAKALIAN-MCKAY, DAVID A. SELIGMAN,
SUZANNE JOHNSON, KELLY SCHMIDT, and SCOTT FRIEDMAN

From time to time, patients laugh while they are talking in psychotherapy sessions, even about matters that do not seem to be laughing matters. That is not news, nor does it differ from people in general. What is news is that a reliable method is available for teasing out from the context of the laughter what may be the person's personal instigators to the laughter. The method of choice is the symptom-context method because it relies on an analysis of the context of thoughts surrounding recurrent symptoms or recurrent behaviors expressed during psychotherapy, or in any conversation, and then compares them with control contexts with no laughs.

The urge to do this study was energized by an old wish: to examine a recurrent nonsymptomatic behavior, such as laughing, to see how its contexts compare with those for the symptomatic behaviors examined in other chapters. A nonsymptomatic behavior should have some basically different contexts from symptomatic behaviors. A *symptom*, as used here, entails an impairment of a normal function (see chap. 16 on theories of symptom formation). For example, momentary forgetting (see chap. 3) qualifies as a symptom because it involves an impairment of a usual memory function—the ability to remember what one is about to say. By contrast, laughter appears to be nonsymptomatic in the sense that it does not involve any impaired psychological function.

METHOD

To study the context of the laughs, I adapted procedures from the symptom-context method (see chap. 2): examination of the patient's words before and after the point of emergence of the laugh and examination of the patient's words before versus after a control point where no laugh appeared. In scoring the session, both symptom and control points were marked with the word *laugh*, so the judge believed that all of them were laugh instances.

Notation of Laughs

To do the job properly, the transcripts were prepared with special care given to accuracy. To be sure that none were missed, all laughs of all kinds were underlined, including chuckles or ironic chuckles such as "hee, hee."

Length of the Units of Context

The length of the unit of context for each real laugh and for each control laugh needed to be marked off before the judging of the transcript could take place. Although in most symptom-context studies a unit based on the number of words was the usual method of segmenting the context to be scored, in the current study I decided to use thought units of the kind identified by Benjamin (1986) because (a) a thought unit is a more meaningful unit than a number-of-words unit and (b) the thought that instigated the laugh appears to be in the thought unit near the laugh. The length of the immediate context to be judged was three thought units before and three thought units after all laughs, both real laughs and control laughs. Laugh contexts were not to be used when the available context was less than three thought units long. The laugh was always in the third thought unit. Usually, it was at the end of the third thought unit, but occasionally it was within the third thought unit.

Most of the thought units around the laughs occurred when the patient was speaking continuously and was not interrupted by the therapist's statements. On a few occasions, a laugh context was used when there had been an interruption by the therapist's speech; inclusion of a few of these probably did not alter the results significantly.

Control Laughs

At the end of the control points, I inserted the word *laugh* (and for strict parity with the real laughs, they were occasionally within the third thought unit). These control laughs were as frequent as the real laughs. The control laughs were at least three and, when possible, four thought units distant from the real laugh contexts. The selection was alternated to be from portions before and then after a real laugh context.

RESULTS

Results are presented for 2 patients, each for their laugh versus control contexts within a single session: Cathy Cunningham, a patient in psychoanalysis for treatment of sexual and other inhibitions, and Sandy Smyth, a patient in short-term psychotherapy for treatment of depression.

CATHY CUNNINGHAM

Method 1: Clinical Review of the Patient's Therapy and Laugh Behavior

The Patient's Course in Psychotherapy

A book about this patient's psychotherapy by Weiss et al. (1986) described the patient at the start of therapy as an attractive 30-year-old social worker in a Catholic agency. Her husband, to whom she had been married for 4 years, was a successful businessman. Her main symptom was a generalized inhibition, especially a sexual inhibition: She held back from having intercourse, she did not have orgasms, and she was unable to relax and enjoy herself. A second symptom was her self-criticalness. A third symptom was passivity: She was afraid of "simply being a nonentity"; she wanted to be more assertive.

In terms of diagnoses from the fourth edition of *Diagnostic and Statistical Manual of Mental Disorders (DSM-IV)*, two conditions were applicable: (a) hypoactive sexual desire disorder (302.71), that is, persistent and recurrent deficient desire for sexual activity that causes marked distress or interpersonal difficulty that is not due to another psychological disorder or to medication or a medical condition; or (b) female orgasmic disorder (302.73), which is a persistent and recurrent absence of orgasm, marked distress, or interpersonal difficulty not due to another psychological disorder or to medication or a medical condition. She also could have had a personality disorder that involved dependency (301.6) or passive-aggressiveness. This patient clearly had personality traits that contributed to her Axis I difficulties, but there was uncertainty about an Axis II diagnosis.

Her mother was a housewife and her father a successful businessman. The patient was the second of four children; she had an older sister, a younger sister, and a younger brother. The parents showed little joy in their lives and little affection toward each other. The father had occasional fits of temper that he used in order to control the mother, and the mother responded passively.

An episode when the patient was 6 years of age showed some of her parents' style of relating to her and to each other. The patient's sister had hit her in the stomach. She complained to her mother but could not get her mother's attention, and so she hit her mother in the stomach. Her mother wept and went to her room. When her father heard about it, he beat the patient and threw her into a closet. She was horrified at her father's loss of control and thought for a while that her father had wanted to kill her. A little while later, she became angry at her younger brother and wanted to kill him.

The analysis was concluded successfully after about 1,300 sessions, spread out over about 4 years. The initial symptoms gradually improved throughout the treatment; she ended the treatment markedly improved and maintained her gains thereafter.

The Patient's Laugh Contexts

Interest in the contexts of laughter was stimulated during Luborsky's reading of Ms. Cunningham's Session 5; the transcription of her session was so faithful to the patient's expressions that it included not just the words of the patient, but the prevalent nonword sounds as well: laughs and chuckles (a slightly nervous short laugh), and other nonword speech qualities, such as pauses, stomach rumbles, sniffs, and throat clearing.

Three examples from Session 5 of the contexts for Ms. Cunningham's chuckles may pique one's puzzle-solving propensities and lead to conjectures about conditions conducive to her laughs.

> *Laugh Context 1 (p. 4).*[1] /[1a] ... I am very free with advice to other people when they ask me,/ [2]and I feel as if I really know the answer./ [3]And sometimes I think my advice is pretty good (chuckle)/ [4]but I can't seem to apply any of it to myself (clears throat, sniff, pause)/ [5]in fact, regarding myself, I find decisions extremely hard./ [6]And, if I do make one, even it's just a minor thing ... /
> *Laugh Context 2 (p. 10).* /[1]... Your reaction to some things I might say./[2] So I suppose there again, it's your approving or disapproving/[3] (pause) and, of course, what it boils down to is I'm sure you're going to (chuckle) disapprove,/[4] so I'm afraid of saying them (pause, stomach rumble)/[5] it's funny how we - I asked David (husband)

---

[1]Raised numbers in boldface refer to the number of each thought unit, marked off by slashes.

about it, too - /[6] and, and I don't know, we, we've been debating how much we should talk./

Laugh Context 3 (p. 1)./[1] I knew what I wanted to do at school/[2] and I didn't have to sit around and think about it very much/[3] and, of course, that didn't last very (chuckle) long./

Finding the common meanings in the contexts of a recurrent behavior requires reading and rereading the samples. In the course of that immersion process, unpredictable saltatorily growing increments of understanding appear. What meanings in common can be seen across these three samples of contexts for chuckles?

Before the chuckle, the patient affirmed something positive about herself or she wished to be affirmed. Afterward, she might have needed to laugh off her boldness by putting herself down or expecting to be put down. As just noted, the chuckle or laugh appears to be positioned to reflect her idea that she has been too bold in saying what she just said. The chuckle or laugh functioned as excusing behavior, a kind of laughing it off. It appeared to convey the idea of "Don't blame me, I'm already blaming myself because of my awareness of my overboldness." Her attitude was one of being too bold or aggressive and needing to put herself down or someone else would.

The chuckle often came at a time of a shift: Before the chuckle the patient appeared to be saying to the therapist and to herself that she was or could be bold or aggressive or self-assured; after the shift she appeared to be thinking, "I'm really too bold, too aggressive, too dominant or too self-assured." The postchuckle thought represented an undoing in the sense that her behavior and speech reflected the opposite of being bold, self-assured, or aggressive, a statement about her uneasiness or about her foibles. At the time just before the shift, there probably was a tension buildup; the laugh or the chuckle might have begun the tension release through a safer, more submissive position.

The content of the thoughts just described were then recognized as an expression in microcosm of the operation of a similar central relationship pattern that was independently discovered through the Core Conflictual Relationship Theme (CCRT). The pattern contains an expression of the main wish, expectation of the response of the other, and an expression of one of the main responses of self.

These results also show that laughs are nonsymptom behaviors, that is, the context of the laughs have only a few of the characteristics of what has appeared in studies of the context for symptoms. One of these is mostly implied rather than explicit in what has been stated so far: The patient behaved as though she was being too bold or too assertive in relation to the therapist. This inference is more than a clinical inference; it also was stated directly by the patient in some of the examples.

All that has just been said was based on the few brief laugh context samples just reviewed. But are these "results" really true for the majority of the chuckle contexts for Ms. Cunningham? The impressions noted in the clinical review were tested by Methods 2 and 3 to determine whether they would hold up in larger samples of laugh contexts at a level that would meet the requirements of relentlessly rigorous psychologists. I also report analyses of the control samples to show the degree to which the trends were just as pervasive in the rest of the session.

Method 2: Ratings of Laugh Versus Control Contexts

Ms. Cunningham's transcript for Session 5 was marked off in thought units around each laugh: three thought units before each laugh and three thought units after each laugh. There was a total of 36 laugh contexts, 21 real laugh contexts and 15 control contexts.

Variables

The symptom-context procedures were based on independent ratings of 10 variables (see Exhibit 1). These variables were selected from the set of variables used in the other symptom-context studies in this book, plus armchair additions that might be relevant to laughter, plus the last three of the 10 variables were the three main components in the patient's CCRT.

EXHIBIT 1
Rating Scales for Judgments of the Laugh Contexts for
Cathy Cunningham and Sandy Smyth

Each of the thought units (three before and three after the laugh) must be rated for each of the following:

1. Reference to the therapist (this includes questions to the therapist)
2. Feelings of helplessness
3. Being bold, assertive, aggressive, or controlling toward others
4. Being self-blaming, self-deprecating, self-critical, or feeling guilty
5. Expecting criticism from others
6. Showing poor self-control
7. Humorous ideas
8. Related to the patient's main CCRT wish:
   Ms. Cunningham: to control others, to dominate
   Ms. Smyth: to oppose others; to resist domination
9. Related to the patient's main CCRT Response from Other:
   Ms. Cunningham: controlling, dominating
   Ms. Smyth: rejecting, disapproving, critical
10. Related to the patient's main CCRT Response of Self:
    Ms. Cunningham: feel helpless, incompetent, inadequate
    Ms. Smyth: feel angry, resentful, irritated, frustrated

CCRT = Core Conflictual Relationship Theme.

Agreement of Judges

The mean agreement on the 10 variables by two independent judges (RKM and SF) for the three thought units before the laugh was .59 (see Table 1). The percentage of agreement was 91.7%; the correlations and percentage of agreement were slightly less after the laugh. The level of agreement of the same two independent judges on this case was similar to the agreement for the other case (Sandy Smyth) discussed in the latter part of this chapter.

Additional Ratings on More Variables

These 10 variables were added for greater comparability with the other cases in this book. They all were rated by RKM following the definitions and scales provided in previous chapters (chap. 3); they included Hopelessness, Anxiety, Blocked, Concern about Supplies, Hostility to Therapist, Hostility to Others, Involvement with Therapist, Depression, Separation Concern, and Lack of Control. Reference to Therapist also was added, but in an unusual form: as a rating rather than as the usual scoring system.

Differences in Ratings Between Laugh Segments and Control Segments

I present the significant results of the original analyses, together with the additional ratings (see Table 2). As in previous chapters, the main focus was on the unit just before the laugh; in this case it is Thought Unit 3. For Thought Unit 3, these were the variables with significant differences (in order, beginning with the most significantly different): Involvement with Therapist ($p < .001$), Reference to Therapist (rating; $p < .001$), Anxiety ($p < .002$), Hostility to Therapist ($p < .015$), and Expects Criticism ($p < .020$). From these significant variables and with the impressions from

TABLE 1
Agreement of Independent Judges' (RKM and SF's) Ratings, Original 10 Variables for Cathy Cunningham's Session 5 (Original Set)

Condition	Thought unit	Correlation	% Agreement
Prelaugh	1	.52	92.8
	2	.58	93.7
	3	.66	88.6
M		.59	91.7
Laugh →			
Postlaugh	4	.51	88.9
	5	.49	88.1
	6	.49	87.0
M		.50	88.0

Note. All correlations were significant at the .0001 level.

TABLE 2
Significant Differences on All Variables for Cathy Cunningham Between Ratings of Laugh Contexts and Control (Nonlaugh) Contexts (for Judges RKM and SF or RKM Alone) for Each of Three Thought Units Before and After Each Laugh

Ratings of variable (RKM)	Before laugh								After laugh							
	1st TU		2nd TU		3rd TU		Units 1–3		4th TU		5th TU		6th TU		Units 4–6	
	t	p	t	p	t	p	t	p	t	p	t	p	t	p	t	p
Hopelessness	N/A		1.45	.081	1.45	.089	1.70	.052	-1.47	.082	-1.47	.082	-.24	.406	-1.32	.103
Anxiety	3.11	.002	2.75	.005	2.98	.002	3.43	.001	2.40	.011	2.75	.005	4.42	.00	3.39	.001
Hostility to Therapist	1.45	.081	1.45	.081	2.34	.015	2.35	.014	1.45	.081	1.42	.086	1.83	.042	1.65	.058
Involvement with Therapist	2.14	.021	2.87	.005	3.56	.001	3.20	.002	2.87	.004	2.23	.019	2.01	.029	2.72	.007
Reference to Therapist[a]	2.00	.027	2.66	.007	3.03	.002	3.17	.003	2.05	.024	1.80	.040	1.65	.054	2.56	.009
Expects Criticism[a]	2.22	.018	0.98	.168	2.41	.011	2.01	.026	-0.03	.487	0.53	.300	1.92	.032	0.40	.345

Note. All probability values were one-tailed. N/A = means not ascertainable because both standard deviations were zero; TU = thought unit.
[a]Judged at a different time by RKM and SF.

the clinical review, I inferred this sequence: Before the laugh, the patient became more involved with the therapist and felt hostile toward him, expected criticism from him, and felt anxious about it. The relationship with the therapist seemed to be especially crucial; note how many of these variables manifestly involved the heating-up of that relationship: Reference to Therapist, Involvement with Therapist, Hostility to Therapist, and Expects Criticism (undoubtedly, from the therapist).

The intercorrelations of the discriminating variables (see Table 3) show that at the heart of the matrix are two expected variables: Involvement with Therapist and Hostility to Therapist.

The shape of the time trend in relation to the appearance of the laugh is well illustrated by a graph for two of the outstanding significant qualities: Involvement with Therapist and Anxiety (see Figures 1 and 2) showed that the rapid increase in these two qualities begins between the second and third thought unit before the laugh and rapidly declines after it.

The conclusion from the ratings on this case of recurrent nonsymptom behavior compared with the findings from the symptom cases suggests that the significant variables for the thought unit just before the laugh had a slightly different context than was usual for the recurrent symptom behavior as reported in the other chapters. But considering all three thought units before the laugh, the same significant variables were found but with the addition of Hopelessness (.052). It was only that variable, and only as part of the larger set of thought units, that suggests some commonality of the laugh context for this patient with the context that comes before actual symptoms.

Method 3: Scoring Systems

The scoring systems did not add much to the findings from the rating systems. The laugh segments were not significantly more filled with Ref-

TABLE 3
Intercorrelations of Rated Variables That Significantly Discriminated
Between Laugh and Control Segments (Ms. Cunningham)

Variable	1	2	3	4	M[a]
1. Expects criticism	—	.14	.37	.49	.33
2. Anxiety		—	.40	.42	.32
3. Hostility to Therapist			—	.79	.52
4. Involvement with Therapist				—	.56

Note. Data are based on Ms. Cunningham's Thought Unit 3 (just before laugh) for laughs only.
[a]The mean of the correlations for that variable.

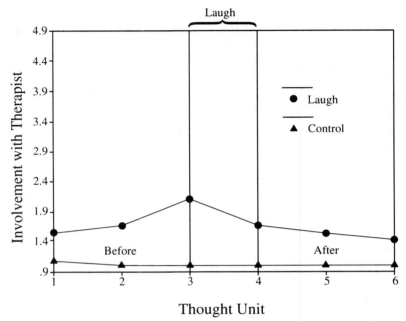

Figure 1. Ratings of Involvement with Therapist for three thought units before and three thought units after laughing for Ms. Cunningham.

erences to Therapist than the controls before the laugh. (By contrast, as noted earlier, the rated version did significantly discriminate the laugh segments from the controls.) Only after the laugh did Reference to Therapist significantly discriminate between laugh segments and controls. There was significantly more Speech Disturbance in laugh segments than in controls in the thought unit before the laugh. Finally, Cognitive Disturbance showed no significant discrimination.

SANDY SMYTH

Method 1: Clinical Review of the Therapy and Her Laugh Behavior

The Patient's Course in Psychotherapy

Sandy Smyth was in short-term psychodynamic psychotherapy as part of a study on the psychotherapeutic treatment of major depression (Luborsky, Diguer, et al., in press). The treatment was supportive–expressive psychotherapy (Luborsky, 1984), as adapted for the treatment of major depression (Luborsky, Mark, et al., 1995).

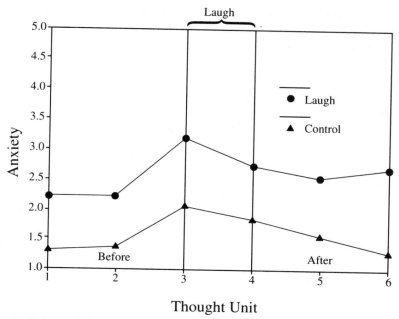

Figure 2. Ratings of Anxiety for three thought units before and three thought units after laughing for Ms. Cunningham.

Ms. Smyth was a 32-year-old single woman who was a recovering alcoholic and had been abstinent for 3 years. Her Beck Depression Inventory (BDI) score of 25, obtained when she came for treatment, indicated severe depression. She was evaluated with the Schedule for Affective Disorders and Schizophrenia (SADS) interview (Spitzer & Endicott, 1979).

In terms of the *DSM-IV*, she was diagnosed with alcohol dependence (303.90); sustained full remission, major depressive disorder, recurrent, moderate severity (296.32); and dysthymic disorder (300.4). This was her diagnostic profile based on the semistructured interviews. She also was evaluated for Axis II personality disorders but did not meet the criteria.

At the time she came for treatment, she had become depressed after failing a job training program. She showed up 30 min late for the first session and said she was unable to schedule the next appointment. The therapist felt anger but did not express it; instead the therapist used the awareness of her own anger to become aware of what the patient was conveying to her. The patient said she was afraid of "sabotaging herself," to which the therapist replied that she thought the patient was correct to be concerned.

By the time of termination, the patient was doing much better, although she still had some difficulty in keeping appointments. Her great progress surprised the therapist. At termination her depression had lifted; her BDI score was 6. The therapist commented to the interviewer in the termination interview, "I would not have thought someone with such a severe depression and who already was making full use of self-help therapeutic groups, such as Alcoholics Anonymous (AA), could have resolved her depression without the use of psychopharmacotherapy."

In the termination interview, the patient spoke about seeing a new male friend for the past 5-months, almost ever since she began therapy, and she was pleased with him. She was working regularly in a clerical job and was doing her job and doing it satisfactorily. She seemed less upset, less pessimistic, more confident, and more capable of taking care of herself. Her one concern was that she might have become pregnant.

At the 6-month follow-up, she still continued to be free of depression, although her BDI score was 9. Her full-time work continued. In fact, she had found out that she was pregnant by the man with whom she was in a relationship. She wanted to be married, but the man was uncertain. Although she felt angry and anxious, she felt she could deal with whatever happened and decided that she would have the baby. She and her boyfriend had entered couples therapy, and she maintained her attendance at AA. Although she was initially upset about the pregnancy, she had resolved to manage and was. She was not on any medication for depression or anxiety.

The Patient's Laugh Contexts

I provide three examples of her laugh contexts, as divided into thought units.

> *Laugh Context 1* (about her brother Jeff and his wife). /[1]I just can't stand it./ [2]Jeff and—Jeff's just pretty worried/ [3]and his wife's stupid (laughing)./ [4]She's a big ignoramous/ [5]and she's kind of, very, very negative./ [6]I don't know why he married her./

In Laugh Context 1, she laughed just after she criticized her brother's wife by calling her "stupid." The implication might be that she laughed as a way to show that she felt guilty for her criticism of the brother's wife, although there also might have been some satisfaction in expressing herself in such a critical fashion.

> *Laugh Context 2* (about her brother Jeff and his wife). /[1][they're] jocks—/[2]I mean I'm not even going to bring them up any more/ [3]but they're just not (chuckle) very nice people to live with/ [4][pause], and the only time he's nice to me is when he wants something./ [5]I'm not being paranoid./ [6]It's true./

Laugh Context 2 came in a similar context. In Thought Unit 3, which is the one that contains the chuckle, she was critical of her brother and sister-in-law. The thought that was responsible for the laugh probably was similar to the one in the first laugh.

> *Laugh Context 3* (about her boyfriend). /[1]. . . it's real perverted too./ [2]I went to see him last week/ [3]and, ah, for some reason he had his wife's (<u>chuckle</u>)/ [4]and the xxx[2] is getting to me, too./ [5]His wife's fur coat out xxx/ [6]and laid it on me./

Laugh Context 3 came when the patient said, "and for some reason he laid his wife's (<u>chuckle</u>)." The part that was not said, but was absolutely clear, was that he laid his wife's "fur coat" on the patient. Possibly, Ms. Smyth was feeling guilty about this reminder that the man has a wife and she (and he) were cheating on the wife. She also said, "If we get caught or something," meaning that she was afraid of criticism or blame.

The three laugh contexts showed strong criticism to the other person. If all of the real laughs had similar contexts to the three in this sample, one would expect that the real and control laughs would be clearly distinguishable. My impression was that many of them were similar but that all of them were not as clear as the three samples.

Method 2: Ratings of Laugh Segments Versus Control Contexts

The analyses were based on Session 3, with 11 real laughs and 10 control laughs. Each of these 21 contexts were marked off with three thought units before the laugh and three thought units after it. These 21 contexts were rated by two independent judges (SF and RKM). The variables (see Exhibit 1), included those that were significantly differentiating in other studies of other symptoms as well as a few that were especially likely to be differentiating in this study.

Agreement of Judges

The reliability results are presented for each of the six thought units. Remember that the laugh appeared at the end of the third thought unit. A more complete picture of the reliability is given by presenting it in two ways: by Pearson correlation and by percentage agreement. Percentage agreement means that the two judges gave exactly the same rating or differed by only one point on the 5-point scale.

The correlations in Table 4 between the two judges, RKM and SF, were only moderate. However, note that the correlations were somewhat higher for Thought Unit 3, in which the laugh typically appears; in fact, the first three thought units typically had higher reliability correlations. For these first three thought units, the mean correlation was .61; the mean

---

[2]xxx indicates a word that the transcriber could not hear.

TABLE 4
Agreement by Two Independent Judges (RKM and SF) on Ratings of 10 Variables for Sandy Smyth for Session 3

Condition	Thought unit	Correlation	% Agreement
Prelaugh	1	.56	88.1
	2	.61	89.1
	3	.67	90.0
M		.61	89.1
Laugh → Postlaugh	4	.59	85.7
	5	.43	80.9
	6	.54	84.8
M		.52	83.8

Note. All correlations were significant at the .0001 level.

percentage agreement for these three thought units was 89.1% (all correlations were significant at the .0001 level). The samples of laugh contexts that were rated were all taken from Session 3 of Ms. Smyth with its total of 21 segments, with each segment having six thought units.

Differences in Ratings Between Laugh Segments Versus Controls

The differences between laugh segments and controls are shown in Tables 5 and 6, which give for each of the 10 variables rated the means and standard deviations for the laugh and control segments.

One can see in Tables 5 and 6 an unusual set of results: There were few significant differences here compared with the tables for differences that appeared in other studies in this book. The laugh segments tended to show less than the controls after the laugh and significantly so for Helplessness, Self-blame, and CCRT response of self–angry. When the three thought units before laughs were taken together (see Table 6), no rating scale showed a significant difference, and, after the laugh only, Helplessness showed a significant difference; again, it was less for the laugh segments than for the controls.

Additional Ratings on More Variables

Ten additional variables were rated by RKM (see Table 5), but none of these showed significant differences in the predicted direction between laugh segments versus controls.

Method 3: Scoring Systems

The scoring systems showed hardly any differences between laugh segments and controls: Reference to Therapist was not significantly differ-

TABLE 5

Significant Differences on All Rated Variables for Sandy Smyth Between Laugh Units and Control (Nonlaughs) Contexts (by Judges RKM and SF and for RKM Alone) for Each of Three Thought Units Before and After Each Laugh

Ratings of variables (RKM)	Before							TUs 1–3		After							
	1st TU		2nd TU		3rd TU					4th TU		5th TU		6th TU		TUs 4–6	
	t	p	t	p	t	p	t	p		t	p	t	p	t	p	t	p
Depression	−0.23	.419	−1.51	.075	−2.61	.011	−1.72	.051		−2.89	.008	−3.07	.006	−3.35	.003	−3.46	.003
CCRT RS–Angry[a]	−0.43	.334	−1.38	.092	−2.50	.011	−1.94	.034		−0.17	.431	−0.78	.221	−3.86	.000	−2.00	.030

Note. All probability values were one-tailed. TU = thought unit; CCRT = Core Conflictual Relationship Theme; RS = Response of Self.
[a]Judged at a different time by RKM and SF.

ent in laugh segments and controls before the laugh. However, there were significantly more References to Therapist in the laugh segments after the laugh. As with Ms. Cunningham, Speech Disturbances significantly discriminated between laugh segments and controls before the laugh, but Cognitive Disturbance did not.

SUMMARY AND CONCLUSIONS

- The variable that was significantly different for laugh segments versus controls differed for the two patients. For Ms. Cunningham's thought unit just before the laughs, several variables were significantly different in the ratings for the symptom segments versus for the controls (see Table 2): References to Therapist just before the laugh showed the most highly significant differences in the comparison between the laugh segments and controls ($p < .002$); for Expects Criticism, the significance level was .020. The additional variables that were significant for the third thought unit (see Table 2) were Anxiety ($p < .002$). Hostility to Therapist ($p < .015$), and Involvement with Therapist ($p < .001$). Their intercorrelations are given in Table 3, in which the highest mean intercorrelation was for Involvement with Therapist ($r = .563$) and next highest was for Hostility to Therapist ($r = .519$). It seems fitting from these results to suggest that the laughing matter that had a part in instigating the laugh was greater Involvement with Therapist because of the greater Hostility to the Therapist, which left her Anxious and Expecting Criticism.

By contrast, for Ms. Smyth, the significant differences between laugh segments and controls was being angry ($p < .011$; see Table 5), and that occurred as expected, exactly in Thought Unit 3, just before the laugh, but unexpectedly the greater Anger was in the controls. The additional variables rated (by RKM) consistent with the other ratings showed only one significant difference for the third thought unit, Depression, and that also was that the controls showed more.

It is obvious that the antecedents of the laughs differed markedly for the two patients. This is the first time this has been shown by the symptom-context method for the context for laughs in psychotherapy. However, a finding that probably is related was reported long ago. Self-consistent differences among people in their preferences for humorous material have been shown before (Cattell & Luborsky, 1947; Luborsky & Cattell, 1947).

- For these 2 patients, as is generally found, it was the unit immediately before the symptom or behavior that showed the greater significant difference between laugh segments and controls. One can see that trend by comparing the level of significance for Thought Unit 3 with that of the three units together. This was especially clear for Ms. Cunningham, as illustrated in two sample graphs for all three thought units for Involvement with Therapist and for Anxiety.
- The types of variables that distinguished laugh segments and controls appeared to be different from those that emerged from other symptom-context studies. Although the antecedents to symptoms revealed in other chapters tended to include Helplessness, Hopelessness, and Anxiety, these were much less evident in the context for these two patients' antecedents for laughs. Of the 2 patients, Ms. Cunningham had at least one of these variables: Anxiety. Ms. Smyth has none of these variables. That is the main implication: Recurrent nonsymptom behaviors, such as laughs, have fewer and different immediately antecedent variables than the recurrent symptoms I examined in the seven symptom cases in earlier chapters.
- However, several factors might have contributed slightly to the low yield of significantly discriminating rating scales for the contexts of laugh segments versus controls: (a) The samples of just three thought units before and three thought units after each laugh might have been too brief; (b) the number of laugh contexts for Ms. Smyth of only 10 might have been too few in light of Ms. Cunningham's 21; and (c) the patients selected might have been too unrevealing of their thoughts adjacent to the laughs, especially Ms. Smyth, who uttered only about half as many words per thought unit as Ms. Cunningham.

REFERENCES

Benjamin, L. S. (1986). Operational definition and measure of dynamics shown in the stream of free associations. *Psychiatry, 49,* 104–129.

Cattell, R. B., & Luborsky, L. B. (1947). Personality factors in response to humor. *Journal of Abnormal and Social Psychology, 42,* 402–421.

Luborsky, L. (1984). *Principles of psychoanalytic psychotherapy: A manual for supportive-expressive (SE) treatment.* New York: Basic Books.

Luborsky, L. B., & Cattell, R. B. (1947). The validation of personality factors in humor. *Journal of Personality, 15,* 283–291.

Luborsky, L., Diguer, L., Barber, J. P., Cacciola, J., Moras, K., Schmidt, K., & DeRubeis, R. (in press). Outcomes of short-term dynamic psychotherapy for chronic versus non-chronic major depression. *Journal of Psychotherapy Research and Practice*.

Luborsky, L., Mark, D., Hole, A. V., Popp, C., Goldsmith, B., & Cacciola, J. (1995). Supportive-expressive dynamic psychotherapy of depression: A time-limited version. In J. P. Barber & P. Crits-Christoph (Eds.), *Psychodynamic psychotherapies for psychiatric disorders (Axis I)* (pp. 13–42). New York: Basic Books.

Spitzer, R., & Endicott, J. (1979). *Schedule for Affective Disorders and Schizophrenia–Lifetime Version* (3rd ed.). New York: New York State Psychiatric Initiative, Biometrics Research.

Weiss, J., Sampson, H., & the Mount Zion Psychotherapy Research Group. (1986). *The psychoanalytic process: Theory, clinical observations, and empirical research.* New York: Guilford Press.

12

A SYMPTOM-CONTEXT STUDY OF FAMILY THERAPY: WHAT MAKES SUZIE CRY?

PAUL CRITS-CHRISTOPH, LESTER LUBORSKY, ELLEN GAY,
THOMAS TODD, JACQUES P. BARBER, and ELLEN LUBORSKY

The purpose of this study was to locate the immediate conditions that influence the onset of a recurrent behavior during family therapy. It is the first attempt to apply the symptom-context method to family therapy and to examine the relative influence of variables that tap social versus internal psychodynamic functions of a symptom.

There are few controlled studies of the onset conditions for symptoms or other recurrent behaviors in which observations are made at the moment an event is occurring rather than through reconstruction of the situation on the basis of retrospective recall, except for those pioneered by Luborsky (1970). Although psychological states that preceded the formation of symptoms in the studies in this book differed somewhat with the type of symptom and with the particular patient studied, a consistent and prominent state usually involved helplessness, as was first suggested by Freud's (1926/1959) general theory of symptom formation.

An earlier version of this chapter appeared in Crits-Christoph, P., Luborsky, L., Gay, E., Todd, T., Barber, J. P., & Luborsky, E. (1991). What makes Susie cry? A symptom-context study of family therapy. *Family Process, 30,* 337–345. It has been adapted with permission of the publisher.

The work was supported in part by United States Public Health Service Career Development Award MH00756 to Paul Crits-Christoph and by Research Scientist Award MH40710 and National Institute of Mental Health Grants MH40472 and MH39673 to Lester Luborsky. I give special thanks to Salvador Minuchin and Bernice Rosman of the Philadelphia Child Guidance Clinic.

These symptom-context studies, however, were limited to the usual individual therapy setting with only a patient and therapist present. An examination of a recurrent symptomatic behavior within family therapy sessions allows a comparison between variables that focus on the individual versus the family context of symptom formation. In this study, I investigated the antecedents of recurrent crying during family sessions, a symptom that is obvious to the family, by having judges rate variables derived from previous symptom-context studies and from family models of symptomatology (Minuchin, 1974).

METHOD 1: CLINICAL REVIEW

The family that took part in this case study had been in treatment at the Philadelphia Child Guidance Clinic for 10 sessions of structural family therapy conducted by Salvador Minuchin (Minuchin, Rosman, & Baker, 1978). The family sessions were attended by both parents as well as by a sister and two brothers. I drew on a clinical analysis of this case, done independently by Rosman (1988), for the description of the family.

Suzie was a 17-year-old superlabile diabetic patient who was prone to frequent crying. The crying episodes were associated, in the opinion of her parents, with her becoming upset and going into diabetic acidosis. When Suzie cried or threw tantrums, her parents were afraid she would go into shock or get sick, which she occasionally did. Suzie had been diagnosed with juvenile diabetes since age 10 and had settled into a poor adjustment to it, experiencing many episodes of acetonuria, hospitalizations to evaluate the poor diabetic control, frequent school absences, and a deficient sense of responsibility for her care. Although the crying behavior may, in many cases, be seen as an appropriate response to a disturbing context rather than as a "symptom" per se, with this patient the crying was selected as the focal behavior for study because the crying appeared to be symptomatic of a dysfunction of normal assertion and control and also was associated with her physical symptom of diabetic acidosis. Therefore, the crying is clearly a symptom-related behavior; for this reason, I refer to it as a symptom, although it is not an obvious symptom in the way the other seven symptoms described in this book are. It also was convenient for my study of the symptom-context that the crying was an easily recognized behavior. One of the aims of the treatment was to increase her control over becoming upset, as indicated by her crying, and therefore to get more control over her physical state.

Suzie was the oldest of seven children, but she was treated by the other children as a younger sibling. She was rejected by the siblings because they were angry and hurt by her favored status with the parents and repelled by her childish behavior.

METHOD 2: RATINGS

From videotapes of the sessions, I located 25 separate instances in which Suzie cried. For each instance of crying, a 400-word segment of the transcript of the session was selected from before the onset of the symptom and another 400-word segment was selected after the point of onset. A similar number of control segments during which there was no crying was drawn from the same sessions as the symptom segments. In total, 27 control segments were selected. A 400-word unit was selected because in other symptom-context studies, significant findings had been found for theoretically important variables within an interval of only 150 words before the symptom. Of course, variables that might have required a larger interval than 400 words to assess were not measured in this study.

Two undergraduates were trained to rate the segments on a number of variables. The raters were unaware of whether a segment came before or after the onset of crying or whether it was a control segment. The following variables were selected from other symptom-context studies and rated on the segments from Suzie's sessions: Concern about Supplies, Helplessness, Lack of Control, Rejection, Involvement with Others in the room. The definitions of these variables are consistent with the definitions in other studies. The variable Concern about Supplies needs further explanation; it refers to the degree to which the patient feared being cut off from sustaining conditions such as love, care, approval, support, or encouragement.

In addition, the variable Asserts Opinion or Belief was added from the clinical formulation of the case, and the variable Blurring of Identities was added on the basis of the structural theory of family therapy (Minuchin, 1974; Minuchin et al., 1978). Blurring of Identities was defined as (a) The rated person speaks to another person about a third person in such a way as to imply a special kind of ownership, relationship, or exclusive knowledge about the third person or says what the third person feels or thinks when the third person has not so indicated; (b) the person being rated speaks to another person in such a way as to imply knowledge of the other's opinions or feelings; (c) the person being rated says "you" or "we" when he or she is speaking of himself or herself, or the person says "we" when he or she really means "you" or "he or she"; or (d) the person being rated enters into an interaction between two or more other people when such is not requested or elicited by the individuals who are interacting.

These seven variables also were rated for each of the other participants (father, mother, a sister Linda, a brother John, a brother Robert, and the therapist) as the unit of focus.

The family group scales included the following: Patient Receives Hostility and Resentment from Others, General Level of Family Tension, and Family Discussion about Patient. The definition of Family Discussion about

Patient is as follows: One or more persons focus on the patient in such a way as to imply that she has (or had in the past) some difficulty, inadequacy, weakness, illness, or shortcoming. Family members may speak in a protective or apparently helpful way about the patient's difficulties, may compliment the patient about improvement, may attack the patient about the difficulties, or may disapprove of the patient's difficulties. All ratings were made on 1–5 scales (1 = *none*, 5 = *very much*), except for Family Discussion and Blurring of Identities, which were rated on 1–3 scales. Finally, a measure of each participant's activity (number of words spoken) was used in the analysis.

The variables were used to test the following hypotheses:

Hypotheses 1: Consistent with the earlier symptom-context studies, a buildup of specific conditions (particularly Helplessness, Concern about Supplies, and Rejection) will occur in Suzie, the young woman with the symptom, before the onset of crying, and a decline in these conditions will occur after the onset.

Hypothesis 2: Consistent with structural family systems theory, the symptom will appear in the context of family conflict, particularly conflict between the parents. With the emergence of the symptom, focus will move away from the family conflict and the family (particularly the parents) will then focus on Suzie by attacking or protecting her.

Hypothesis 3: The symptom will follow the family's discussing Suzie in such a way as to imply she has some difficulty, inadequacy or illness. According to Hypothesis 2, although the conflict allegedly stimulates the symptom, which in turn rescues or protects the family from the conflictual situation, here a focus on the child is the cue for emergence of the symptom. Focusing on the child in this fashion may follow conflict and may thus be the family's means of directly cueing the protective symptom.

Hypothesis 4: Consistent with the structural family systems "enmeshment" construct, the child with symptoms will cry in a context of becoming confused over boundaries between herself and others. Before the symptom emerges, she will intrude into others' conversations, take up others' causes, and speak for others.

Agreement of Judges

Reliability of the judges' ratings on all the study variables was assessed during training and was found to be adequate. The median intraclass correlation of ratings between two judges was .70. During the study, reliability coefficients of ratings were computed for Family Tension, Family Discussion, Patient Receives Hostility, Concern about Supplies and Helplessness; the same median intraclass correlation (.70) was obtained on the measures. The mean of the two judges' ratings, when available, was used in the remaining analyses.

Comparison of Symptom Segments With Control Segments

The following reports of statistical significance are best viewed as a heuristic guide rather than as inferential statistics because of the problems of inference with a single case study. For each of the variables, I computed t tests to compare the level of each variable before the occurrence of crying with levels during the control segments. Table 1 shows the means and probability values for the variables that significantly discriminated the symptom segments from the control segments. Three variables with the patient as the unit of focus were significant: Involvement with Others in the Room (Suzie), Rejection (Suzie), and Concern about Supplies (Suzie). Two family group variables also were significant: Family Discussion and Patient Receives Hostility.

A stepwise discriminant function analysis was performed on the variables that distinguished the symptom segment from the control segments to further examine which measures were most important in signaling the onset of crying in this patient. In this analysis, Family Discussion entered first, as expected, on the basis of the highly significant t test for it (see Table 1). No other variables significantly added to the discriminant function, implying that there was much redundancy among the measures listed in Table 1. The intercorrelations among these measures are given in Table 2. Apparently, the variables Involvement with Others, Rejection, Concern about Supplies, and Patient Receives Hostility from Others were related only to the type of segment through their association with Family Discussion.

As mentioned, statistical significance testing within a single-case study is questionable. As described by Gottman (1973), the major concern with the application of standard statistical analyses (such as t tests) to single-case data is that observations over time are often dependent (or autocorrelated), thereby violating the independence assumption of the analysis. To examine the extent of my violation of the assumption of in-

TABLE 1
Means on Variables that Significantly Discriminated Before-Crying Segments From Before-Control Segments (t Values)

Variable	Mean control	Mean before	p
Involvement with Others (Suzie)	2.3	3.3	.01
Rejection (Suzie)	1.5	2.3	.05
Concern about Supplies (Suzie)	1.2	1.7	.05
Family Discussion	1.4	2.2	.0001
Patient receives Hostility	1.2	1.6	.05

Note. The family discussion variable was rated on a 1–3 scale and the other four variables on a 1–5 scale.

TABLE 2
Intercorrelations of Variables That Significantly Discriminated Before-Crying From Control Segments

Variable	1	2	3	4	5
1. Involvement with Others (Suzie)	—				
2. Rejection (Suzie)	.67	—			
3. Concern about Supplies (Suzie)	.51	.55	—		
4. Family Discussion	.68	.59	.52	—	
5. Patient receives Hostility	.58	.51	.33	.54	—

Note. $N = 77$. All correlations were significant at the .005 level or greater.

dependence, I computed lag correlations pairing each score with the score for the next segment in time for the five variables that demonstrated significant univariate relationships to the type of segment. The median lag correlation of these five variables was .10 (range $= -.10$ to .21), indicating minimal autocorrelation. Therefore, at the least, my analysis was not influenced by autocorrelation of observations over time.

Many of the variables of secondary interest (that is, ratings on other family members) were consistently rated as 1s, and it is therefore not surprising that they did not relate to type of segment.

Changes From Before to After a Crying Episode

Although not the main focus of this study, changes from before to after crying episodes were examined to shed light on the consequences of crying episodes for Suzie, for the therapist, and for the rest of the family. Table 3 gives the variables that significantly discriminated (by paired t test) before-crying segments from after-crying segments.

The main consequence of crying appears to be that Suzie asserted her opinion or belief more. Again, she might have achieved some benefit in terms of assertion by having cried. This finding is consistent with the clinical formulation of the case presented by Rosman (1988). In addition, Suzie felt out of control and showed some blurring of identities. The mother talked less after a crying episode. The therapist became more involved with others in the room and asserted his opinion or belief more. Again, the median lag correlation of these variables was small (.11).

METHOD 3: BROAD BACKGROUND CONTEXT

Changes Over the 10 Sessions

Dividing the 25 crying episodes approximately into fifths, the following levels of the main variable, Family Discussion, were obtained over the

TABLE 3
Variables That Significantly Discriminated Ratings of Before-Crying Segments From After-Crying Segments: Means and Probability Values of *t* Tests

Variable	Before	After	*p*
Blurring of Identities–Type A (Suzie)	1.24	1.52	.05
Mother's Activity (no. of words)	70.20	34.90	.05
Involvement with Others (therapist)	2.68	3.08	.05
Lack of Control (Suzie)	1.40	2.16	.05
Asserts Opinion or Belief (Suzie)	1.40	2.40	.01
Asserts Opinion or Belief (therapist)	2.20	2.92	.02

course of treatment: 2.3, 2.2, 2.1, 2.7, and 1.3. Thus, the level of Family Discussion about the patient increased later in treatment (2.7) and fell off sharply at the end (1.3). In the last session of treatment in particular, Family Discussion averaged 1.0 for two episodes of crying. Note that the differences between early treatment and the last session in mean levels of Family Discussion before crying episodes (2.3 – 1.0 = difference of 1.3 on the 3-point scale) was substantially larger than the difference between the before-crying segments and the control segments (2.1 – 1.5 = 0.6).

Changes at Follow-Up

Note here the important changes in the original symptoms that emerged in the follow-up, which took place 1 year from the start of the treatment. Suzie "looked and acted so differently that it was hard to recognize her; the sickly and preadolescent-looking girl had been transformed into a self-possessed and assertive young woman" (Rosman, 1988, p. 306). The mother said that she no longer had anything to do with the management of the diabetes because Suzie managed it herself. In fact, an entirely new development occurred in the patient's self-management of the diabetes: She learned her own version of biofeedback. She began to recognize that when she had to take a test in school, she became anxious, which increased her blood sugar. Just by becoming more aware of her anxiety she was able to reduce it and get her blood sugar down. Furthermore, she no longer refused to eat as a way of getting control, as she had done before the treatment. The refusal to eat had risked the setting off of hypoglycemia. There had been one incident reported in the initial evaluation in which she had wanted to go shopping with her mother and because she was not permitted she did not eat at proper times.

In the initial evaluation it came out that although she was the oldest child, she was treated by the siblings as a younger sibling. The others would physically attack her and she felt helpless to do anything about it. At follow-up, she was reintegrated into the sibling system and had regained her authority as the oldest sister in terms of getting the siblings to do chores. She was able to help her mother manage the other children. She became more mature-looking; she looked older, as befit her age.

DISCUSSION

This application of the symptom-context method represents the development of a method for measuring both the situation and the personal dispositions as well as their interaction. It fit Maher's (1978) proposal in his book review:

> The task of the personality psychologist is to develop . . . methods that will make it possible to measure situations and dispositions . . . to assign separate values to them, and to develop laws describing their interaction. . . . By and large psychologists of personality have paid much less attention to measuring situations than to measuring dispositions. (p. 739)

In this study, a method for examining the contribution of a social situation was demonstrated. I attempted to investigate the relative contribution of individual and social factors simultaneously using the symptom-context method.

The finding that only a family-as-unit variable reliably discriminated the onset of crying from control segments is consistent with the family theories that emphasize the social context in which symptoms arise and are maintained. The intrapsychic view found little support in the data in this case. The patient-as-unit variables that yielded significant findings seemed to be, like crying itself, more a consequence of the Family Discussion about Suzie's problem, for example, she then felt Rejected and showed Concern about Supplies. The individual variables added little information to what was learned from the social context in terms of predicting the occurrence of crying. There is still a good possibility, however, that the lack of findings for the individual variables was the result of the relatively high correlation of these variables with the family variables.

Yet, the findings from my family therapy study may not be as different from those in symptom-context studies of individual therapy as they appear to be. Of course, family context variables were not measured in the individual psychotherapy studies reported in other chapters, and so their relative importance to intrapsychic variables was not assessed. However, the nature of the immediate social context in the individual psychotherapy, particularly the relationship with the therapist, was often an important predictor of symptom formation in those studies. Second, when the broad stimulus of the social context, as is provided by the important family members, is not immediately present, the individual therapy patient's reconstruction of it through thoughts, images, and expectations is likely to have the same kind of consequences. Thus, the following sequences can be hypothesized to be occurring in individual therapy: Patients' thoughts and images of a difficult social situation lead to feelings of helplessness and inability to cope, which in turn may lead to symptoms (Freud, 1926/1959). In family therapy, the sequence was: The difficult social context leads to the patient's feeling bad and unable to cope, which then may lead to the symptom. The main difference is whether the social context is currently physically present or present only in thoughts and images.

The symptom in the case I examined had a specific family involvement. It occurred consistently when the family discussed the patient in a scapegoating way, talking about the patient's problem, blaming her, or directing hostility toward her. But the symptom was not predicted by Family Tension; for example, Suzie apparently did not cry in an attempt to rescue her parents when she perceived tension between them. It appears, then, that Suzie has not "chosen" this role in order to reduce parental or family conflict (not supporting Hypothesis 2). Rather, the family placed her within the role to serve their own function (supporting Hypothesis 3), that is, the parents used her role as a means of avoiding their conflicts. The dimension of Family Discussion about the patient, particularly with the implication by the father that Suzie had a difficulty or was inadequate, can be seen in the following transcript of one of the crying episodes that was included in my study. Also, to be seen in the transcript is the sequence that led to the symptoms in this family: a difficult social context that led the patient to feel bad (afraid and rejected) and unable to cope.

Father: No, no, no, I say it's nothing real personal, I have no objection to you as a person. It's just that I'm afraid that maybe if this thing backfires, then we're in . . .

Therapist: In what way? I am interested in your point of view. In what way?

Father: Well, if we don't get Suzie drawn out, she might go farther into a shell. And then in order to get her out it's that much harder on me. You know, and the family.

Therapist: Can you ask, because Suzie's here, let's see what she says. Can you ask her, can, can you explain to her what are your concerns and see how she responds to that?

Father: Well, I think I talked with Suzie a little about it. Suzie, what is it that you're afraid of?

(Suzie shakes her head slowly)

Therapist: No, first it was that *you* are concerned. You know.

Father: Yes, well, I am concerned, and I think Suzie knows I'm concerned. But what it is, will this harm you, honey? (pause) Do you think that sitting here talking that you will go get . . .

Suzie: (whining) I don't like it here.

Father: . . . more afraid of us? Will you get more afraid of us?

Suzie: (crying) I don't know. I haven't been here long enough.

Father: Well, what was it I said to you Sunday we won't be afraid. There's nothing to be afraid of. That we could stop anytime. Hmm? That until you know what it is that you're afraid of none of us can help you.

Suzie: (sniffs)

Father: (looking at therapist) That it's something back in her childhood, you wonder . . .

Therapist: No, you know I am a person that likes to deal with things that exist now.

Father: Oh.

Therapist: Like, for instance, maybe you could discuss with Suzie that, to talk to you. You mostly talk and Suzie listens to. I would like you to help Suzie to talk to you. Like, Suzie just now, helped Linda to talk with me. I think it's important to not talk *to* Suzie, but to talk *with* Suzie. Can you, for instance, just now it happened that you begin to talk, and Suzie began to cry. Maybe you can explore, what happened just now.

Father: Did I say something to make you cry?

Suzie: (shakes head no)

Father: Now why were you crying?

Suzie: I don't know. I was frightened. (Suzie goes into a crying episode for several minutes)

The fact that the family discussion about the patient was reduced by the time of the last session and no longer served as a cue for Suzie to cry illustrates that a change in the family relationship patterns had resulted from the structural family therapy.

To some extent, the content of the family sessions might have been shaped by the hypotheses of the participants, particularly the therapist, so that the judgments of the clinical raters may reflect their picking up these therapist-shaped participant hypotheses. This may be a factor, but it is unlikely to be the main explanation for the findings: Not all of the hypotheses were confirmed, and many of the specific behaviors and interactions of the family members appeared to have been there before the therapist came on the scene.

These findings also may be a function of the nature of the symptom selected, that of crying episodes. Such a symptom is different from those studied before by the symptom-context method, such as momentary forgetting or precipitous shifts in depression. Crying does not fit the definition of impairment of a usual function. However, with this patient, crying had two functions that showed it to be symptom related: (a) It was a behavior that loudly announced Suzie's lack of maturity and lowly social position in her family and (b) it was a behavior that was closely associated with the physical sign of acetone, which was a probable symptom of her diabetes.

SUMMARY AND CONCLUSIONS

I set out to examine the conditions influencing symptom formation in a study of both social and individual variables within a 10-session videotaped structural family therapy. The measures included in this study covered both intrapsychic and family variables; it was from this broad coverage of variables that it was possible for me to determine which had the greatest role in the symptom context of episodes of crying during family therapy.

- *Conditions before crying.* Univariate comparisons of symptom segments (crying) with control segments (noncrying) showed that three rated patient variables differed significantly: Involvement with Others in the Room (Suzie), Rejection (Suzie), and Concern about Supplies (Suzie).

  Two family variables also were significant: Family Discussion and Patient Receives Hostility.

  A stepwise discriminant function analysis was done to understand which measures were likely to be most important in signaling the onset of crying. Family Discussion entered first, with no other variables adding significantly. Therefore, a family discussion about the patient in her presence was the most important in signaling the onset of crying.

- *Consequences of crying.* The changes from before to after a crying episode indicated that the main consequence of crying appeared to be that Suzie asserted her opinion or belief more to her family and admitted (by crying) to her feeling out of control along with experiencing some blurring of identities.

Apparently, her crying had the additional consequences of the mother talking less and the therapist becoming more involved.

- *Time course over the treatment for crying episodes.* The level of Family Discussion about the patient increased later in the treatment, but it fell off sharply at the end.

Family variables appeared to be the most potent in instigating crying. However, because of the limitation involved in a case study, it was difficult to know whether the finding about the prepotency of the family variables relative to the symptom may have some generality to other cases or apply only to this case. It could be that in both individual and family therapy treatments, social variables are important, but with individual treatments, they are present in terms of relationships with internal representations of others, and with family therapy, they are present in terms both of internal representations and of the presence of people themselves.

REFERENCES

Crits-Christoph, P., Luborsky, L., Gay, E., Todd, T., Barber, J. P., & Luborsky, E. (1991). What makes Suzie cry? A symptom-context study of family therapy. *Family Process, 30,* 337–345.

Freud, S. (1959). *Inhibitions, symptoms and anxiety.* In J. Strachey (Ed. & Trans.), *Standard edition of the complete psychologic works of Sigmund Freud* (Vol. 2), pp. 87–174). London: Hogarth Press. (Original work published 1926)

Gottman, J. (1973). N-of-one and N-of-two research in psychotherapy. *Psychological Bulletin, 80,* 93–105.

Luborsky, L. (1970). New directions in research on neurotic and psychosomatic symptoms. *American Scientist, 58,* 661–668.

Maher, B. (1978). Interaction at the intersection. *Contemporary Psychology, 23,* 739–740.

Minuchin, S. (1974). *Families and family therapy.* Cambridge, MA: Harvard University Press.

Minuchin, S., Rosman, B. L., & Baker, L. (1978). *Psychosomatic families: Anorexia nervosa in context.* Cambridge, MA: Harvard University Press.

Rosman, B. (1988). Family development and a child's chronic illness. In C. Falicov (Ed.), *Family transitions.* New York: Guilford Press.

13

THE CONTEXT FOR CHILDREN'S TOUCHING OF TREASURED OBJECTS: BUNNIES, BEARS, AND BLANKETS

ELLEN GAY

A fascinating fact about young children is that sometime between birth and 4 years of age, many form a tenacious attachment to some object, usually a blanket or a fuzzy stuffed animal. The object to which the child becomes attached I call in this article the *blanket*, *treasured blanket*, or *treasured object*. Generally, the attachment is no passing fancy; it is an intense affair—often lasting several years—and one that makes separation from the blanket highly upsetting to the child (Gay & Hyson, 1977). Tales abound from mothers, the comic strips, and the literature about the frenzy caused by a misplaced or lost treasured object. For instance, one mother said, "I'll kill myself if anything ever happens to that blanket!" Another told about her son's stiff resistance to having his blanket taken from him to be washed. After the laundering was finally done, he would stand in the yard grasping onto a corner of the wet blanket until it dried on the line (Gay & Hyson, 1977).

The phenomenon of a child's strong attachment to a specific inanimate object seems a particularly interesting one in the study of early human development. It is one that may well have relationships with attachment

An earlier version of this chapter appeared in Gay, E. L., & Hyson, M. C. (1977). Blankets, bears, and bunnies: Studies of children's contacts with treasured objects. *Psychoanalysis and Contemporary Science*, 5, 271–316. It has been adapted, revised, and expanded by the author with permission of the publisher.

in general, with individuation, with the child's gradual understanding of the world of objects, with the process of learning to adapt to stress, and with the origins and mechanisms of psychopathological symptoms (Bowlby, 1969, 1973). Indeed, there are a number of theories about how and why these attachments occur. The literature contains descriptions of particular cases and reports from mothers, including speculation about the reasons for the special attachment. However, as far as I know, few researchers have attempted systematic empirical investigation of the phenomenon. There are undoubtedly many reasons for this. Probably one is that "transitional objects," as Winnicott (1958) labeled them, have been discussed primarily by the psychoanalysts, whose methods of investigation traditionally do not include systematic or quantified measures. Furthermore, investigation of children and their blankets does not lend itself easily to laboratory experimentation. Treasured objects seem very much tied to the child's natural environment; the conditions under which children use them and the manner of use are not well understood enough to provide material for extensive laboratory manipulation of variables. What seems to be called for in preliminary work in this area are observations of children in their usual settings at home or at school. However, the ethnological study of behavior has until recently been considered by many behavioral scientists to be of questionable reliability and validity (Hutt & Hutt, 1970; Jones, 1972).

The research strategy used in the current study appears to be a promising one for examining recurrent behaviors in general, not only for children with their blankets. Luborsky (chap. 2) devised the basic technique to examine verbalizations of patients whose symptoms appear repeatedly during psychotherapy. The preliminary study by Gay and Hyson (1977) was the first to use the method for anything other than rating portions of psychotherapy transcripts.

One of the primary purposes of the current project, then, was to develop further a methodology that can be used for observational investigations in which the goal is to begin to understand specific behaviors or patterns that are seen repeatedly. It is a methodology that should be used in the early phases of investigating particular behavior patterns as a way to develop causal hypotheses that can later be experimentally tested. It seems particularly amenable to use in studies of child development because normal development involves an evolution of recurring patterns of behavior. The possibilities seem almost unlimited for studying normal individual phenomena such as tantrums, angry outbursts, crying, joyful behavior, expressions of affection, yawning, personal habits, and specified types of mastery play, messy play, or fantasy. In groups, phenomena such as scapegoating, "group glee" (Sherman, 1975), or competitive patterns might be examined, along with the many possible applications for systematically investigating disturbed child behaviors such as compulsions, phobic responses, excessive fears, withdrawal patterns, hyperactivity, frequent biting, and enuresis. The present study is aimed at demonstrating the usefulness of the methodology for such purposes; it describes the instruments used, the hypotheses tested, and the main results.

A few of the main theories of the treasured objects relative to the child's developing mental structure were described by Gay (1977). These theories include the presymbolic view; psychoanalytic views; and developmental stage theory including Piagetian, cognitive stages, and Hyson's cognitive–emotional stages (Hyson, 1974).

RESEARCH ON CHILDREN AND THEIR BLANKETS

Methods and Measures

The methods used for the study were designed to gather information about the history and use of children's treasured objects and to test hypotheses about what sorts of conditions precede, accompany, and follow the child's contacts with the object. It was not within the scope of this study to test hypotheses about the causes of contacts with blanket. It is the charting of sequences that allows for the formulation and testing of hypotheses concerning why the behavior occurs. Therefore, the current research should ultimately lead to an experimental approach.

Much of this study was similar to or overlapped the preliminary study by Gay and Hyson (1977). Hence, roughly the same age groups of children were observed, a similar parent questionnaire was used to provide a broad background on the context of touching, and the observation method and rating scales were much the same. The hope was that the promising results of the preliminary study might be more securely supported by this tighter, more systematic, and better controlled effort.

Selection of Children

Several nursery schools and day-care centers, including a range of socioeconomic levels, were contacted for permission to send letters to their parents asking for study volunteers. Letters were sent out, and individuals who replied were contacted by telephone. The parents were asked about the nature of the child's attachment to a blanket and the frequency of contacts with it. The major criteria used in selecting the children to be observed, aside from a willingness to participate, were as follows:

1. The child had to be aged between 2 years and 2 years 6 months of age or 4 years and 4 years 6 months of age.

2. The child had to be strongly attached to an inanimate object. The parents reported that this object was special and much needed by the child. A score of 6 or above on Weisberg and Russell's (1971) 10-point scale of attachment was necessary. This scale merely required that the parent rate the child's attachment along a continuum (1 = *not attached*, 10 = *very strongly attached*).

3. The parents reported that the child had to have contact with the object frequently enough that an observer would be likely to see at least a few contacts in a 2-hr observation period.

Eight children were originally selected to be observed in their homes. There were 4 boys and 4 girls, with 2 of each group being aged 2 years to 2 years 6 months and 2 each being 4 years to 4 years 6 months.

Although the criteria for selecting children to be observed seemed suitable as the study got underway, it was discovered after the observations were done that 1 child (CD) did not meet the criteria. Her mother had initially implied that this child "needed" the blanket but then later told me that the blanket was just one among many playthings and was not really "special." For this reason, I did not include CD in the blanket portion of the study. CD, was, however, a replacement for another girl, (LF) who dropped out of the study after one observation. LF's one observation period was included in the study.

This means that, for blanket segments, 8 children were studied and data are presented on them. For mother segments, 9 children were studied (CD was included in this portion of the study). Fathers were present during some of the children's observations, and the contexts of these children's contacts with their fathers were rated.

The Observations

Study of complex recurrent behavior patterns requires preliminary naturalistic observation so that categories of behavior can be defined and causative hypotheses drawn. The observation should at first be broad based and then become more specific, requiring less and less inference on the observer's part as observation categories are established and refined. Finally, when the variables under study are well defined, observation should become more specific, requiring less and less inference on the observer's part. Finally, when the variables under study are well defined and specific, they may be subjected to experimental tests.

In the current study, I used an observation method that requires the observer to sequentially write down as much as possible of what the child does and appears to feel. Ratings on behavior categories are done at a later time. I attempted to devise means that would capture accurately as much of the child's behavior and verbalizations as possible, given financial limitations and the limitations inherent in observing children roaming around in their own homes.

Observer Training and Reliability of Observations

A single observer was trained to observe young children. She was instructed to write down as much as possible of what the child did, said, and appeared to feel, as well as information about interactions with other people, including what others said to the child. Practice observations were done with another observer, and interobserver reliability was established using Singer's (1973) method of having an outside judge determine the closeness of the two observers' observations. This method required that the two observers' process notes of the same child be examined by a qualified judge, my dissertation advisor, who decided whether the fit was close enough.

Number and Length of Observations

Each child was observed for 2 continuous hours on three different days, for a total of 6 hr. Observation sessions were in the morning or afternoon and were approximately 1 week apart. Children were prepared for the observations by the observer, who spent a short time in the house before the first observation and explained what would be happening.

The observer was equipped with a flip-style notebook and a portable tape recorder that recorded throughout the observation period. The tape merely indicated each 2-min interval, which the observer marked with a slash on her process recordings so that a record could be kept of time intervals during the observations.

Preparation of Observations and Tapes for Ratings

The method to divide up the material around the blanket contact, to select controls, and to compare contact contexts with controls was adapted from the symptom-context strategies (see chap. 2). Luborsky and others have used his method with considerable success to study the verbalizations of patients in psychotherapy sessions just before and after the emergence of a symptom. He found that certain conditions build up just before the onset of the symptom and then decline after the onset. Although there are individual differences in what the build-up conditions are, intraindividual patterns tend to be consistent. Furthermore, there are some indicators, such as hopelessness, that are part of the build-up pattern for all patients.

In the current study, each observation period yielded a set of process notes. For each period of contact with the blanket in the presence of the mother or the father, or for each period that the child engaged in a particular habit such as thumbsucking, the 50 words of process notes just before contact (presegment) and the 50-word period just after contact ended (postsegment) were marked.

The original plan was to use 2-min intervals, marked with the aid of the tape recorder, as the pre- and postsegments. This was unfeasible because there was no way of estimating just when a contact period would begin and hence no method of marking when 2 min before contact began. Fifty-word segments were chosen instead because this length was usually close to 2 min. If the contact period (a during-segment) was longer than 75 words, it, too, was divided into smaller segments. The segments that were marked, then, were the during-segments, the presegments, and the postsegments.

Contact with the blanket (or other treasured object) was described as follows: The onset of contact could occur when the child began to touch or hold the blanket with some part of the body or when the child indicated that he/or she wanted to find the blanket and it culminated in physical contact with it. A period of continuous play or fantasy that included blanket contact was considered a single contact even if there were short periods when the child was not actually touching the blanket. However, no more than 1 min without touching it could elapse for one contact segment.

Contact with the mother was described as follows: Contact began when the child, by his or her own initiation, moved toward the mother and touched her with some part of his or her body or when the child called for the mother to come or listen, directly after which she moved toward the child and they touched. Contact was not scored if the mother initiated it. Contact ended when touching stopped.

Contact with a thumb or pacifier began when the child put a thumb or pacifier into his or her mouth and ended when he or she took it out.

The beginning and ending of other habits were determined, as necessary, for the individual child. In general, the habit was marked as beginning as soon as it was manifested and was marked as ending when the child stopped engaging in it. Rules applying to continuous and discontinuous blanket contact were applied to other forms of contact and habit.

Control segments were randomly chosen from observation material that was separated by at least 100 words of process notes from any presegment, contact, or postsegment. Presegments and postsegments and their controls were nearly always close to 50 words long. Contact segments, however, varied in length. To provide an adequate control for these contact segments, the controls had to at least roughly correspond to the contacts in length. The match was achieved by cutting down the length from the end of a designated control segment to fit any contact segment that was less than 50 words. When contact segments were longer than 50 words, two adjacent control segments were used and cut from the end to fit.

So that the rater would not know the difference between blanket contact or habit segments and their controls, each control had a phony reference to the child's going to the blanket or engaging in a habit. By doing this, all contact and habit segments, both real ones and controls, appeared to be real blanket or habit segments.

In addition to these segments, "pre presegments" and "post postsegments" (and, in a few cases, pre-pre-presegments and post-post-postsegments) were marked off when there was enough process material to do it. When there was, controls were chosen for these segments and all segments were rated. Therefore, for a few children 100–150 words were rated prior to and after blanket contact, mother contact, or use of a habit. One 2-hr observation was rated in its entirety.

Once the presegments, during-segments, and postsegments and their controls for a given 2-hr period were marked or selected, the process notes, which had now been typed, were arranged in random order for rating.

METHOD 1: CLINICAL REVIEW OF THE CONTEXT FOR TOUCHING TREASURED OBJECTS

A method was used that included observation with process reporting of children's behavior in their own homes. The design was based on a preliminary study by Gay and Hyson (1977), who attempted an initial testing of the general hypothesis that children take up their blankets in the context of a state of stress or "loss of ego control" and that the contact is followed by a return to a more usual state. Gay and Hyson observed 4 children who were attached to blankets, pieces of fabric, or stuffed animals in their homes. Later, they rated the portions of the observational notes that came before, during, and after the children's contacts with their blankets and compared them with control portions randomly selected from notes in which there was no contact with the blanket. Gay and Hyson then used rating scales they had devised from theoretical material, reports from parents, and the literature on conditions leading to contacts with treasured objects.

Gay and Hyson's (1977) results strongly suggested that a number of conditions tested did in fact precede the child's search for or contact with the blanket and that, after a snuggle or a brief period of play with it, the situation regarding these conditions returned to normal. In other words, it appears that children may need the blanket when they have experienced some stress or have been upset and that somehow the blanket helps them cope so that they could resume their usual activities or play.

METHOD 2: RATINGS OF TOUCHING EPISODES AND CONTROLS

The Scales

Many of the rating scales used were taken directly from Gay and Hyson (1977). These were devised from the theoretical literature (especially Freud, 1965) and from the interviews with parents. They constitute descriptions of a set of behaviors, events or affects that are reported to precede or cause contact with treasured blankets or that are considered to lead to the operation of defense mechanisms. Interrater agreement on these scales for the preliminary study was better than 90%, and many were found to discriminate contact contexts from their controls. Note that at the start of the current study, I considered that there might be overlap among some of the scales within each category. For these reasons, I was careful while working on interrater reliability to try to eliminate overlap and strengthen reliability. One scale—aimless physical activity—was dropped because it appeared to overlap too heavily with the lability of affect scale.

I felt after the preliminary study that certain important behaviors and affects were not being picked up by the scales, so I derived several more scales relating to the child's cognitive and emotional state. In addition, differences in the contents or themes of play between the 2-year-olds and the 4-year-olds were evident in the preliminary study. For this reason, a new group of "thematic" scales was added. I hoped that they might differentiate between the two age groups. These scales are consistent with the theoretical literature suggesting that toilet training and issues surrounding the child's need for autonomy are typical conflictual matters for 2- or 2½-year-olds and that an emerging moral sense, along with sexual identity and a beginning awareness of the self and others as potential sexual partners, are matters causing conflict and stress for children aged 4 to 4 years 6 months (Erikson, 1963). The scales also are partially based on the differences found between the 2- and 4-year-olds in the preliminary study.

One other set of new scales, the object contact scales, was used only for the contact segments and their controls. These were designed to measure the three types of blanket contacts observed in Gay and Hyson's (1977) study.

All scales were used to rate all observational segments, except the three object contact scales, which were used only for the blanket contact segments and their controls. Each indicator was given a 0 (none of the indicator), 1 (some of the indicator), or 2 (much of the indicator) for each segment rated. The completed set of indicators, along with definitions, is shown in the Appendix to this chapter.

Doing the Ratings

The observer (DK) and an outside rater (DM) who had no information on the study except that it related to treasured objects were trained to use the scales. Practice segments were used until interrater agreement on the presence or absence of an indicator was 75% or better. For the majority of scales, it was possible to get 75% or better agreement on ratings of 0 (none of indicator), 1 (some of indicator), and 2 (much of indicator). For a few scales, however, this was not possible, and I settled for 75% or better agreement on presence (ratings of 1 or 2) or absence (ratings of 0) of the indicator. Combining ratings of 1 and 2 in this fashion also seemed justified by the fact that one of the raters (DM) consistently rated more conservatively than the other. Hence, when DK rated a segment 2 on a particular indicator, DM was likely to give it a 1. A breakdown of scales and the level of agreement at the end of the rater training period are listed in Table 1.

When reliability was established, both raters rated all the observational segments for the study. Ratings of the raters were combined by adding the two ratings for each segment on each scale and dividing by 2. Averages of ratings for the total group of children or a subgroup of scales or single scales were then computed by (a) calculating an average rating on each scale or subgroup of scales for each child and (b) combining these averages to make an average for the total group or a subgroup of children. This meant that average scores for the stress and regression subgroups of scales (and all other subgroups) reflected an equal contribution from each child and did not reflect an equal contribution from each segment rated.

Before I present the results of the study, I note a few problems that arose in the analysis of the data, and method of presentation.

Because the study was primarily descriptive and was designed to explore potentials of the methodology used in addition to investigating the subject of treasured objects, I present the results informally. Statistical analysis was minimal because the sample sizes were small and there were substantially fewer control segments than there were real segments (and for some children no controls could be assigned for some categories of real segments), and trends are meant to be suggestive rather than to be viewed as significantly supporting one or another hypothesis. A number of t tests for correlated and noncorrelated samples were done on the findings. Because of the small samples sizes (tested samples were never greater than 9), I used a significance level of .10. When $.10 < p < .20$, I also note it. Specific scales and some of the material on subgroups and individuals within the study are treated only descriptively.

Because there was not enough remaining observational material to assign control segments to all real segments, the graphs and tables do not

TABLE 1
Interrater Agreement on Scales at the End of Rater Training

Scale	% Agreement
1. Tension	80[a]
2. Fearfulness	100
3. Upset/angry	81
4. Frustrated	78
5. Interactional conflict	92
6. Control	87[a]
7. Unfulfilled need	81
8. Affront	93
9. Self-consciousness	96
10. Tired/sleepy	96
11. Physical and verbal passivity	81
12. Habits	89
13. Lability of affect	78[a]
14. Age-inappropriate use of language	96
15. Age-inappropriate behavior	96
16. Need for closeness	85
17. Change to a more mature set	93
18. Morality and guilt	93
19. Mastery play	89
20. Separation	89
21. Toileting	93
22. Autonomy	96
23. Difference between self and others	89
24. Dressing/undressing	85
25. Romance	100
26. Sex play	100
27. Regression/progression	100
28. Power and destruction	96
29. Food	96
30. Soothing	96
31. Magic	100
32. Progressive fantasy	100

Note. From Gay and Hyson (1977). Adapted from "Appendix 2: Rating Scales," pp. 313–315 with permission.
[a]Agreement on presence (rated 1 or 2) or absence (rated 0) of indicator. Nonmarked scales show percentage of perfect agreement on ratings.

always provide a fair picture of the differences between real and control segments. For example, some blanket ratings represented the average of 20 or more segments, whereas the control ratings might have included five or fewer segments. One would expect, then, greater variability in the averaged control segments than in the averaged real ones, and it is likely that the averaged figures for the real segments generally represent more accurately what occurred in the context of object contact or habits than the averaged controls represent what occurred at times removed from such contact.

The method used for combining ratings for all children (or subgroups) on individual scales or various subgroups of scales (see Gay, 1977, p. 91) had both positive and negative effects. On the positive side, it was a method that allowed each child's ratings to have the same weight when ratings across children were combined. Some children had many more rated segments than others (see Gay, 1977, Appendix 8), and a method that did not give each child equal weight would have reflected the rating patterns of some children more than others. On the other hand, there were few segments in some categories for some children; for example DW had only one segment in each of the pre-, during-, and postblanket control categories (see Gay, 1977, Appendix 8). This meant that mean rating scores for the whole group or a subgroup of children might have been heavily biased by ratings on one or two segments. For example, DW's single control for during-blanket contacts was given as much weight in total averages or ratings as were JM's 24.

Hypotheses and Results for Touching Episodes Versus Controls

Each observational hypothesis is summarized and is followed by the findings and a discussion.

Hypothesis: Stress and Regression Together

If one sums the ratings of the blanket segments and their controls for all children on stress and regression indicators and an average is calculated for the pre-, during-, and post-, and control segments, a graph can be plotted that shows a buildup of indicators before contact with the blanket, a peaking during contact, and a sharp decline after contact. Average ratings for pre- and during-segments will be significantly greater than those for their control segments.

Results

The means on stress and regression for the 8 children for whom I had blanket contexts were analyzed. The hypothesized level of average ratings for the real presegments was found, followed by a slight increase for the during-segments and the expected drop for the postsegments (see Table 2). Significance levels for differences between real and control segment means and differences between categories of real (pre-, during-, and post-) segments are shown in Table 3.

All differences were significant, except for those between real presegments and during-segments and between during real and control segments.

For this sample, then, no peaking occurred for the real during-segments. However, the drop from pre- to posttime periods was highly significant. The average value for the during-segment controls was unexpectedly high; therefore, the difference in means between real segments and controls was not significant. A good proportion of the high mean for

TABLE 2
Mean Ratings on Total Stress[a] and Regression[b] Indicators for the 8 Children

Child	Presegments		During-segments		Postsegments	
	Real	Control	Real	Control	Real	Control
BC	1.96	2.32	2.30	2.13	1.84	0.70
BW	2.59	2.20	2.67	2.16	1.45	1.00
BP	1.13	0.51	2.74	1.72	0.29	0.28
JM	3.50	1.60	2.48	2.54	2.50	2.20
TB	1.13	1.03	1.10	1.00	1.60	1.40
LF	4.83	0.67	3.53	—	4.00	0.00
ML	6.38	0.88	6.65	1.88	4.38	1.63
DW	2.50	0.50	3.35	6.50	1.25	0.00
M	3.00	1.21	3.10	2.56	2.16	0.90

Note. Dash indicates no data.

[a]The mean ratings on total stress include the nine scales in the Appendix under Indicators of Stress: tension, fearfulness, upset/angry, frustrated, interactional conflict, control, unfulfilled need, affront, and self-consciousness.

[b]The mean ratings on total regression indicators include the items 10 to 16 in the Appendix: tired/sleepy, physical and/or verbal passivity, habits, lability of affect, age-inappropriate use of language, age-inappropriate behavior, and need for closeness.

control during-segments was accounted for by the ratings on 1 child DW, whose single during-segment control was rated high on stress indicators. Although DW had 26 real during-segments, there was only enough material left to assign one during-segment control. Again, note that controls for the during-segments included a phony reference to blanket contact. This might have spuriously inflated ratings because raters might have assumed the presence of other behaviors that they thought must accompany blanket contact.

Even though the touching episode's postsegment mean decreased, it did not approach the control level, which was still considerably lower. Mean ratings on combined stress and regression indicators for the 8 children are shown in Table 2. The significant difference between real postsegments and their controls might lead one to question whether ratings do in fact drop to control levels after blanket contact. If, as supposed, the blanket acted to alleviate stress so that the child could resume his or her usual activities, and regression usually accompanied blanket contact, then sometime after blanket contact ended combined stress and regression indicators should have fallen to normal levels. It may be that this did happen because of the necessarily short pre- and postsegments (50 words, or about 2 min) used in the study.

For the most part, then, the hypothesis was supported: Real means were in two of three cases significantly greater than control means, which indicates higher stress and regression in the context of blanket contact than at other times. In addition, stress and regression built up before blan-

TABLE 3
Differences Between Real and Control Segment Means and Differences
Between Categories of Real Segments (Pre, During, and Post)

Segment	t	p
Real vs. control		
Pre	2.43	.05
During	ns	ns
Post	2.52	.05
Between categories		
Pre vs. during	ns	ns
During vs. post	2.14	.05
Pre vs. post	3.19	.001

ket contact and dropped significantly after contact. The findings support the view that the blanket serves to alleviate high levels of stress and that regression occurs in the context of blanket contact.

Hypothesis: Stress and Regression Separately

If the ratings of all children on the stress and on the regression indicators for blanket contexts are summed separately, there will be different

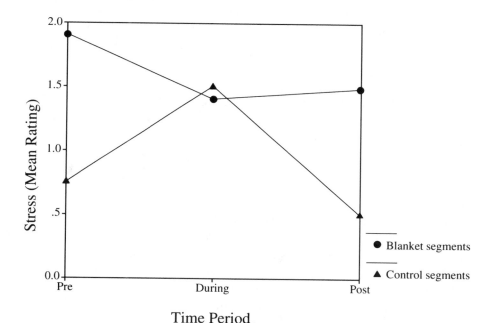

Figure 1. Ratings of stress for blanket and for control segments in 8 children.

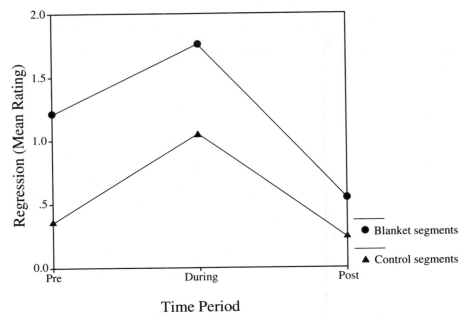

Figure 2. Ratings of regression for blanket and for control segments in 8 children.

graphic patterns for the two. Stress will build up prior to contact, decline during contact, and decline further after contact. Regression will be higher than the control level prior to contact, will sharply increase during contact, and will decline to the control level after contact.

Results

The stress and regression graphs (see Figures 1 and 2) only partially support the hypothesis. Although the ratings of stress were high before blanket contact and declined during contact, there was no further decline in stress after contact. Also, there was still a considerable difference between the postblanket contact mean and its control mean on stress indicators. For regression, the hypothesized buildup prior to contact and peaking during contact was seen. However, there remained, as with stress, a significant difference between the postsegment real regression mean and its control. Significance levels are shown in Table 4.

On the whole, the results do support the hypothesized buildup of stress before contact and the peaking of regression during contact. Furthermore, both stress and regression were significantly lower after blanket contact than before. It appears, however, that the reduction in stress occurred while the child was with the blanket and that it did not go down further immediately after contact.

TABLE 4
Differences Between Real and Control Segment Means and Differences
Between Categories of Real Segments (Pre, During, and Post) for Stress
and Regression

Segment	Stress		Regression	
	t	p	t	p
Reals vs. controls				
Pre	1.71	.10	4.39	.005
During	ns	ns	3.06	.025
Post	2.25	.05	2.41	.05
Between categories				
Pre vs. during	1.81	.10	−2.93	.025
During vs. post	ns	ns	3.59	.005
Pre vs. post	1.67	.10	2.60	.025

What is most important is that stress and regression were significantly higher in blanket contexts, that the child regressed while he or she had the blanket, and that this process of holding the blanket and regressing appeared to help the child cope with the stress so that he or she could leave the blanket and move on to some other activity.

In summary, this hypothesis was generally, but not completely, confirmed by the results. Also, contrary to prediction, regression did increase sharply for during-blanket segments, but a similar increase occurred for the controls, which included a phony reference to the child's taking up the blanket. If one were to eliminate the alleged effect of this reference in the real segments to match a flattened control curve, it would no longer appear that regression increases during blanket contact.

It does appear, though, that high stress and regression do precede the child's move to the blanket, that stress decreases during contact and regression either increases or remains fairly stable, and that both stress and regression decline after contact.

Hypothesis: Mother Contact

The graphs of stress and regression (see Figures 1 and 2) pre-, during-, and postsegments for the child's self-initiated contacts with the mother will be similar to those for contact with the blanket. However, there will be differences in the indicators that discriminate real segments from controls.

This hypothesis would support the view that the blanket may be used in place of the mother but that it is more than simply a mother substitute.

TABLE 5
Differences Between Real Versus Control and Between Categories for
Self-Initiated Contacts With the Mother

Segment	Stress		Regression		Stress and regression	
	t	p	t	p	t	p
Reals vs. controls						
Pre	ns	ns	3.45	.01	ns	ns
During	1.48	.10	3.75	.005	3.00	.005
Post	ns	ns	ns	ns	ns	ns
Between categories						
Pre vs. during	ns	ns	ns	ns	ns	ns
During vs. post	ns	ns	1.52	.10–.20	1.07	.10–.20
Pre vs. post	0.94	.10–.20	3.18	.01	2.41	.025

Results

Significance levels of means for mother contacts are shown in Table 5.
A comparison of the mother graphs with the blanket graphs (see
Figures 3 and 4) shows both similarities and differences. All real mother
and blanket graphs show significant (or close to significant) declines in

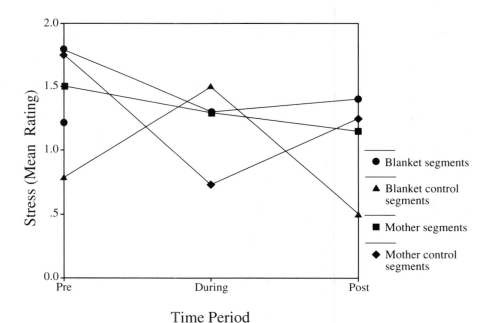

Time Period

Figure 3. Ratings of stress for blanket and control segments and for mother and
control segments.

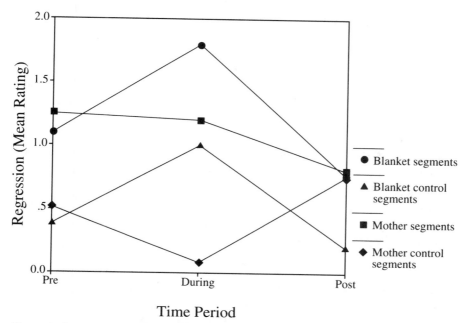

Figure 4. Ratings of regression for blanket and control and for mother control segments.

means of ratings from pre- to postsegments. Although all blanket graphs showed significantly higher ratings for pre- than postsegments, during-segments rose significantly above the presegments for the regression graph. If one were to eliminate from blanket during-segments the alleged effect of reference to the blanket, this rise in regression for blanket during-segments would decrease, and the regression graphs for the blanket and the mother would look highly similar. The stress graph for blanket contexts shows a significant decline from presegment to during-segment contexts, followed by no further decrease in indicators for the postsegments; for the mother, the change in stress from presegment to during-segment contexts was not significant, but the change from during-segment to postsegment contexts approached significance. Blanket and mother contexts were similar, then, in that stress and regression were higher before contact with the object (blanket or mother) than after contact; for example, contact was followed by a reduction in stress and regression in both cases. It is also possible that regression worked much the same in the blanket and mother contexts. However, the contexts were different in that stress declined during blanket contact but not afterward, whereas stress declined more after contact with the mother than before.

Another difference between the blanket and mother contexts is that there were no significant differences between pre- and postsegments for blanket contexts, which were rated significantly higher on stress than were their controls.

The difference on stress between during-mother segments and their controls was significant; in contrast, the difference between during-blanket segments and their controls was not significant. On the other hand, pre-segment and during-segments were rated significantly higher on regression for both blanket and mother segments than were their controls.

Because the number of control segments varied considerably from child to child and because some children did not have controls matched to some categories of segments, the sometimes-dramatic swings in averages for control segments may make comparisons between real segments and controls for specific categories questionable. It is clear, however, that controls for both blanket and mother segments were generally rated lower than were the real segments. In several cases, the differences were significant, and in no case were control means significantly greater than real means.

These findings suggest that more stress and regression do occur around times when the child seeks out the blanket, the mother, or both than at other times. It would appear that the child tends to go to the mother when he or she is already in a fairly regressed but moderately distressed state and that touching or hugging the mother helps the child get over the regression and cope with the stress. Touching the mother did not seem to be accompanied by further regression in this sample of children. The blanket seemed to be sought out when the child was distressed and somewhat regressed; while he or she was touching the blanket, his or her distress subsided. Whether further regression occurred while he or she held the blanket was not entirely clear. In any case, by the time the child gave up the blanket, he or she no longer needed to be as regressed, and his or her stress level remained about where it was while the child was with the blanket.

The second portion of this hypothesis was that blanket and mother contexts would differ on which specific indicators differentiated real from control segments. There were some interesting differences in stages—presegment during-segment, or postsegment—at which apparent differentiation between real and control segments occurred. Control was much more predominant before blanket contact than before contact with the mother. During blanket contact, control dropped down, but it increased somewhat during mother contact.

In summary, there were not large differences between the blanket and mother on which scales differentiated. One scale differentiated for blanket contexts, failed to do so for mother contexts; and one scale differentiated mother segments from controls but not blanket segments from controls. The remaining 13 scales appeared to discriminate between both mother and blanket contexts. The indication, then, is that many of the same forms of stress and regression surrounded the child's move to his or her mother as surrounded the child's taking up the blanket.

Although the blanket and the mother both appeared to act as stress reducers for the child, there were some differences in the kinds of stress and regression that preceded, accompanied, and followed contact with the mother compared with the blanket. For this group of children, then, the hypothesis was supported.

Hypothesis: Contact Habits Versus Blanket Contacts

The graphs of pre-, during-, and postsegments for children's habits, such as thumbsucking, will be similar to those for contact with the blanket.

However, there may be differences in the indicators that discriminate touching episodes from controls. This hypothesis was generated by the preliminary study and was consistent with the view that autoerotic habits and early attachments to objects fall along a developmental continuum, gratifying changing but overlapping needs as the child grows (Fink, 1962).

Results

Four children (DW, CD, BP, and BW) had "autoerotic" habits that were repeatedly seen during the observation periods. BP and BW sucked their thumbs, DW chewed his tongue, and CD habitually chewed gum. In the cases of BP, BW, and DW, chewing and sucking sometimes occurred simultaneously with blanket contact. To study habits as distinct from blanket contact, completely simultaneous sucking (sucking and blanket contact began and ended together) and blanket contact were not rated. In a few instances, sucking overlapped with blanket contact. That is, the child was sucking and holding the blanket and, while still sucking, put the blanket down. When this occurred, sucking (chewing) was rated. During one of the observations of DW, he sat with his blanket for nearly the entire 2-hr period. Off and on, he also chewed his tongue, and these segments were rated.

To avoid bias attributable to the mention of the habit in during-segments, during-controls included a phony reference to the habit.

Significance levels for the difference in habit means are shown in Table 6.

The graph of total averaged stress and regression for habits is highly similar to its counterpart for the blanket (see Figure 5). In both cases, presegments were rated high and real presegment ratings were significantly greater than controls. However, during the postsegment habit, the segments did not differ significantly from their controls; for blanket segments, the during-segments' mean did not differ significantly from the control mean, but real postsegments were significantly greater than their controls. For

TABLE 6
Comparison of Reals and Controls Between Categories for Differences in
the Children's Habits

Segment	Stress		Regression		Stress and regression	
	t	p	t	p	t	p
Reals vs. controls						
Pre	1.58	.10	8.25	.005	2.90	.05
During	ns	ns	3.61	.025	ns	ns
Post	ns	ns	ns	ns	ns	ns
Between categories						
Pre vs. during	1.47	.10–.20	−2.05	.005	ns	ns
During vs. post	ns	ns	1.80	.10	1.54	.10–.20
Pre vs. post	1.61	.10–.20	1.08	.10–.20	2.14	.10

both blanket and habit, there was a sharp decrease in the postsegment
ratings. The difference between pre- and postsegment means for both blanket and habit were significant.

Separate stress and regression graphs for habits (see Figures 6 and 7)
were also highly similar to stress and regression blanket graphs. For both

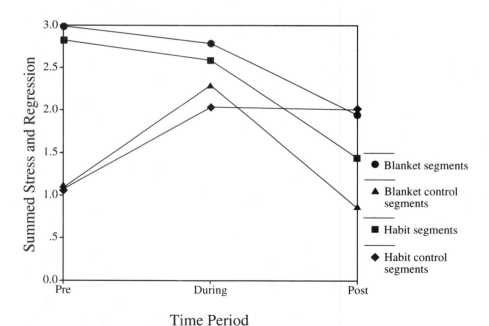

Time Period

Figure 5. Summed stress and regression for habit and control segments and for
blanket and control segments.

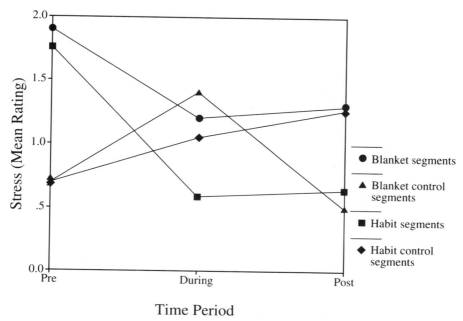

Stress (Mean Rating)

2.0

1.5

1.0

.5

0.0

● Blanket segments

▲ Blanket control segments

■ Habit segments

◆ Habit control segments

Pre   During   Post

Time Period

Figure 6. Ratings of stress for habit and control segments and for blanket and control segments.

blanket and habits, stress was high in presegments, declined in during-segments, and rose just slightly (but insignificantly) in postsegments. Pre-segment means in both cases were significantly greater than their controls. Regression in both habit and blanket contexts were high for presegments, increased sharply for during-segments, and then declined, below preseg-ment level, for postsegments. Pre- and during-segments were significantly greater than their controls in both blanket and habit contexts. Although posthabit segments did not differ significantly from controls, the postblan-ket segment mean for regression indicators was significantly greater than the control mean. The main difference between blanket and habit graphs was that postsegment means in the latter case did not differ significantly from their controls.

In general, however, the first portion of this hypothesis was clearly supported. The second portion of the hypothesis was that blanket and habit contexts would differ on which specific indicators differentiated real from control segments.

Overall, the pattern of stress and regression in blanket and habits contexts was highly similar. Scales that, on scanning the ratings, appeared to discriminate were also similar, except that fewer scales distinguished real from control segments for habit contexts than they did for blanket con-texts. There was a closer fit between blanket and habit patterns, both for

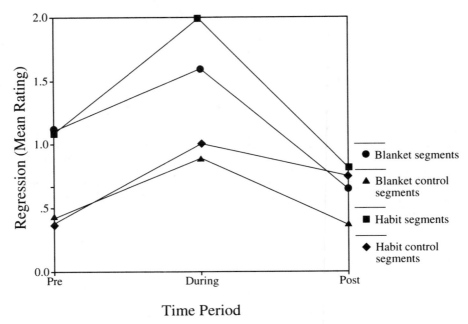

Figure 7. Ratings of regression for habit and control segments and for blanket and control segments.

summed and individual indicators, than between blanket and mother patterns. This tends to support the notion that various childhood autoerotic habits lie along a continuum, filling overlapping needs, and that these habits to some extent grow to be differentiated as stress reducers from the mother, who undoubtedly plays a more complex role in the child's life. Regression may be more prevalent during the time the child uses a habit or holds the blanket than it is during contact with the mother. Ratings on regression scales tended to be high for blanket and habit during-segments, although they were not necessarily high for mother segments. The blanket and the habit may typically involve regression, whereas the child may sometimes regress only while touching the mother. Blanket, mother, and habits were alike, however, in that they all appeared to function as stress reducers for the child.

Hypothesis: Other Qualities Discriminating Reals and Controls

In addition to the stress and regression scales, there may be other indicators that will discriminate real (blanket, mother, father, and habit) contexts from controls. It was predicted that one or more of the following scales would be rated higher for real contexts than for controls: morality and guilt, change to a more mature set, separation, toileting, autonomy, differences between self and others, dressing and undressing, romance, sex play, regression/progression, power and/or destruction, and food.

Results

This hypothesis was supported by the results of the study. Eight of the 12 scales seemed to show some discrimination, either between real segments and controls or between two or more of the pre-, during-, and postsegment categories. In most cases, real segments were rated higher than controls when discrimination occurred; however, in a few instances, controls were rated higher than real segments. Reasons for discrimination generally included a consideration of the possible stress implied in the ratings on the scales.

Hypothesis: Comparison With Mastery Play Scale

The mastery play scale will show a higher average rating for postsegment and control blanket segments than for pre- and during-segments. This was hypothesized to support the view that the blanket, after a period of regression, would help to reestablish normal equilibrium or developmental level. A similar pattern may be evidenced for mother, father, and blanket contexts.

Results

For blanket, mother, and father contexts, controls were rated higher than were real segments. This pattern was less clear for the contexts for habits. However, postsegments were rated higher than were pre- and during-segments in both blanket and habits contexts, although for habits, the change was slight; this supported the hypothesis. For mother contexts, there was little change from pre- to postsegments; and for father contexts, mastery play ratings declined from pre- to postsegments. Significance levels for the blanket and mother contexts are shown in Table 7.

As can be seen, control means for both the mother and blanket contexts were, for the most part, significantly greater than the real means. The mean for real postblanket segments was close to being significantly greater than the real presegment mean; however, the difference between real and presegments and postsegments for the mother context was not significant. The hypothesis, then, tended to be supported.

Hypothesis: Soothing During Blanket Contact

Consistent with previous findings and with the theoretical position predicting flexibility of use of the treasured blanket, it was hypothesized that behavior while the child is in contact with the blanket (during-segments) will tend, more than in their control periods, to fit into one or

TABLE 7
Comparison of Reals and Controls Between Categories for Blanket and Mother Contexts

Segment	Blanket		Mother	
	t	p	t	p
Reals vs. controls				
Pre	−2.27	.05	−1.74	.10
During	−1.52	.10	ns	ns
Post	−1.96	.05	−2.11	.05
Between categories				
Pre vs. post	−1.02	.10–.20	ns	ns

more of the object contact scales, which include soothing, magic, and progressive fantasy. When the child's contact with the blanket is rated high on the progressive fantasy scales, the usual increase of stress and regression ratings before and during blanket contact will be best, and there will be higher-than-usual ratings of mastery play in the pre- and during-segments.

Results

The hypothesis was clearly confirmed, although only for one of these scales, contact segments were rated much higher on soothing than were controls. However, magic and progressive fantasy were hardly rated. Therefore, more hypotheses regarding the latter of these scales could be neither supported nor disconfirmed.

METHOD 4: BROAD BACKGROUND CONTEXTS

The breadth of the immediate context was limited by the brief length of the observation period before and after touching the treasured object. To extend this period, a broad background of observations was provided by a questionnaire for the parents of 40 children, including those 9 children who were observed and rated. Generally, it was the mother who was interviewed, but fathers sometimes took part. Information about the child's behavior relative to treasured objects was much extended by these interviews.

After the children to be observed were selected, all parent volunteers whose children met the criteria, as well as others who claimed their children were strongly attached to bottles, pacifiers, or hard toys, were interviewed in person or over the telephone using a semistructured, exploratory questionnaire. The ages of the children ranged from just under 2 years to 11 years. Two of these children (the 11-year-old and an 8-year old) had given up the blanket by the time of the interview. The median age of children still attached to treasured objects was 4 years 6 months. In the sample of 40 children, there were 14 girls and 26 boys.

To avoid creating possible biases, the parents of observed children were not extensively interviewed until after the observations. The history and nature of the attachment and the use of the object were discussed, along with the parents' role in the attachment, the child's personality, length of attachment, and changes over time.

According to the parents' reports, children usually become attached to treasured objects between the ages of 6 and 12 months; thumbsucking began before 6 months, and attachment to a pacifier or bottle appeared a little later. The most common treasured object was a blanket with a silky binding.

An interesting finding was that although no parent encouraged a child to become attached to a blanket, a majority of parents encouraged the continuance of an already-formed attachment. Encouragement took the form of getting the blanket for an upset or tired child, being sure it was along on a trip, and so on. This finding suggests that parents' actions may be important ingredients in whether an incipient blanket attachment will survive. Going a step further, it may well be that parents could successfully encourage children to form attachments. If attachment enhances development, as was proposed in the theoretical model for this study (Gay, 1977), then encouragement by routinely placing a particular blanket or stuffed animal in the child's bed and wrapping the child in that blanket during feeding might be advisable.

Another finding was that the period of most intense blanket attachment occurred between 19 months and 2½ years of age; intense periods for pacifier and bottle attachments came somewhat earlier, although the period of strongest attachment to stuffed toys was a bit later. This continuum of age and attachments from sucking objects to toys that elicit fantasy play supports the view that the stage of development, with its characteristic conflicts and needs, plays a role in what sort of soother a child will choose as an object of attachment. A parent wishing to encourage the start of an attachment would be well advised to take the child's age and developmental stage into account before selecting an object.

Children were most frequently reported to go to their blankets at bedtime, when tired, while sitting quietly watching TV, when upset in one way or another, and when engaged in fantasy play. The occasions parents mentioned for contact with the treasured object corresponded closely to the stress, regression, and fantasy scales used to rate the child observations for the study. This means that the scales that were derived from the literature, from parent reports and observational material from the preliminary study, were probably sufficient to tap the range of behaviors likely to occur in the context of blanket contact.

Typically, the reaction to a lost or unavailable blanket was moderate distress. Younger children were more likely to get highly upset than were older children.

Neither the parent's report nor observational material indicated that there is a personality stereotype among blanket users or that blanket users differ from other children in their level of mental health.

SUMMARY AND CONCLUSIONS

- Hypotheses about the child's behavior relative to the use of treasured objects were substantially borne out by the current study: (a) the buildup of stress and regression indicators before contact with the blanket; (b) the peaking of regression indicators during contact; and (c) the drop in both groups of scales after contact. In addition, touching episodes were rated significantly higher than were control episodes.

  Whether the rise in regression during blanket contact was genuine or whether it was a consequence of reference in the process notes to the blanket could not be determined clearly. What is clear is that both stress and regression were significantly lower after blanket contact than before, suggesting that the blanket served to reduce stress.

  As hypothesized, most of the individual children showed the predicted stress and regression patterns, whereas specific indicators that differentiated touching episodes from control segments varied (Gay, 1977).

- Stress and regression also were reduced through contact with the mother as well as during and after habits such as thumbsucking. However, unlike the blanket and habits, there was no peaking of regression while the child was in contact with the mother.

  If the blanket and habit regression peaks are not spurious, the absence of peaking for mother contacts would appear to represent a real difference from the blanket and from habits. Although other children may regress with the blanket, behavior while having contact with the mother may be more varied; this is reasonable because the mother could interact with the child and can solve problems for him or her. The blanket's power to reduce stress may be related primarily to the child's use of it to allow himself or herself to regress. Regression, in the form of lying passively, sucking on something, becoming sleepy, and so on, would likely be associated for most children with their infanthood relationships with the mother. By the time a child is 2–4 years old, his or her relationship with the mother will have become much more complex; regression may sometimes occur when he or she goes to her, but many other behaviors, including conversation, requests, complaints, and play, would also take place. The blanket and other autoerotic habits may serve to connect the child to the extensive nurturing received from his or her mother as an infant. Hence, partly with the help of the blanket, the child can separate and individuate from the mother, as the theoretical framework for this chapter suggests, because the child can get the infantile gratification once gotten from her by a different means.

- As predicted, mastery play was more prevalent in control segments than in touching episodes for blanket, habits, mother, and father contexts. In addition, ratings on mastery play were low for pre- and during-blanket segments and then rose in postsegments. No such rise in mastery play after contacts with the mother was evident. The child's contact with the blanket, then, appears to allow the child to return to normal activities that involve mastery. That this should not be so for the mother may point to the different roles the blanket and the mother play for the child.

How the Symptom-Context Method Performed

Overall, the theoretical model for this study was supported by its results. Also, the positive results indicate that the adaptation that was used of the symptom-context methodology (see chap. 2) can be successful in investigating repetitive behaviors or affects shown by children in naturalistic settings.

The method as applied to this topic, however, has some problems. The process of gathering observational data, preparing segments for rating, and the rating itself is laborious; therefore, samples of participants tend to be small and the possibilities for significant results will be reduced. Enough observational material to assign controls to all touching segments was not always available, and so observed differences between mean touching and control levels may not be significant. There are also several stages at which the loss of potentially important data is likely: Process recordings can include only a general picture of the child's behavior, and many nuances are lost; some of these will be remembered by the observer-rater when he or she does the ratings on the scales, but the outside (nonobserver) rater must work from a sparser fund of information and is likely to give less reliable ratings than is the observer-rater; the scales are global and behavioral subtleties will not be picked up in the ratings. All of this means that the final results of the study cannot represent the range or extent of behavior actually exhibited by the child (as would be more fully recorded by a video). However, if the study does yield positive results, as this one clearly did, one can be fairly sure that they are at least partly valid. Keeping these points in mind, the investigator has a tool that can be used profitably to explore behavior as it precedes, accompanies, and follows an unlimited range of repeating events.

The current study was an attempt to understand how and why children need treasured objects. Further work might include a comparison of what follows stress for blanket users compared with nonusers. Studies of emotionally disturbed children and their treasured objects might shed light on differences between normal and pathological attachments. The development of additional scales to more fully represent occasions when children initiate contacts with the mother and father would allow a more thorough study of differences between attachments to inanimate objects and to people. Age differences need to be explored further; studies of infants with their blankets, 12- to 18-month-olds who are learning to walk and get around on their own, and older children who are in process of giving up their blanket attachment would help to further show the continuum of developmental antecedents and uses of the blanket. Longitudinal studies of individuals from the beginning to end of the blanket attachment also would serve this purpose.

It is clear that the recurrent touching behavior for treasured objects cannot be classed as a symptom because there is no significant impairment of function involved. Although the antecedents for the touching were involved with increased stress and a presumably greater sense of helplessness, their touching led to reequilibrization and a return to more usual behavior.

A comparison with other symptom-context studies might be possible if, at least for the 4-year-olds, some of their expressed thoughts could be transcribed for further analyses. It may be that the context for increased stress leading to touching may include some of the relationship conflicts associated with their central relationship pattern, as was suggested by a study of 3- and 5-year-olds' narratives (Luborsky et al., 1995).

As the results of the current study have shown, the young child's attachment to a treasured object appears to be a facet of his or her capacity to cope with stress. The elucidation of a childhood coping mechanism can have important consequences for knowledge of child development, child rearing, and for psychotherapy. If researchers know what the components of coping are, they can better foster their development and their use.

Comparison of the Two Chapters on Touching

The findings of this study on touching treasured objects has a strong common bond with the findings of the study on touching the mouth and face, discussed in chapter 14. The touching in both conditions appears to reduce the buildup of stress and reduce the movement toward regression. Both forms of touching are ways of coping by showing mastery over the stress by a behavior that feels need satisfying and bolstering.

There are obvious limits to being able to do an exact comparison of the conditions for touching with the conditions for the recurrent symptoms described in this book. It would have been valuable to have had a voice recording or a video, to be able to register not just the touching behavior but also the part of the child's experience that was expressed in words. Some of the behavioral ratings suggested that the child was becoming increasingly tense and upset before touching the treasured object. It is possible that if the child's words were available for analysis, I could have assessed the presence of helplessness, hopelessness, and related qualities as was done for the symptom studies.

In the study of touching the mouth by Gottschalk in chapter 14, an association was found between touching the mouth area and thoughts of women; the patient's touching of his mouth area evoked positive memories and associations with females as "good objects." Rather than thinking of the association of the touching in each of the studies only as regressive, it also could be fitting to think of the association as maintaining and bolstering self-sufficiency and as enhancing the capacity for adequate functioning.

APPENDIX
INDICATORS AND DEFINITIONS

Rating Indicators

Scales were rated: 0 (Absence of the indicator)
1 (Some of the indicator)
2 (Much of the indicator)

Indicators of Stress

1. Tension: Child appears to be tense, uncomfortable, or anxious.
2. Fearfulness: Child is fearful. To use this scale, there must be evidence of or talk about something feared by the child.
3. Upset/angry: Unhappy, cranky, irritable, angry, or crying.
4. Frustrated: Child seems to feel he or she cannot do something right, or he or she is trying to do something and cannot. There is a negative reaction to an obstacle (perceived or real) in the way of mastery or success.
5. Interactional conflict: Argument, disagreement, or conflict. Someone may be angry at the child or vice versa.
6. Control: Interaction involving the issue of control. For example, the mother or a friend tells the child to do something or the child tells another to do something. The implication is that the child appears to feel controlled by the other person or that he or she is unsuccessful at controlling the other person.
7. Unfulfilled need: Child's need or desire is unfulfilled by other person. Indicates desire and is turned down or rejected. May rate strong affect even if the need is finally filled. Scale rates the need for goods or for nurturance. Example: Child asks for a cookie and is turned down.
8. Affront: The child is embarrassed or "put down" by another person. May imply a sudden embarrassment or somewhat alarming surprise, but this must be the result of a deliberate affront from another person. Example: Another child says to the target child, "That's dumb," or "You don't do it that way, stupid."
9. Self-consciousness: Child seems to become aware of self or shy or embarrassed in relation to another person without any evident provocation or to an extent that is out of proportion to the particular interpersonal context.

Indicators of Regression

10. Tired, sleepy.
11. Physical passivity, verbal passivity, or both.
12. Habits: Sucking (fingers or something else), rocking (rhythmically, in habitual way), systematically stroking or rubbing something over a part of the body, repeatedly smelling, and so on. (Raters were instructed not to rate the blanket contact on habits.)

13. Lability of affect: Mood swings.

14. Age-inappropriate use of language: Baby talk, silly talk, or nonsense words; talking in a fake voice; or loss of control of logical verbal processes. Regressive use of language (no baby talk as part of a fantasy role) is implied by this scale.

15. Age-inappropriate behavior: Behavior or affect that shows regression from the child's present age level or optimal developmental level. This should include a generally regressive behavior pattern, possibly general babyish silliness or thematic content representative of an earlier age (e.g., silly, giggly "poo-poo" talk or play in a 4½-year-old or play with materials typical of a much younger child). Do not score this unless it is different from or goes beyond the other potentially regressive scales (tired, sleepy; physical and verbal passivity; habits; lability of affect; age-inappropriate use of language; and need for closeness). In other words, this scale should not overlap with the others.

16. Need for closeness: Desire for closeness, hugging, kissing, and being held by or holding another person, especially mother.

Additional Scales

(Includes scales that measure content or themes implied in children's behavior)

17. Change to a more mature set: Child changes from less to more mature behavior, for example, silliness followed by settling down to a puzzle, lolling around in no clothes, fooling aimlessly followed by self-initiated dressing.

18. Morality and guilt: Child verbally or nonverbally shows concern about having done something wrong, about others doing wrong, or about being sorry or feeling bad, right or wrong, or should or ought. There may be indications that the child is being moralistic or condemning.

19. Mastery play: The child, alone or with others, is engaged in a productive problem-solving or work activity that is appropriate for his or her age. This might include, for example, playing a game, solving a puzzle, building something, drawing a picture, attempting to work out or arrange something, thinking or playing through some issue or problem, helping someone else in a productive fashion, and so on.

20. Separation: Separation is about to occur, is occurring, or is being discussed. This may be separation from a place or a person. Rate 2 if there is either high frequency (of discussion, etc.) or high intensity on this scale.

21. Toileting: There is mention of going to the toilet or the child does go to the toilet. Any discussion of toilet activities, including "poo-poo" talk, fit into this category.

22. Autonomy: There is an indication that the child is concerned about being able or allowed to do something himself or herself. For example, the child may refuse assistance in doing a task that is highly difficult for him

or her, may talk about all the things he or she can do, how big he or she is, and so on.

23. Differences between self and others: The child seems highly aware of or talks about differences or similarities between self and others. Differences include those in size or physical attributes, knowledge, ability, activities, possessions, and so forth. Examples include the following: child talks about how much faster she or he can run than a friend or says, "I can draw a house that you can't" (implying that the other person cannot). Hence, there may be an evident competitive aspect.

24. Dressing, undressing: Dressing or undressing oneself or a doll or stuffed animal, or talking about or pretending to do this.

25. Romance: Child fantasizes, plays out, or talks about male–female relations, emphasizing sexual or romantic aspects of the relationship. Examples include talk of an older sister going on a date; pretending with a friend to be a man and woman kissing or dancing together; and saying "I'm gonna marry _____ when I grow up."

26. Sex play: Talking about, examining, touching genitals of one-self or other or a doll or stuffed animal.

27. Regression/progression: Any situation in which the child shows a behavior that contrasts infantlike aspects with adultlike aspects. This may include imitation or fantasy about adult behavior in which mastery beyond the child's years is implied and in which there is characterization of both adult and infant roles. Examples: A young boy plays Superman with his own blanket wrapped around himself as a cape; child covers dolls with own blankets; child dresses, protects, or mothers a baby doll.

28. Power and/or destruction: Talk or fantasy of being big and powerful or destructive and evil in a powerful way. Example: "I am Batman."

29. Food: Rate child discussing food (1) or rate child has or is eating food (2).

The Object Contact Scales

30. Soothing: Behavior that indicates the child is being soothed or is soothing himself or herself in an infantile manner. Child may lie down as if sleeping, close eyes, cuddle up, suck thumb, suck pacifier, and so on.

31. Magic: Child uses or talks about an inanimate object that he or she has or is playing with in a way that indicates he or she believes it has some special qualities that it does not. For example, the object may be used as a kind of protection from harm or as a weapon.

32. Progressive fantasy: Use of an object the child has or is playing with in fantasy in a way that indicates he or she is attempting to work out or practice a problem, conflict, or life issue. Examples would be playing out a birth fantasy with a stuffed animal, dressing or undressing a doll, or pretending to go on a trip with the stuffed animal.

REFERENCES

Bowlby, J. (1969). *Attachment and loss* (Vol. 1). New York: Basic Books.

Bowlby, J. (1973). *Attachment and loss* (Vol. 2). New York: Basic Books.

Erikson, E. (1963). *Childhood and society* (2nd ed.). New York: Norton.

Fink, P. (1962). The pacifier as a transitional object. *Bulletin of the Philadelphia Association for Psychoanalysis, 12,* 69–83.

Freud, A. (1965). *Normality and pathology in childhood: Assessments of development.* Madison, CT: International Universities Press.

Gay, E. (1977). *Blankets, thumbs, and Mom: A comparative study of stress and regression around early childhood habitual behaviors and contacts with treasured objects.* Unpublished doctoral dissertation, Bryn Mawr College, Bryn Mawr, PA.

Gay, E., & Hyson, M. (1977). Blankets, bears and bunnies: Studies of children's contacts with treasured objects. *Psychoanalysis and Contemporary Science, 5,* 271–316.

Hutt, S., & Hutt, C. (1970). *Direct observation and measurement of behavior.* Springfield, IL: Charles C Thomas.

Hyson, M. (1974). *The child's treasured object: The development of defenses and cognitions as seen in blankets and bears.* Unpublished manuscript Bryn Mawr College, Bryn Mawr, PA.

Jones, B. (Ed.). (1972). *Ethological studies of child behavior.* Cambridge, England: Cambridge University Press.

Luborsky, L., Luborsky, E., Diguer, L., Schaffler, P., Schmidt, K., Dengler, D., Faude, J., Morris, M., Buchsbaum, H., Emde, R. (1995). Extending the Core Conflictual Relationship Theme into childhood. In G. Noam & K. Fisher (Eds.), *Development and vulnerability in close relationships* (pp. 287–308). Hillsdale, NJ: Erlbaum.

Sherman, L. (1975). An ecological study of glee in small groups of pre-school children. *Child Development, 46,* 53–61.

Singer, J. (1973). *The child's world of make-believe.* San Diego, CA: Academic Press.

Weisberg, P., & Russell, J. (1971). Proximity and interactional behavior of young children to their "security" blankets. *Child Development, 42,* 1575–1579.

Winnicott, D. (1958). *Collected papers.* New York: Basic Books.

14

THE CONTEXT FOR TOUCHING
THE MOUTH AREA DURING
PSYCHOANALYTIC SESSIONS

LOUIS A. GOTTSCHALK

The opportunity to study the relationship between the content of free association and a repeated physical gesture was provided by the psychoanalysis of a 40-year-old married psychologist. During his treatment, the patient not infrequently moved one hand from alongside his body toward his mouth and then fingered his lips, oral cavity, nose, or cheek or rubbed his closed eyes with his fingers or fist. I decided to investigate the recurrent relationship of the content of his free associations and these various hand–face approximations (as reported by Gottschalk, 1974).

The content of verbal material during psychoanalysis and its correlation with various behaviors or manifestations of the involuntary nervous system have long been of interest to analysts. Ferenczi (1912/1950) wrote of the relationship of associative content to a variety of transient symptoms during the psychoanalytic session. I have reported psychoanalytic observations on the recurring epileptic manifestations of an 8-year-old boy (Gottschalk, 1956) and on the psychophysiological relationship between the content of free associations and paroxysmal electroencephalographic activity in a 24-year-old soldier who was prone to having grand mal seizures (Gottschalk, 1955). My findings have been reconfirmed by a more rigorous

An earlier, expanded version of this chapter appeared in Gottschalk, L. A. (1974). The psychoanalytic study of hand-mouth approximations. *Psychoanalysis and Contemporary Science, 3,* 269–291. It has been adapted with permission of the publisher.

analysis of the data (Luborsky, 1970; Luborsky et al., 1975) and by others (Haggard & Isaacs, 1966; Scheflen, 1964, 1966).

Editorial note: The place of the study in symptom-context research. It is important for the reader to know that this chapter is included in the book because it illustrates an innovative and informative method of showing the parallels between the verbal level and the bodily movement level in data from psychotherapy. Although in its present form it lacks some of the essential qualities of the symptom-context method, such as the comparison with controls, it is likely to stimulate other researchers to conduct similar studies in a symptom-context format. In future studies, a researcher could note the timing of the hand position relative to the thoughts and arrange for ratings of the thoughts before different hand positions (as in Method 2) as well as evaluations of the background state.

This chapter is included in this book for another reason as well: Its results parallel those from chapter 13 on the role of physical contact with treasured objects. In the current chapter, a positive supportive role is shown in an adult for touching the mouth area. In the previous chapter, a similar role is shown in children for physical contact with treasured objects. Both of these physical contact-seeking behaviors might be interpretable as regressive behavior, but they both also are interpretable as forms of regression in the service of control or mastery, a kind of beneficially supportive and remedial role for the physical contact.

RÉSUMÉ OF THE PATIENT'S ANALYSIS

The patient, a psychologist, was an unusually mature, perceptive man, with a long-standing penchant for self-reflection and introspection. Some combination of these traits—and probably others that cannot be specified—made it possible for him to start his analysis and get well involved in it with a minimum of defensiveness and intellectualization. This is not to say that he presented himself as the epitome of normality and mental health. Rather, he could at the outset detail systematically and lucidly his lifetime traumas and experiences and his ensuing neurotic struggles and real achievements. He was able to point to those genetic and psychodynamic factors that he understood and those areas of comprehension that eluded him and apparently left him with recurring symptoms. These symptoms included occasional doubts about his real abilities; disturbing feelings that his wife, an attractive woman, did not sufficiently match his ideal of feminine beauty (the important missing characteristic was fuller breasts); occasional impotence (in the form of loss of erection during intercourse or retarded ejaculation); and chronic, nonallergic rhinitis.

During his treatment, the patient, Mr. B, made excellent progress in the analysis and resynthesis of himself. This was shown by dynamic and structural changes as well as by definite symptomatic changes. His chronic rhinitis became practically nonexistent. His episodes of sexual impotence stopped. His self-concept of possibly being inadequate or damaged—depicted, for example, in dreams by having a false tooth or being minus a jawbone—disappeared. Mr. B's mind was a busy and inquiring one, yet he was critical and skeptical about easy or hastily arrived-at formulations.

The earlier portions of his analysis were characterized by involvement in feelings and thoughts about his mother and people like her. His mother died of an infection when he was 5 months old. His rearing was taken over by a paternal aunt, but he later spent much time with another aunt and his paternal grandmother, with all three women having the role of mother surrogate for him. His father, an architect, was so grief-stricken at the death of his wife that he played a relatively minor role in Mr. B's rearing for several years.

The manifest theme of his first dream in analysis was of his sucking on the breasts of a young woman and finding the milk sweet. The second dream dealt with a frightening erotic attraction to three women: his three mother surrogates. It is likely that the focus of the analysis on early mother–child relationships was enhanced by Mr. B's wife becoming pregnant with the couple's second child about 3 months before his analysis started; she gave birth to a baby girl 6 months after the beginning of his analysis.

The frustration of oral–passive urges in the analytic situation led him to reflect that, although he lost his mother while he was still nursing at the breast, he was overindulged by his substitute "three mothers," certainly until the age of 4 years. At the age of 4, he developed a strange malady—obviously a conversion reaction—consisting of his being unable to walk. After ailing for several weeks, he was tricked into a recovery by being tempted to go after a gift, a fuzzy toy animal. Analysis revealed that this episode of "paralysis" was triggered by the marriage and first pregnancy of one of his aunts, his principal mother surrogate at that time, and his anxiety at losing his place in her affections. Anal smearing fantasies and impulses toward the analyst and key parental figures appeared, which were superseded and defended against by reaction formations and a preoccupation with cleanliness and orderliness. These reaction formations were re-enactments of the aggressive reactions he had to early childhood frustrations of dependency. The reaction formations to the hostile aspect of these anal urges were presumably quick to develop because of the threat of further withdrawal of love and support.

At this point, Mr. B disclosed that prepubertally he had had an eating problem characterized by his subsisting primarily on milk and candy. With adolescence this eating pattern gave way to a more balanced menu, and with this change in diet there arose a reaction formation against passive dependence: He almost made a fetish of independence, self-reliance, and autonomy. Whereas at an earlier age he fantasized about a reunion with his deceased mother in a far-off place or that his mother was nearby, always watching over him, he renounced or forgot about these solaces. In adolescence, he renounced his adherence to and faith in religion. In analysis, being able to trace the vicissitudes of his oral needs and frustrations, he could realize the defensive and self-defeating nature of his excessive striving for independence and repudiation and intolerance of his legitimate and appropriate need for support and love.

When this kind of material came into focus in the transference, he initially expressed inappropriate resentment and bitterness toward the analyst. When the defensive nature of this resentment was pointed out—that it was a coverup for his affection—he burst into tears of relief and insight.

During the later portion of his analysis, the transference manifested itself mostly as a father–uncle transference, which was characterized by phallic competitive urges, a feeling of inferiority, a fear of retaliation, and thoughts of renouncing ambitious striving intermingled with new zest and self-confidence.

The termination of Mr. B's analysis was associated with a continuing sense of self-assurance and equanimity. He now had a capacity to love his wife more intimately without the preoccupation that her breasts were too small. His nonallergic vasomotor rhinitis—previously unresponsive to a variety of medical treatments—was cured. Finally, he was more assertive and creative in his professional work.

Method 1: Clinical Review of Associations Between Touching Facial Areas and Thought Content

The patient was seen for 612 analytic sessions over a period of almost 4 years. During one phase of his analysis, beginning in the second year and lasting 6 months, verbatim notes were kept of his associations as well as notations about the placement and movement of his hands and fingers. On many random occasions, the patient's analytic sessions were tape recorded and the tapes transcribed and then erased. The analyst's notations of the patient's hand movements were then edited into the verbatim transcripts.

About 6 years after the termination of the patient's analysis, these progress notes were systematically studied in an investigation of the temporal relationship between hand–mouth activity and the content of associations. The data obtained in the psychoanalytic situation were analyzed in several different ways.

In the clinical review, as part of Method 1, the analyst reviewed handwritten notes or verbatim transcripts (including hand movement observations) and impressionistically summarized the content and flow of free associations. The summaries appeared to indicate the nature of the patient's transference to the analyst at the time. To illustrate this procedure, I present a random selection of summaries of the hand movements and free associations produced by this patient during a segment of the middle phase of his analysis. A clear-cut relationship between hand movements and nonsexual and sexual child–mother associations occurred when the patient's hands were at his sides and away from the face and "snout" area. Nevertheless, an elusive patterning of associational content and hand location did become apparent that defied simple formulation and easy consensus among the different psychiatrists who examined these chronological sequences. My own attempt to synthesize these hand movement–verbal content relationships is reflected by these hypotheses:

1. The analysand touches a part of his anatomy related to a psychological or biological function he is experiencing and describing.
2. The relationship of the hand activity and position to the content of thought may be concrete or highly symbolic.
3. Immediately before, during, or after hand movements near or at his mouth, the patient's thoughts concern a longing for the breast or for the whole body, or to be part of a woman, in a sexual or nonsexual context. These associations tend to be affectionate or positive rather than negative.
4. Hand movements away from the mouth area or static hand positions away from this area (e.g., hands at sides) are more often associated with the expression of negative affects toward people.
5. More specifically, touching the lips and mouth is often related to talking about women and intimacy and gastrointestinal function. The latter more often occurs when a finger is inserted into the mouth.
6. Touching the eyelids is often related to talking about seeing or understanding.
7. Touching the nose is associated with sexual interest in forbidden women or discussing diarrhea after his mother-in-law's leaving his home.

Method 2: Scoring Systems for Verification of Hypotheses

Transcripts of 14 psychoanalytic sessions, tape recorded over a 1-year period, were divided into the smallest possible communication units (grammatical clauses). (Notations of hand movements were not included in the typescripts.) Two content analysis technicians independently scored each clause according to an object relations scale (Gottschalk, 1974) for references to females, males, sexually unspecified humans, and inanimate objects, and for valence: positive, neutral, and negative feelings toward any objects. Differences in classification by the two technicians were subsequently resolved by review and consensus. Each clause was then scored for the accompanying hand position: hand touching mouth or lips (1), hands on face but not touching lips (2), and hands away from face (3). Eight hundred thirty-six statements were scored along the three dimensions: object relations, valence, and hand position during utterance.

Results

There was no reason to expect the statements to be equally distributed among the categories within any dimension, and, in fact, they were not. In the object relations classification, 53% of the statements were about males, 20% were about females, 16% were about humans and unspecified sex, and 11% were about inanimate objects. This finding, by the way, is consistent with those of an earlier study by Gottschalk and Gleser (1969), which indicated that in general males make many more references to males (excluding all self-references) and females make many more references to females. In the valence classification, 49% of the statements were neutral, 35% were negative, and 16% were positive. In the hand position classification, 49% of the statements were made during Position 2, 34% during Position 1, and 17% during Position 3.

More important than the question of how the statements were distributed among the dimensions was the question of interaction between one dimension and another. For example, does the proportion of statements referring to different objects vary from one hand position to another? Does the proportion of statements of different valence vary with hand position? Figure 1 presents the findings relevant to these questions.

The proportion of female responses decreased as one went from Hand Position 1 to Hand Position 2, and Hand Position 3 was accompanied by fewer positive and more neutral responses than were Hand Positions 2 and 1.

There was a significant relationship in this patient between the position of the hand and the kind of object he was likely to mention, $\chi^2 = 15.28$, $df = 6$, $p < .02$. The proportion of female references made during Hand Position 1 was significantly greater than the proportion made during Positions 2 and 3, $\chi^2 = 8.95$, $df = 1$, $p < .01$ (Castellan, 1965). The number of female references made during Hand Position 2 was larger than the number made during Hand Position 3, χ^2 of 2.67, $df = 1$, but the difference was not significant ($p < .10$).

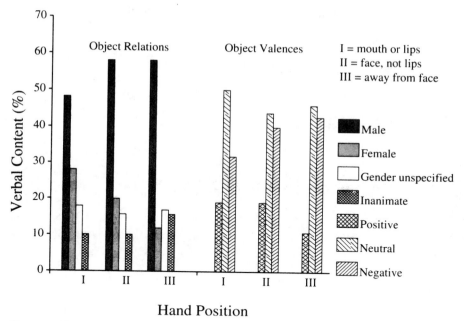

Figure 1. The association of hand position in relation to the mouth, lips, and face with talking about people with different valences.

A similar statistical analysis on the relationship between hand position and valence revealed a significant association, $\chi^2 = 9.84$, $df = 4$, $p < .05$. The ratio of neutral statements to positive statements during Hand Position 3 was 5.19, whereas the comparable ratio during Hand Positions 1 and 2 combined was 2.82, a statistically significant difference, $\chi^2 = 4.58$, $df = 1$, $p < .05$.

Another way to examine the data would be to determine whether there would be a consistent tendency over the 14 sessions for a particular object reference or valence to be associated with a particular hand position. Unfortunately, not all hand positions occurred in every session; therefore, sessions that lacked a particular hand position could not be included in some analyses, thus weakening the statistical evaluation. Nevertheless, some trends were noted. In 9 of 11 sessions, the proportion of negative statements was higher during Hand Position 2 than during Hand Position 1 (sign test, $p < .01$). In 8 of 8 sessions, the proportion of negative statements was higher during Hand Position 3 than during Hand Position 1 ($p < .01$). In 7 of 8 sessions, the proportion of female references was higher during Hand Position 1 than during Hand Position 3 ($p < .05$). In 10 of 11 sessions, the proportion of references to females or positive references to all objects was higher during Hand Position 1 than during Hand Position

2 ($p < .01$). In 6 of 8 sessions, the proportion of such references was higher during Hand Position 1 than during Hand Position 3 ($p < .05$).

Another finding, not related to hand position, was of an interaction between object references and valence, $\chi^2 = 42.60$, $df = 6$, $p < .001$: Female references were more likely to be positive than were nonfemale references, $\chi^2 = 24.71$, $df = 1$, $p < .001$, and male references were more likely to be positive than inanimate or other sex-unspecified references, $\chi^2 = 5.81$, $df = 1$, $p < .02$.

SUMMARY AND CONCLUSIONS

The opportunity to make refined observations provided by the psychoanalytic situation allows insights into the associations of touching body parts with the kinds of thought content and vice versa.

- The even more precise observations permitted by Method 2 helped with testing the clinically based hypotheses generated by Method 1. The more objective methods in Method 2 have supported some of the bases for my clinical impressions.
- In Mr. B, thoughts of women or of gratifying relationships with people regardless of gender were more often associated with hand placement on or near his mouth than with hand placement away from his face. Verbalizations of neutral or negative feelings toward others occurred less often when his hand was touching his lips than when it was not. In most instances, these findings reach a convincing level of statistical significance, raising the clinical impressionistic hypotheses to a greater level of certainty.
- The main points here are that the patient's "free associations" were not "free" and were not entirely revealed by his speech. Others, including Freud (1913/1958a, 1914/1958b, 1917/1963), have also pointed out how unfree free associations are. Reich's (1949) pioneer observations about character "armoring" and body activity as a façade for deeper covert motivations and conflicts are reconfirmed by this case study.
- The results of the current study illustrate how the developmental steps toward autonomy and self-sufficiency may be aided by body activity. The patient's touching his oral area with his fingers evoked memories and associations of a supportive type, of females, and of good objects, affects, and ideation. It is not sufficient to dismiss these as autoerotic or masturbatory equivalents and thus to imply that they are

pathological remnants or signs of an unresolved narcissism or mother fixation. Fleeting, nonfeeding hand–mouth or hand–face movements typify every human being, regardless of how well subliminated his or her drives are (Adatto, 1957, 1970). An appropriate and valuable function is provided by this analysand's sampling his environment with the positive perspectives (references to females or positive reference to all others) evoked when his hand was in the oral area and the negative perspectives aroused when his hands were at his side.

- The analysis of this patient brings out the adaptive function of hand–mouth actions, illustrating how they lay a groundwork for the maintenance of self-sufficiency and autonomy. The potency of oral stimulation in enhancing a person's integrative capacity to deal with the frustrations of everyday life was supported. Other studies (Gottschalk & Uliana, 1979a, 1979b) also have demonstrated relations of lip caressing with hope, oral references, shame, and hostility.

REFERENCES

Adatto, C. P. (1957). On pouting. *Journal of the American Psychoanalytical Association*, 5, 245–249.

Adatto, C. P. (1970). Snout-hand behavior in an adult patient. *Journal of American Psychoanalytical Association*, 18, 823–830.

Castellan, M. J., Jr. (1965). On the partitioning of contingency tables. *Psychological Bulletin*, 64, 330–338.

Ferenczi, S. (1950). On transitory symptom-constructions during the analysis. In S. Ferenczi (Ed.), *Sex in psychoanalysis* (pp. 164–180). New York: Dover. (Original work published 1912)

Freud, S. (1958a). On beginning the treatment (further recommendations of technique of psychoanalysis I). In J. Strachey (Ed. and Trans.), *The standard edition of the complete psychological works of Sigmund Freud* (Vol. 12, pp. 123–144). London: Hogarth Press. (Original work published 1913)

Freud, S. (1958b). Remembering, repeating and working through (further recommendations on the technique of psychoanalysis II). In J. Strachey (Ed. and Trans.), *The standard edition of the complete psychological works of Sigmund Freud* (Vol. 12, pp. 147–156). London: Hogarth Press. (Original work published 1914)

Freud, S. (1963). Introductory lectures on psychoanalysis: III. Resistance and repression. In J. Strachey (Ed. and Trans.), *The standard edition of the complete psychological works of Sigmund Freud* (Vol. 16, pp. 286–302). London: Hogarth Press. (Original work published 1917)

Gottschalk, L. A. (1955). Psychologic conflict and electroencephalographic patterns: Some notes on the problem with psychologic conflicts. *American Medical Association Archives of Neurological Psychiatry, 73,* 656–662.

Gottschalk, L. A. (1956). The relationship of psychological state and epileptic activity: Psychoanalytic observations on epileptic child. *Psychoanalytic Study of the Child, 11,* 352–380.

Gottschalk, L. A. (1974). The psychoanalytic study of hand-mouth appropriations. *Psychoanalytic and Contemporary Science, 3,* 269–291.

Gottschalk, L. A., & Gleser, G. C. (1969). *The measurement of psychological states through the content analysis of verbal behavior.* Berkeley: University of California Press.

Gottschalk, L. A., & Uliana, R. L. (1979a). A study of the relationship of nonverbal to verbal behavior: Effect of lip caressing on hope and oral references as expressed in the content of speech. In L. A. Gottschalk (Ed.), *The content analysis of verbal behavior: Further studies* (pp. 773–792). Jamaica, NY: Spectrum.

Gottschalk, L. A., & Uliana, R. L. (1979b). A study of the relationship of nonverbal to verbal behavior: Effect of lip caressing on shame, hostility, and other variables as expressed in the content of speech. In L. A. Gottschalk (Ed.), *The content analysis of verbal behavior: Further studies* (pp. 793–810). Jamaica, NY: Spectrum.

Haggard, E. A., & Isaacs, K. S. (1966). Micromomentary facial expression as indicators of ego mechanisms in psychotherapy. In L. A. Gottschalk & A. H. Auerbach (Eds.), *Methods of research in psychotherapy* (pp. 154–165). New York: Appleton-Century-Crofts.

Luborsky, L. (1970). New directions in research on neurotic and psychosomatic symptoms. *American Scientist, 58,* 661–668.

Luborsky, L., Docherty, J., Todd, T., Knapp, P., Mirsky, A., & Gottschalk, L. (1975). A context analysis of psychological states prior to petit-mal seizures. *Journal of Nervous and Mental Disease, 160,* 282–298.

Reich, W. (1949). *Character analysis* (3rd ed.). New York: Orgone Institute Press.

Scheflen, A. E. (1964). The significance of posture in communication systems. *Psychiatry, 27,* 316–331.

Scheflen, A. E. (1966). Natural history method in psychotherapy: Communicational research. In L. A. Gottschalk & A. H. Auerbach (Eds.), *Methods of research in psychotherapy* (pp. 263–289). New York: Appleton-Century-Crofts.

V

THERAPEUTIC USES, THEORIES, AND A NEW THEORY OF THE CONDITIONS FOR SYMPTOM FORMATION

15

A GUIDE TO THERAPEUTIC USES OF SYMPTOM-CONTEXT METHODS

LESTER LUBORSKY

As will be seen in this chapter, the labor of using the symptom-context method therapeutically can be richly repaid in the form of benefits to the patient.

HOW THE THERAPIST COMES TO UNDERSTAND THE PRESYMPTOM THEME

The popping up of a symptom in the midst of a psychotherapy session is a moment to be grabbed by the patient and therapist—the segment of the session that came just before the symptom emerges can reveal the most about preconditions for the symptom, as the studies in this book have shown. It is not enough just to notice the symptom's appearance; the symptom's context must be deciphered to decide how to deal with the symptom therapeutically. Deciphering it requires clinical skill, and this skill can most easily be drawn on when a series of presymptom contexts are available for review.

My main examples here are of deciphering the symptom's contexts and of their clinical use. These examples are of two kinds: the emergence of shifts to increased depression and the emergence of phobic anxiety.

These two offer a useful selection of examples because depression and anxiety are the most common of symptoms.

Example: Mr. Quinn's Symptom-Context Theme Before His Shifts in Depression

A good example of the benefits of the patient's (P's) and therapist's (T's) attunement to the symptom context was shown by Mr. Quinn, a patient who was vulnerable to precipitous shifts in depression (see chap. 5). He had begun in Session 144 to feel guilty and then reported a shift to increased depression after speaking of hating his father:

> T: What did you say right then that made you not feel good?

> P: It was something about my father. . . . I was fighting him. . . . I hated him. . . . [I felt] guilty about hating him.

The benefit from this patient–therapist exchange was set off by the therapist's inquiry about the patient's pre- and postsymptom states. It helped the patient to see the role of specific feelings in instigating his shift toward depression. It became clearer to the patient and therapist that the patient typically became more depressed when he compared himself with another man—he then felt guilty, inferior, inadequate, and then helpless. The exchange gave Mr. Quinn an experience in learning to attend to his predepression state, an experience that helped to develop his gradually greater capacity to cope with the preliminaries to depression.

One also can infer the other qualities related to helplessness and hopelessness: Lowered self-esteem and guilt were associated with this conflict and appeared to be involved in setting off Mr. Quinn's depression. Another ingredient in Freud's (1917/1963) earlier theories of depression also appeared to operate, but not as clearly—that is, the turning of his hostility inward in the form of guilt instead of outward in the form of anger.

Another good example of the benefits of the patient's and the therapist's attunement to the presymptom state can be found in the example that follows.

Example: Ms. Deborah Lewis's Symptom-Context Theme Before Increased Depression (From Luborsky, 1984, pp. 96–97)

For the first 10 min of the session, Ms. Lewis spoke with enthusiasm about her involvement in many different activities, such as being involved in a research study. But then her mood began to shift to greater depression, she became less excited, and her speech began to slow.

T: What's happening?

P: I began to be depressed when I sensed you were losing interest and I was therefore isolated and could do nothing about it.

T: At first you had felt I *was* interested.

P: Yes, but then you began to lose interest. That's what people tend to do. Like when I told the class about the research of a woman who treated diabetes. Now a man has come along as though he were the first to make a contribution and has shown the same effect with animals.

T: So you caught your whole sequence of thoughts beginning with a good feeling and then noting that when you saw me as being less interested, you began to feel depressed and alone.

P: Yes, I began to feel like a cloud was on my brain. I think of it physically. I've discovered that the way to pull out of it is to become active--and that does work.

She then began to speak again, talking avidly about the history of the cure of diabetes.

During the just-retold exchange in the example, the therapist had commented on the patient's shift from spontaneity and enthusiasm to boredom and depression; depression was one of her main initial symptoms. She recognized that she had gone through a mood shift. The mood shift gradually became understood in terms of her central relationship problem: her fear of showing her spontaneity and fear of being thought to be dull. This fear was not only experienced with the therapist, but she also was afraid of showing her thoughts and feelings to her boyfriend, and earlier she had been similarly afraid with her parents. It was the central frustration she experienced during her growing up: She felt that what she wanted was unimportant compared with pleasing her parents by being quiet and by not expressing what she wanted. If she persisted, she became afraid she would hurt them, especially her father, whom she saw as fragile and depressed. She then would retreat and become quiet.

The recommendation to therapists to attend to the symptom's context, as is illustrated by the examples, is consistent with the recommendation to attend to shifts in the patient's state of consciousness because such shifts in state tend to come before outbreaks of symptoms. The reward for attending to shifts in the patient's state comes from the observation that the workings of a psychological system tend to be more fully exposed to view during its shifts rather than during its stasis (see also the similar recommendation to attend to shifts in state in Horowitz, Marmar, & Wilner, 1979, and Horowitz, 1979).

Another example follows of a shift in symptom level starting outside of the session.

Example: Mr. John Alton's Increases and Decreases in His Phobia From Accounts About the Symptom Appearances Outside of the Session (From Chap. 6)

In this short-term (24-session) psychotherapy, a gradual improvement had been made in his phobia. There were decreases in anxiety and in phobic restriction. Yet in Session 17, the patient began by reporting an upsurge outside of the session in the restrictions from his phobia. He explained that he could not go on a trip with his wife and partner because of an upsurge in phobic behavior. He was highly conflicted about not being able to go and concerned that he was "using his symptom."

In essence, the beginning of this session was marked by a narrative about an obvious revival of the phobia that prevented his airplane travel. But the therapist recognized this and launched interventions to deal with the upsurge of the patient's conflictual pattern that involved the phobic symptoms.

A phobia, in contrast to the other kinds of symptoms presented in this book, often does not involve an increase in expression of the symptom directly in the session but an increase in accounts of the phobia outside the session. Chapter 6 therefore illustrates a modified form of the symptom-context method that takes into account this typical manner of presentation of such symptoms by a symptom-context analysis on these accounts.

MAKING INTERPRETATIONS OF THE SYMPTOM'S CONTEXT

Three recommendations on techniques are needed here because they can be of tremendous help to the patient; especially the first and third are insufficiently dealt with in almost all treatment guides.

1. *Find ways to interpret the main symptom-context theme and still maintain the alliance.* Therapists often shy away from interpretation in favor of staying just safely supportive. This fact about a common therapeutic style is not generally recognized. Cautious reticence appears to come from the concern of many therapists that to be interpretative runs the risk of interfering with the supportive relationship and biasing the patient's self-observations. Although it is often true that there is increased resistance in response to interpretations, negative responses to interpretations can usually be avoided or reduced. Interpretations, when given properly in timing and wording, have a positive effect on the alliance. This positive effect can be heightened by the manner of conveying the interpretation so

that it facilitates the alliance. Several principles of style of interpretation illustrated by Wachtel (1994) serve to reduce defensiveness and lead to positive responses. As an example, Mr. Quinn's therapist managed to get across nonconfrontationally the meaning of the patient's shift toward increased depression by a joint examination with the patient of what the patient experienced. The therapist launched this benefit by his question, "What did you say right then that made you feel not good?"

2. *Find ways to work through the main symptom-context theme.* The main symptom-context theme of each patient needs to be worked through to achieve a good outcome of psychotherapy. Early in the symptom-context research, as was noted in the last paragraph of chapter 3 on momentary forgetting, this technical principle was suggested: An individually specific recurrent theme preceding a symptom that appears during the treatment sessions may be crucial to work through to ensure a good outcome.

This principle was obviously operative in each of the symptom-context studies, as these examples show.

- For the momentary-forgetting patient, her main symptom-context of expectation of painful rejection clearly was not worked through and the patient's treatment ended with only minimal benefits.
- For the patient with depressive mood shifts, his main theme of inadequacy in competition with other men was worked through and the treatment ended with moderate benefits.
- For the phobia patient, there was considerable working through of the main symptom-context theme of an inability to directly express an independent view to a person on whom he depended. Therefore, the patient's brief treatment was a resounding success in terms of overcoming his phobia.
- For the patient with the stomach ulcer pains, the same principle was true. His main theme of helpless concern about getting "supplies" from others was much improved and the outcome of the treatment was good.
- The principle applies to the patient with migraine headaches for whom the symptom-context theme of a hopeless state about getting continued interest and attention from a man was not sufficiently worked through and the benefits of the treatment were therefore limited.

The crucial issue in each case example in the working through of the symptom-context theme was not just change in the content of the Core Conflictual Relationship Theme's (CCRT) main theme by the end of the treatment, but changes in the level of mastery of the content of the CCRT's main theme. A single interpretation is rarely enough. The therapist must continue to follow through with recurrent interpretations that address the same and related facets of the main theme. These interpretations do not become boringly repetitious; instead, they can set up and keep moving an exciting process of the patient's learning to master the conflicts that are associated with the symptoms. Supporting this conclusion was the result of a study that reported a significant correlation for mastery of the main theme with the outcomes of psychotherapy (Grenyer & Luborsky, in press).

There is much evidence for the principle of technique that requires a focus on working through the qualities of the symptom context that are most central and significant for each patient. As shown in this book (a) there is considerable evidence of a main symptom-context theme for each patient. (b) There is further evidence that the symptom-context theme has parallels with the CCRT (as summarized in chap. 17). (c) There is even evidence that therapists who maintain a focus on interpretations that are a part of each patient's central relationship pattern, as measured by the CCRT, provide their patients with greater benefits (Crits-Christoph, Cooper, & Luborsky, 1988).[1] Similar research findings from the Mt. Zion psychotherapy research group (Silberschatz & Curtis, 1993) show that therapists who focus on interpretations that are consistent with the patient's goals for therapy and that disconfirm the patient's pathogenic beliefs will show signs of improvement that contribute to the patient's benefits in terms of positive outcomes from the treatment.

---

[1]There is evidence that it is helpful to the patient to keep to interpretations that are congruent with the patient's central relationship conflicts, but comparative treatment studies for phobias imply that much different kinds of treatments with different interpretations can be effective. A stimulating question on this topic came from a student at the University of Barcelona, where I gave a talk in 1993 on the treatment of Mr. Alton's phobia. The question was, How can we be sure that the main interpretation given to Mr. Alton was the responsible therapeutic agent for his cure? The question is provocative because of the likelihood that other therapies probably could have benefited this patient. The suggestion was even made, to further this discussion (by Emilio Gutierrez of the University of Santiago de Compostela), that the treatment that the patient needed was training in communication skills. Presumably, the training would teach him how to be able to tell others when he needed to disagree with them and to counter their control of him. My reply to these questions was that probably other treatments could have benefited this patient but that there was a special appropriateness of the form of treatment described in the example for Mr. Alton. There was, in fact, a congruence between the interpretations and the central relationship conflicts of this patient. Also, this patient would be an unwilling student for learning communication skills because he had strong feelings of guilt about presenting to someone to whom he was close an opposing view that would cause the other person to be upset. That issue would be, and was, appropriate for him to work through in psychotherapy.

3. *Find ways to examine the parallel of the symptom-context theme and the CCRT.* The symptom-context theme, as might be expected, turns out to be much like another broad theme, the CCRT. The correspondence with the CCRT is most clear in the interpersonal pattern part of the symptom-context theme. The correspondence can be seen in the example from Mr. Quinn, based on Session 144 (see chap. 5), and it also can be seen with almost any of the sessions of this patient. In this session, there were six relationship episodes: with his first girlfriend, with his second girlfriend, with his therapist, with his first girlfriend, with a teacher, and with his father. As is usually found, the main themes across the relationship episodes are highly redundant, so that a clinician listening to the session as it progressed could easily identify in the episodes the three components that make up the CCRT: what the patient wanted from the other person, how the other person responded, and how the patient responded. The method of extracting the CCRT from a session is easily understandable as depicted in Table 1 (and even more precisely in Luborsky, in press-a, in press-b). Table 1 briefly lists each relationship episode in the session, with the three components for each episode: the wishes, responses from others, and responses of self. The CCRT is always defined as the most pervasive of each type of component across the relationship episodes. The brief version of the CCRT in this session is: "I wish to relate to others without self-blame; the other puts me down; I blame myself."

The target symptom of increased depression appeared as part of the symptom-context theme, and the responses of self in the CCRT were much like the symptom contexts' significant variables (see Table 2).

Why should there be a parallel between the symptom-context theme and the CCRT? In large part, the answer emerges in chapters 16 and 17 on the symptom-context theories of the variables that precipitate symptoms: One prominent part of the explanation is the heating up of the CCRT during the presymptom state, which, together with the other conditions, erupts into symptom formation.

CONCLUSIONS ON THE SYMPTOM-CONTEXT METHOD IN CLINICAL PRACTICE

- The patterns of relationships and the conflicts within them can be inferred from the context in which a symptom appears in the session.

TABLE 1
Mr. Quinn's (Session 144) REs and CCRT Scores for Each Episode

Other person completeness rating (1–5)	Summary RE	Wish	Response from Other (RO)	Response of Self (RS)
Girlfriend 1 (2)	I went to visit a girlfriend. I wasn't relating. I could look her in the eye only because I had three beers.	W1: To relate without self-blame W2: To feel adequate		RS1: Self-blame for not relating
Girlfriend 2 (2)	I walked home with J (Girlfriend 2). That's just another woman I can't—I don't know how to respond to. I can't do right.	W1: To relate without self-blame W2: To feel adequate		RS1: I don't know how; I can't do right. Everything is so rotten. RS2: No sense in doing anything anymore (depressive mood)
Therapist (3)	Did you see that Strecker psychiatry book? An idiotic stupid book.	W1: To tear down Strecker's book W2: To relate to T as a peer W3: To put T down?	RO: Strecker said "people who are depressed once are likely to get it again," implying I have no hope.	RS1: anger at stupidity of Strecker.
Girlfriend 1 (2)	I am going out with that girl.	W1: I guess I could (would like to) lay her this weekend. W2: To feel superior to the girl		RS: Maybe it's wrong I should go there because I'm supposed to be bright. I feel at ease with nursing students (i.e., self-blame).
Teacher (2)	I have to go hear that goddam idiot, Dr. ——.	W1: To tear him down "he's not worth anything" W2: To relate without tearing him down		RS: "I don't know why I should be so intolerant of everybody, him included (self-blame for his anger).
Father (3)	Father was just nothing. He got mad at me once my freshman year I guess I was feeling my oats.	W1: To beat the shit out of father (and brother) W2: To feel his oats in relation to father	RO: From father "I can still put you on your ass"	RS1: At college you don't want to see your parents with the other guys (ashamed of father). RS2: Anger at father

Note. REs = relationship episodes; CCRT = Core Conflictual Relationship Theme; W1 = Wish 1; W2 = Wish 2; W3 = Wish 3.

TABLE 2
Comparison of the CCRT With the Symptom-Context (S-C) Theme

Mr. Quinn's CCRT	Mr. Quinn's S-C theme
W1: To relate to others without self-blame	
W2: To feel he is adequate	
W3: To put the other person down	
RO: Puts him down	
RS1: To blame himself	1. Guilt[a]
RS2: To feel inadequate	2. Loss of self-esteem
RS3: To feel shame	3. Hostility toward self
RS4: To feel hopeless and de-pressed	4. Hopelessness
RS5: To be angry with others	

Note. CCRT = Core Conflictual Relationship Theme; W = Wish; RO = Response from Other; RS = Response of Self.
[a]Ranks of variables based on significance of differences of ratings between increased versus decreased depression segments (see chap. 5).

- The therapist's recognition of the ups and downs of the patient's symptoms and their contexts can lead to powerfully effective interpretations, as in Mr. Alton's Session 17 (described earlier).
- Although in this book most of the examples are of symptoms that suddenly emerge in the session, in everyday clinical practice symptoms more often gradually increase and decline. Yet the same principles still apply. Both the sudden occurrence of a recurrent symptom and the gradual buildup of the symptom are fair game for special attention by the therapist, and the symptom-context method can be helpful with both.

REFERENCES

Crits-Christoph, P., Cooper, A., & Luborsky, L. (1988). The accuracy of therapists' interpretations and the outcome of dynamic psychotherapy. *Journal of Consulting and Clinical Psychology, 56,* 490–495.

Freud, S. (1963). Transference. In J. Strachey (Ed. and Trans.), *The standard edition of the complete psychological works of Sigmund Freud* (Vol. 16, pp. 431–447). London: Hogarth Press. (Original work published 1917)

Grenyer, B., & Luborsky, L. (in press). Mastery of transference-related conflicts as an outcome of psychotherapy. *Journal of Consulting and Clinical Psychology.*

Horowitz, M. J. (1979). *States of mind: Analysis of change in psychotherapy.* New York: Plenum.

Horowitz, M. J., Marmar, C., & Wilner, N. (1979). Analysis of patients states and state transitions. *Journal of Nervous and Mental Disease, 167,* 91–99.

Luborsky, L. (1984). *Principles of psychoanalytic psychotherapy: A manual for supportive-expressive (SE) treatment.* New York: Basic Books.

Luborsky, L. (in press-a). Core Conflictual Relationship Theme (CCRT): A basic case formulation method. In T. Eells (Ed.), *Handbook of psychotherapy case formulation.* New York: Guilford Press.

Luborsky, L. (in press-b). A guide to the CCRT method. In L. Luborsky & P. Crits-Christoph (Eds.), *The CCRT method for understanding transference* (Rev. ed.). Washington, DC: American Psychological Association.

Silberschatz, G., & Curtis, J. T. (1993). Measuring the therapist's impact on the patient's therapeutic progress. *Journal of Consulting and Clinical Psychology, 61,* 403–411.

Wachtel, P. (1994). *Therapeutic communication: Principles and effective practice.* New York: Guilford Press.

16

CLASSICAL THEORIES OF SYMPTOM FORMATION: FREUD, ENGEL AND SCHMALE, GOLDSTEIN, ANGYAL, AND SELIGMAN

LESTER LUBORSKY and GERALD ARONSON

Five classical theories of symptom formation are summarized in this chapter. To make the essence of each theory stand out, each one is shaped into a diagram of the main steps of the theory leading to a symptom. Freud's (1926/1959) theories of symptom formation are most fully reviewed because his theories have had the greatest influence in stimulating the symptom-context studies. In the final chapter these five theories are compared with the theory that emerges from the symptom-context studies.

Other theories of symptom formation abound, but the five selected ones give a fair sample of the theories. Among the general theories of symptom formation not included were those of Arlow (1969), Brenner (1973), and Rangell (1959, 1990). There also are some specific disorders with empirically based theories that have not been adequately covered, for example Grace and Graham (1952), Mirsky (1958) and Weiner, Thaler, Reiser, and Mirsky (1957).

FREUD'S THEORY OF SYMPTOM FORMATION

One of Freud's (1926/1959) central hypotheses about symptom formation is that a neurotic symptom is part of an attempted solution to a situation that is evaluated to be so dangerous that the person feels helpless. The danger typically emanates from the person's own impulses. For example, each time Ms. Apfel (see chap. 3) suffered a momentary forgetting, it was preceded by associations that caused her to recall a situation she evaluated as being too dangerous to cope with, a situation involving her wish to avoid rejection. Our method should tell us whether, as specified in Freud's hypotheses, the patient's language in treatment would regularly reveal specific verbal contents corresponding to such latent meanings of the symptom such as "I'm in danger and helpless to cope." The method also should show whether these specific contents appear more frequently before a symptom than at other times and whether different kinds of psychological symptoms are similar in their psychological preconditions.

Propositions in Freud's Theory of Symptom Formation and the Definition of a Symptom

Among the psychological symptoms we examined were momentary forgetting, sudden shifts in depression, and phobic behavior; among the somatic symptoms examined were stomach ulcer pains, migraine headaches, absence epilepsy episodes, electroencephalographic paroxysmal states (petit mal), and premature ventricular contractions of the heart. What is common among these diverse symptoms? The most general definition of a symptom—an impairment of a usual function (Freud, 1905/1953)—encompasses enough to include them all. Do they have any of the other characteristics of symptoms as postulated by Freud (1926/1959)? Do they substitute for psychological conflicts? I attempt to answer these questions.

Most of what Freud wrote on the topic of the nature of psychological symptoms is contained in his studies on hysteria (Freud, 1905/1953) and in "Inhibitions, Symptoms, and Anxiety" (Freud, 1926/1959). He used the term *symptom* in a general sense, as almost equal to a dysfunction. A dysfunction can be an inhibition, a disturbance, or an alteration of function:

> A symptom . . . actually denotes the presence of some pathological process. Linguistic usage, then, employs the word inhibition when there is a simple lowering of function, and symptom when a function has undergone some unusual change or when a new phenomenon has arisen out of it. (Freud, 1926/1959, p. 87)

As examples of symptoms, Freud (1926/1959) listed disturbances in sexual function, nutritional function, motor function, and work functioning. However, in this work, Freud (1926/1959) was thinking of symptoms that take the form of phobias, conversion hysteria, and obsessional neuroses. As in most of his work, Freud did not consider the types of symptoms that have in recent decades come to be called *psychosomatic symptoms*.

For Freud, anxiety was an important aspect of symptom formation, and he offered an account of the role of physical sensations in anxiety: "We notice that anxiety is accompanied by fairly definite physical sensations which can be referred to particular organs of the body. . . . The clearest and most frequent ones are those connected with the respiratory organs and with the heart" (Freud, 1926/1959, p. 132).

Freud (1926/1959) then defined the terms *inhibition* and *symptom* more completely. Inhibitions "are restrictions of the functions of the ego which have been either imposed as a measure of precaution or brought about as a result of an impoverishment of energy" (Freud, 1926/1959, p. 90). By contrast, a symptom cannot be described as a process taking place within the ego.

Both the concepts of anxiety and of the danger situation are involved in the generation of symptoms:

> Symptoms are created in order to remove the ego from a situation of danger. If the symptoms are prevented from being formed, the danger does, in fact, materialize; that is, a situation analogous to birth is established in which the ego is helpless in the face of a constantly increasing instinctual demand—the earliest and original determinant of anxiety. Thus, in our view, the relation between anxiety and symptom is less close than was supposed for we have inserted the factor of the danger situation between them. (Freud, 1926/1959, p. 144)

Anxiety may not appear along with the symptom after its development, but it is involved in the formation of symptoms (Freud, 1926/1959).

In his Addendum, Freud (1926/1959) continued to develop this last line of thinking by adding the concept of helplessness:

> A danger situation . . . consists in the subject's estimation of his own strength compared to the magnitude of the danger and in his admission of helplessness in the face of it—physical helplessness if the danger is real and physical helplessness if it is instinctual. . . . Let us call a situation of helplessness of this kind that has been actually experienced, a traumatic situation. . . .
>
> It is in this situation that the signal of anxiety is given. The signal announces: "I am expecting a situation of helplessness to set in" or: "The present situation reminds me of one of the traumatic experiences I have had before. Therefore, I will anticipate the trauma and behave as though it had already come, while there is yet time to turn it aside."

Anxiety is therefore on the one hand an expectation of a trauma, and on the other, a repetition of it in a mitigated form. . . .

Taking this sequence, anxiety-danger-helplessness (trauma), we can now summarize what has been said: A danger situation is a recognized, remembered, expected situation of helplessness. Anxiety is the original reaction to helplessness in the trauma and is reproduced later on in the danger situation as a signal for help. (Freud, 1926/1959, pp. 166–167)

Summary of Freud's propositions about symptom formation in terms of states: For Freud (1926/1959), the danger was the recognition of an expected situation of helplessness. Anxiety is the original reaction to helplessness. The symptom appears as one way to cope with the helplessness. It is both an expression of the helplessness and a way of coping with it. Freud's theory can be diagrammed (as in Figure 1) in terms of a sequence of somewhat separable states. Although Freud did not refer to these as *states*, I do so because the idea of a state appears to fit what he described.

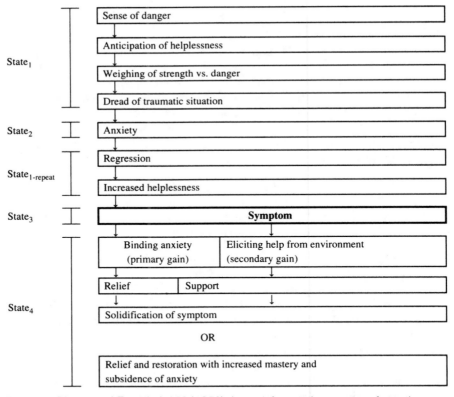

Figure 1. Diagram of Freud's (1926/1959) theory of neurotic symptom formation. (The state labels refer to the presentation in the chapter in terms of states.)

The essence of each state is formulated as a proposition to be tested by the symptom-context research.

State 1 (and State$_1$-Repeat)

Proposition: Evaluation of the situation as containing a danger situation. It "consists in the subject's estimation of his own strength compared to the magnitude of the danger and in his admission of helplessness in the face of it—physical helplessness if the danger is real and psychical helplessness if it is instinctual" (Freud, 1926/1959, p. 166). The process of estimating strength versus danger is partly conscious and partly unconscious. Typical danger situations include birth, loss of the mother, loss of the penis, loss of the love object, and superego criticism.

Proposition: It is the anticipation of psychical helplessness (especially to instinctual dangers) that is involved in symptom formation. Note that in the sequence shown in Figure 1, there are two phases of helplessness: in "State$_1$" where helplessness is anticipated and in "State$_1$-Repeat" where helplessness increases.

State 2

Proposition: Some anxiety may be present before a symptom appears. The amount of anxiety may be small because it is "signal anxiety," an amount just sufficient to announce that a danger situation is about to appear. State 2 is implied in the following quote, in which some anxiety appears:

> It is in this [danger] situation that the signal of anxiety is given. The signal announces: "I am expecting a situation of helplessness to set in," or: "The present situation reminds me of one of the traumatic experiences I have had before. Therefore I will . . . behave as though it had already come, while there is yet time to turn it aside." Anxiety is . . . an expectation of a trauma and . . . a repetition of it in a mitigated form. . . . Anxiety is the original reaction to helplessness in the trauma and reproduced later on in a danger situation as a signal for help. (Freud, 1926/1959, p. 166)

State 3

Proposition: Neurotic symptoms may appear as a way to deal with the helplessness and potential (signal) anxiety or actual anxiety generated by danger situations. The neurotic symptoms may represent a "substitute formation." The conditional "may" is important: Many other outcomes to states of helplessness and anxiety are usual, for example, the danger situation subsides, the person ultimately evaluates his or her strength as adequate, or a variety of defensive behaviors may appear to protect the person.

Therefore, a "one-way direction" for predicting symptom occurrence is usual: Whenever symptoms have appeared, the helplessness will frequently have appeared before it; but whenever helplessness has appeared, symptoms will only occasionally follow it.

State 4

Proposition: After the symptom appears, the degree of helplessness and of anxiety tends to lessen. This proposition is clearly implied by Freud's (1926/1959) theory of symptom formation. As shown in Figure 1, the symptom has two effects: It binds anxiety (which is a primary gain), and it attracts help from the environment (which is a secondary gain). The binding of anxiety affords relief; the getting of help from the environment affords support. Once the symptom appears, there is a double possibility: There can be a solidification of the symptom or there can be relief and restoration with increased mastery and a decrease of anxiety.

ENGEL AND SCHMALE'S THEORY OF SYMPTOM FORMATION

The theory of symptom formation developed by Engel and his associates (Engel & Schmale, 1967; Schmale, 1972) is similar to Freud's but gives more attention to the inclusion of somatic symptoms. In Engel and Schmale's theory (see Figure 2), the core of the ego state that gives rise to both somatic and neurotic symptoms is termed the *giving up–given up complex*. This "complex" is a nonspecific presymptom state with helplessness and hopelessness as its corresponding affects, together with some related qualities, including lessened control; lessened security; a lessened sense of ability to rely on one's perceptions of the environment and of past experience; some loss of a sense of continuity between past and future; and a revival of feelings, memories, and behavior connected with similar past experiences.

There is no direct relation between the existence of the "complex" and the development of a somatic disorder. Outstanding among other necessary conditions are biological dispositions, about which more should be known.

The only one of these theories in which a distinction is made between helplessness and hopelessness is that of Engel and Schmale (1967). As the reader has seen in the symptom-context studies and will see summarized in chapter 17, that distinction turned out to be a useful one because both hopelessness and helplessness were associated with the development of symptoms, with hopelessness even more so than helplessness. Next to, or

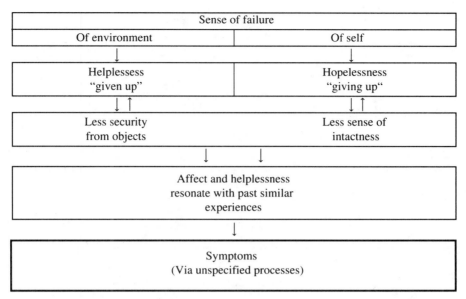

Figure 2. Diagram of Engel and Schmale's (1967) theory of neurotic and somatic symptom formation.

alongside of Freud's, Engel and Schmale's studies, with their focus on the disease onset situation, have benefited the symptom-context studies.

GOLDSTEIN'S THEORY OF SYMPTOM FORMATION

Goldstein (1939) distinguished between (a) a situation of which the person is afraid and (b) the even more frightening possibility of experiencing a catastrophic breakdown that is based on feeling absolutely worthless and absolute rejection (see Figure 3). The expectation of catastrophic breakdown and the fear of it involves not so much a fear of a specific threat as a fear of a threat to the integrity of the personality.

Goldstein (1939) made a distinction between substitute reactions and catastrophic reactions. Substitute reactions are organized and serve the purpose of solving a problem. By contrast, catastrophic behavior is "inadequate, disorderly, inconsistent, inconstant, and embedded in physical and mental shock" (Goldstein, 1939, p. 37). Substitute reactions attempt to avoid catastrophic situations that would result in breakdown and disorganization.

In summary, people attempt to actualize their being to act in the world in an ordered manner. When this ordered functioning is threatened (by defeat, inadequacy, etc.), a catastrophic reaction impends, producing

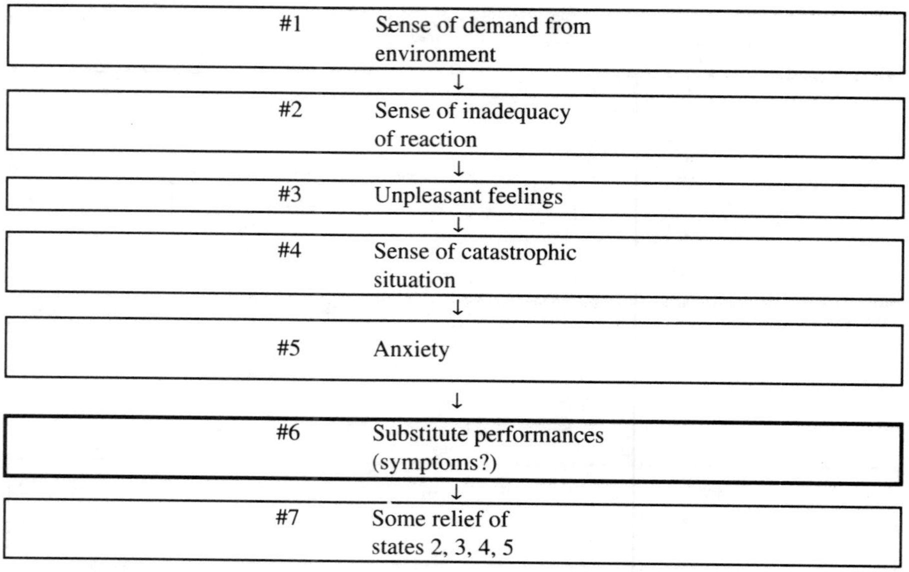

#1	Sense of demand from environment

↓

#2	Sense of inadequacy of reaction

↓

#3	Unpleasant feelings

↓

#4	Sense of catastrophic situation

↓

#5	Anxiety

↓

#6	Substitute performances (symptoms?)

↓

#7	Some relief of states 2, 3, 4, 5

Figure 3. Diagram of Goldstein's (1939) theory of symptom formation.

anxiety, which is defended against and/or prevented by substitute perform-ances, that is, by symptoms.

The theory is presented in more detail through two quotes from Gold-stein (1939), which explain more of his concepts of substitute reactions and catastrophic reactions, as well as the central role of anxiety:

> Substitute performances enable the organism to come to terms with the environment. . . . When we tried to force [the patient] into a situation he had identified as catastrophic, he deliberately seeks to escape through some other performance—a "substitute performance." . . . He will be less disturbed by [the substitute performance] than if he were compelled to yield to demands of the situation with which he is actually confronted. (p. 41)

> Serious catastrophic reactions are subjectively experienced as shock or as anxiety. Thus we see that the phenomena of anxiety occupies an important place in the whole process of coming to terms of the organism with the world. (p. 286)

ANGYAL'S THEORY OF SYMPTOM FORMATION

Angyal (1965) presented what was once a well-known theory about symptom formation; however, he did not refer to symptoms, not even in his index. He referred instead to the healthy organization and the neurotic one within each person. In his theory (see Figure 4) the threat of depri-

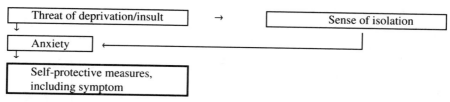

Figure 4. Diagram of Angyal's (1965) theory of symptom formation.

vation and insult leads to a sense of isolation, which leads to anxiety, which in turn leads to self-protective measures, including symptoms.

These two quotes from Angyal (1965) offer more of the flavor of this theory and the role of the concepts of the threat of dissolution, anxiety, and isolation:

> Anxiety arises not only out of the state of isolation but also out of anticipating such a state. Consequently anxiety will appear whenever the dominant organization is threatened with dissolution. (p. 116)

> Anxiety signals the existence of a threat . . . and leads to the enhancement of self-protective measure. . . . It serves indiscriminately as a safeguard of the status quo. (p. 116)

SELIGMAN'S LEARNED HELPLESSNESS AND EXPLANATORY STYLE THEORY OF DEPRESSION

Seligman's (1975) theory states that when a person experiences a negative event and explains it by pessimistic explanations, the person's vulnerability to symptom formation, especially to depression, is increased. The theory got its start from observations about learned helplessness (Seligman, 1975, 1990), a state that showed similarities to the state of depression. People or animals who developed learned helplessness showed passivity, cognitive deficits, diminished self-esteem, loss of aggression, loss of appetite, negative affect, and catecholamine changes. The experience with studies of learned helplessness led to the hypotheses that uncontrollable events set up an expectation that similar events in the future also will be uncontrollable. The expectation reflects learned helplessness.

A reformulation of the learned helplessness theory (see Figure 5) has added the concept of negative explanatory style (Abramson, Seligman, & Teasdale, 1978). A person's causal explanation of negative events determines the generality and chronicity of the helplessness and diminished self-esteem. Those who typically explain negative events as being caused by internal, global, and stable factors are more likely to suffer longer and more general symptoms of depression than people who explain negative events by a more optimistic explanatory style.

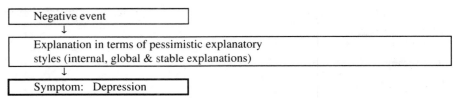

Figure 5. Diagram of Seligman's (1975) theory of learned helplessness and explanatory style in symptom formation (depression).

The predicted relationship was confirmed in a meta-analysis of 104 studies (Sweeney, Anderson, & Bailey, 1986). The clinically depressed samples showed an even stronger relationship between pessimistic explanatory style and depression (Sweeney et al., 1986). Further confirmation of the relationship comes from two studies reporting that pessimistic explanatory style at the end of successful therapy for depression predicted relapse or recurrence (Evans et al., 1992; Hollon et al., 1988); see also Seligman & Elder, 1985; Seligman & Nolen-Hoeksema, 1987; Buchanan & Seligman, 1995).

SUMMARY AND INTEGRATION OF THE MAIN FACTORS IN THE THEORIES

Each of the main theories of symptom formation—those of Freud (1926/1959), Engel and Schmale (1967), Goldstein (1939), Angyal (1965), and Seligman (1975)—are presented in terms of the main precipitants of symptoms in each theory. These precipitants are summarized and compared.

None of the theories of symptom formation presented are encompassing theories of symptom formation in the sense that each of the theories has particular symptoms in mind as the target of explanations. Freud (1926/1959) primarily tried to explain the antecedent conditions of phobias and to a lesser extent of obsessional neurosis. Engel and Schmale (1967) came the closest to offering a broad theory, and Angyal's was broad as well. Goldstein's (1939) theory was directed toward explaining the conditions for schizophrenia and other psychoses. Seligman's theory (1975) focused on the conditions leading to depression.

Despite these different foci, it is of interest to list the components of each theory and to compare them with each other and with the theory we extracted from the diverse symptoms in this book. We found considerable overlap in most of the theories. In most theories, helplessness, hopelessness, or both were important as preconditions, including those of Freud, Engel and Schmale, and, by implication, Goldstein, Angyal, and Seligman. Anxiety is a mediating affect in most of the theories, certainly in Freud and to some extent in Engel and Schmale with their "less security from objects"; anxiety is clear in Goldstein and in Angyal, but not in Seligman. Some of the theories specify a relief or restoration after the symptom is formed; this is true especially for Freud and Goldstein.

The final chapter shows how the components of the five theories overlap and do not overlap with the symptom-context theory's components that emerged from the symptoms analyzed in this book.

REFERENCES

Abramson, L. Y., Seligman, M. E. P., & Teasdale, J. D. (1978). Learned helplessness in humans: Critique and reformulation. *Journal of Abnormal Psychology, 87,* 49–74.

Angyal, A. (1965). Neurosis and treatment: A holistic theory. In E. Hanfman & R. M. Jones (Eds.), *Neurosis and treatment: A holistic theory.* New York: Wiley.

Arlow, J. (1969). Unconscious fantasy and disturbances of conscious experience. *Psychoanalytic Quarterly, 38,* 1–27.

Brenner, C. (1973). *An elementary textbook of psychoanalysis* (2nd ed.), Garden City, NY: Doubleday.

Buchanan, G. M., & Seligman, M. E. P. (Eds.). (1995). *Explanatory style.* Hillsdale, NJ: Erlbaum.

Engel, G., & Schmale, A. (1967). Psychoanalytic theory of somatic disorders: Conversion, specificity and the disease onset situation. *Journal of the American Psychoanalytic Association, 15,* 344–365.

Evans, M. D., Hollon, S. D., DeRubeis, R. J., Piascecki, J. M., Grove, W. M., Garvey, M. J., & Tuason, V. B. (1992). Differential relapse following cognitive therapy, pharmacotherapy, and combined cognitive-pharmacotherapy for depression: IV. A two-year follow-up of the CPT Project. *Archives of General Psychiatry, 49,* 802–808.

Freud, S. (1953). Fragment of an analysis of a case of hysteria. In J. Strachey (Ed. and Trans.), *The standard edition of the complete psychological works of Sigmund Freud* (Vol. 7, pp. 15–122). London: Hogarth Press. (Original work published 1901–1905)

Freud, S. (1959). Inhibitions, symptoms and anxiety. In J. Strachey (Ed. and Trans.), *The standard edition of the complete psychological works of Sigmund Freud* (Vol. 20, pp. 87–174). London: Hogarth Press. (Original work published 1926)

Goldstein, K. (1939). *The organism.* New York: American Books.

Grace, N. J., & Graham, D. T. (1952). Relationship of specific attitudes and emotions to certain bodily diseases. *Psychosomatic Medicine, 14,* 243–251.

Hollon, S. D., DeRubeis, R. J., Evans, M. D., Wiemer, M. J., Garvey, M. J., Grove, W. M., & Tuason, V. B. (1992). Cognitive therapy and pharmacotherapy for depression, singly and in combination: I. Differential outcome in the CPT project. *Archives of General Psychiatry, 49,* 774–781.

Mirsky, I. (1958). Physiologic, psychologic, and social determinants in the etiology of duodenal ulcer. *American Journal of Digestive Disorders, 3,* 285–314.

Rangell, L. (1959). The nature of conversion. *Journal of the American Psychoanalytic Association, 7,* 632–662.

Rangell, L. (1990). *The human core: The intrapsychic base of behavior* (Vol. 1). Madison, CT: International Universities Press.

Schmale, A. H. (1972). Depression as affect, character style, and symptom formation. In R. Holt & E. Peterfreund (Eds.), *Psychoanalysis and contemporary science.* (pp. 327–354). Madison, CT: International Universities Press.

Seligman, M. (1975). *Helplessness: On depression, development and death.* New York: Freeman.

Seligman, M. E. P. (1990). *Learned optimism.* New York: Pocket Books.

Seligman, M. E. P., & Elder, G. (1985). Learned helplessness and life-span development. In A. Sorenson, F. Weinert, & L. Sherrod (Eds.), *Human development and the life course: Multidisciplinary perspectives* (pp. 377–427). Hillsdale, NJ: Erlbaum.

Seligman, M. E. P., & Nolen-Hoeksema, S. (1987). Explanatory style and depression. In D. Magnussn & A. Ohman (Eds.), *Psychopathology: An interactional perspective* (pp. 125–139). San Diego, CA: Academic Press.

Sweeney, P. D., Anderson, K., & Bailey, S. (1986). Attributional style in depression: A meta-analytic review. *Journal of Personality and Social Psychology, 50,* 974–997.

Weiner, H., Thaler, M., Reiser, M., & Mirsky, I. (1957). Etiology of duodenal ulcer: I. Relation of specific psychological characteristics to rate of gastric secretion (serum pepsinogen). *Psychosomatic Medicine, 19,* 1–10.

17

LOOKING AHEAD TO A NEW SYMPTOM-CONTEXT THEORY OF HOW PSYCHOLOGICAL AND PSYCHOSOMATIC SYMPTOMS FORM

LESTER LUBORSKY

We come now to two timely ending phases: a time for summing up the discoveries from symptom-context studies and a time for looking ahead to where they are leading.

SUMMING UP

Symptom-context methods were applied to the seven types of recurrent symptoms whose results are the centerpiece of this book: three types of psychological symptoms—momentary forgetting, sudden depressive shifts, and phobic behaviors; and four types of somatic symptoms—stomach ulcer pains, migraine headaches, absence episodes (petit mal), and premature ventricular contractions (PVCs) of the heart.

Looking at this centerpiece skeptically as the glass-is-half-empty leads one to mourning the lack of more patients in this sample. But looking at it as the glass-is-half-full leads one to savoring the realization that these seven intra-individual studies are a unique set, the only set of patients with recurrent symptoms ever analyzed by the symptom-context method.

These symptoms, although they differ from each other in severity and character, all fit Freud's (1926/1959) basic definition of a symptom as an impairment of a usual function, such as the inability to remember what one has just intended to say or an episode of heart arrhythmia. Yet, they also are diverse in terms of needing a self-report from the patient to locate the moment of the appearance of the symptom; the last two symptoms, the episodes of absence epilepsy (petit mal) and the episodes of PVCs of the heart, were purposely measured directly from a physiological marker so there was no need for the patient's self-report. They reveal that a symptom's preconditions could be known even without the patient's report.

To offer yet another kind of contrast, I also included symptom-context analyses of nonsymptom recurrent behaviors: laughing, crying, touching treasured objects, and touching the mouth while talking. Of these, the two cases of recurrent episodes of laughing were the most suitable for comparison with the seven recurrent symptom cases. I found that there appears to be differences between recurrent symptom antecedents and recurrent nonsymptom antecedents.

All nine symptom or behavior patients were in psychotherapy, except for the patient with PVCs, and even he had had 12 sessions of psychotherapy-like free-association interviews. One of the three patients with absence epilepsy (petit mal) who are included was in psychotherapy; the other two patients with absence epilepsy (petit mal) were not included because they were not in psychotherapy. My findings are therefore limited to patients in psychotherapy, that is, to people who might have a significant psychological component to their recurrent symptoms or behaviors.

The Five Basic Symptom-Context Principles of the Symptom-Context Methods

The symptom-context (S-C) principles that have served best in guiding the analyses need to be summed up. It was allegiance to these principles that earned what has been learned by the research.

S-C Principle 1: There is a special virtue in collecting data on recurrent symptom contexts that have formed at the moment they are observed, not just as has usually been done through retrospection and reconstruction through the memory of the symptom contexts. The virtue is in the opportunity to examine the actual antecedents of the symptom, not a remembered version of it.

S-C Principle 2: The basic method relies on a baseline control made up of the same patient's words when no target symptom follows them. This is a vital control because the antecedents before the symptom also may appear with equal frequency and intensity throughout the session. What needs to be identified is what is special that appears before the symptom.

S-C Principle 3: The use of psychotherapy sessions provides a high-yield context for examining symptom formation because of these reasons:

- The patient is likely to say at least some of the thoughts that are associated with the symptom. The observer needs only to go back over the thoughts that the patient expressed just before the symptom in order to summarize these presymptom recurrent thoughts.
- Psychotherapy contains instances of recurrent current psychological and psychosomatic symptoms.
- Psychotherapy sessions were the basic milieu from which the main concepts of psychoanalysis were generated; it is therefore only fitting that I return to them to reexamine the concepts but now better armed, clinically and quantitatively, by the controlled symptom-context methods. By contrast, others have argued for the importance of shifting the research arena to outside-of-treatment data in order to reexamine psychoanalytic concepts (Grünbaum, 1984; Holzman & Aronson, 1992). Outside-of-treatment studies are fine, but only in addition to the type of controlled reexamination presented here, based on Freud's usual research milieu of psychotherapy sessions.
- It is a basic assumption of these studies that psychotherapy sessions are a slice of life—the preconditions for symptoms in sessions are a fair sample of the preconditions for symptoms that appear in everyday life. Yet, it is worth mentioning as an unlikely possibility that the therapeutic environment may naturally highlight some of the preconditions in the symptom-context theory, such as the current conditions, the relationships with people, and the components of the Core Conflictual Relationship Theme (CCRT).
- The therapist, the patient, other listeners to the recordings, and readers of the transcripts of the therapy can then serve as multiple vantage point observers of the conditions for the emergence of the symptom.
- Psychotherapy sessions are convenient to use, in the sense that the patients and therapists come to appointments and they almost always agree to be tape recorded.

S-C Principle 4: The within-person analysis over time is the primary unit for measuring the consistencies for the recurrent context of the symptom. This principle is in contrast to the practice in traditional research studies of reliance on cross-sectional methods that deal in aggregates across patients; these show presymptom levels only across cases rather than presymptom levels within each person over time.

S-C Principle 5: It is useful to generate a multilayered perspective from a set of methods at different levels of observation: (a) clinical review of the contexts, (b) rated categories derived from the clinical review, (c) scored categories derived from the clinical review and from the ratings, and (d) concurrent physiological substrate variables. All four of these layers can be generated both for the immediate and for the broad background contexts.

The Heart of the Findings About Onset Conditions

The symptom-context methods have turned up a range of discoveries about the conditions before the onset of recurrent symptoms in psychotherapy. These discoveries are listed in this chapter in italics and preceded by a dark square, starting with the most crucial ones:

■ *Certain basic psychological antecedents almost always appear within cases before recurrent psychological and recurrent somatic symptoms.*

In this book I have examined the types of psychological antecedents that appear within each case for each of seven types of recurrent symptoms. Although I report significance tests, I tried to take heed of Cohen's (1994) warning against overreliance on such tests by examining (a) the within-case, most established variables and (b) the replication of within-case variables across cases. Both of these types of results are in Tables 1, 2, 3, and 4.

Table 1: The Number of Significant Cases for Each Rated Variable

A ratio is given for each variable. The numerator is the number of studies in which the variable showed significant discrimination between symptom segments and control segments for the 50-word unit before (or at the start of) the symptom; the denominator is the total number of the seven studies for which I obtained data.

The main findings in Table 1 show that the most frequent significantly discriminating within-case rated variables were Hopelessness (in seven of seven cases), Helplessness (in six of seven cases), Anxiety (in six of seven cases), and Lack of Control (in four of four cases).

Table 2: A Meta-Analysis of Rated Variables for Recurrent Symptoms

The trends across the seven within-case patients with recurrent symptoms are fairly clear, but another type of summary in Tables 2 and 3 makes them even clearer. This more precise summary was suggested by Rosenthal's (1991) guide to meta-analysis, which recommends effect size methods for combining results. The results in Table 2 are listed for the 12 rated variables that were most often included in each of the seven symptom studies.[1] For

---

[1]As can be found in the chapters on each case, a few other variables were significant: forgetting (Rejection); Depression (Loss of Self-esteem, Oedipal Conflict); and migraine (Doubt, Dependency).

TABLE 1
Number of the Seven Symptom Cases for Each Variable With Significant
Differences Before Symptoms Versus Before Controls for Rated and
Scored Variables

Rating	Single cases/ all cases[a]	Scoring	Single cases/ all cases[a]
Hopelessness	7/7		
Lack of Control	4/4		
Anxiety	6/7 →	Anxiety (G-G)	1/5
Blocked	4/6		
Helplessness	6/7 →	Helplessness manual (LL)	2/7
Concern about Supplies	4/5		
Hostility to Therapist	4/6		
Involvement with Therapist	4/7 →	Reference to Therapist (LL)	1/7
Depression	3/6 →	Hostility-Inward (G-G)	1/5
Guilt	2/7		
Hostility to Others	1/6 →	Hostility-Outward (G-G)	0/1
Separation Concern	2/5		
Attention Difficulties	0/1 →	Cognitive Disturbance (LL)	2/7
		Speech Disturbance (GM)	1/7
		Cognitive Impairment (G-G)	0/5

Note. The arrows connect the rated variables with the intended-to-be-similar scored variables.
[a]The numerator is the number of cases with significant differences between symptom segments versus controls; the denominator is the number of cases studied.

each variable, the differences and their significance levels are given for the symptom segments versus control segments for the 50-word unit just before the symptom. (For shifts in depression, the unit is just after the start of the shift in depression.) The main results in Tables 2 and 3 emerge from the same variables as those listed in Table 1. Most of the variables showed significant within-case differences. The largest effect sizes across the cases were Hopelessness (.53), Lack of Control (.53), Anxiety (.52), Feeling Blocked (.51), and Helplessness (.47).[2] Figure 1 depicts in graphic form the relative effect sizes of the rated variables.

It is of special interest that the brief unit just before the symptom was sufficient to capture the distinction between symptom segments and control segments. That brief unit is usually only about 50 words, which is a "thin slice" of behavior, as Ambady and Rosenthal (1992) called such brief units; they found that such thin slices of behavior can be predictive for a variety of behaviors.

---

[2]The final column significance is a one-tailed *p* value, which is justified because most of the studies' results are in the same direction (see Tables 2 and 3).

TABLE 2
Summary of Symptom-Context Rated Variables for the 50-Word Unit Before the Symptom Versus Controls

Rated variable	Momentary forgetting		Depression[a]		Phobia		Stomach Pain[b]	
	t/p	r	t/p	r	t/p	r	t/p	r
Hopelessness	2.04 .027	.391	2.85 .013	.733	2.65 .017	.578	1.53 .068	.278 (R)
Lack of Control							1.82 .040	.325
Anxiety	0.85 .203	.175	2.43 .023	.676	2.78 .015	.596	2.37 .013	.409
Blocked			2.41 .024	.673	2.49 .021	.554	0.68 .252	.127
Helplessness	1.80 .043	.351	+		3.97 .003	.728	1.73 .048	.311
Concern about Supplies			1.99 .044	.601	2.60 .011	.571	2.09 .023	.367
Hostility to Therapist	1.80 .043	.351	−0.65 .268	−.239			0.80 .216	.149
Involvement with Therapist	4.20 .00	.659	−1.88 .051	−.579	0.06 .477	.016	0.30 .382	.057 (R)
Depression			+		0.09 .463	.024	0.00 .500	.000
Guilt (self-blame)	−0.77 .224	−.159	4.15 .002	.843	1.55 .086	.383	0.00 .500	.000
Hostility to Others	0.55 .293	.114	0.34 .371	.127			0.72 .237	.135 (R)
Separation Concern	2.13 .022	.406	0.61 .282	.225			1.00 .167	.186
Instances compared	13 symptoms 12 controls		4 increases 5 decreases		8 increases 8 controls		15 symptoms 15 controls	

continues

Note. A negative t value means a smaller symptom than the control. Probability values are one-tailed. Correlations are translations of t values. Blank cells mean the variables were not rated. PVC = premature ventricular contraction; ES = effect size; CC = Cathy Cunningham; SS = Sandy Smyth; (R) = a recent rating by RKM; + = appears to have been significant, but data are missing.
[a]The 100-word unit just after the shift to increased depression. The t indicates increased versus decreased depression.
[b]Stomach pain used about 30 words before the symptom. Only AA's ratings were used.

TABLE 2 *(Continued)*

7 Symptom cases						2 Nonsymptom cases				
						Laughing[f]				
Migraine[c]		Absence (petit mal)[d]		PVC[e]		Ms. CC		Ms. SS		ES summary[g]
t/p	r	t/p	r	t/p	r	t/p	r	t/p	r	r/p
3.51 .003	.743	2.71 .006	.412	1.87 .040	.403	1.45 .081	.241 (R)	−0.85 .204	−.187 (R)	.530 .000
3.86 .002	.774	2.11 .021	.332	2.94 .005	.570	1.18 .123	.198 (R)	−0.99 .169	−.216 (R)	.530 .000
2.14 .029	.560	2.55 .008	.391	4.19 .000	.703	2.98 .002	.455 (R)	0.00 .500	0.00 (R)	.523 .000
4.07 .003	.790	3.90 .000	.545	0.68 .260	.158	−0.34 .367	−.058 (R)	−1.46 .081	−.310 (R)	.515 .000
2.79 .010	.662	2.41 .010	.373	1.05 .150	.240	1.37 .089	.229	−0.40 .348	−.088	.470 .000
0.45 .332	.141	1.77 .042	.283			−0.35 .365	−.060 (R)	−0.45 .330	−.100 (R)	.405 .000
2.39 .019	.603	2.69 .007	.409	2.33 .020	.481	2.34 .015	.372 (R)	−1.49 .084	−.316 (R)	.310 .000
1.71 .065	.476 (R)	3.70 .000	.525	1.43 .090	.319	3.56 .001	.521 (R)	0.35 .364	.078 (R)	.236 .001
0.89 .198	.271 (R)	4.90 .000	.633	2.93 .010	.568	0.84 .203	.143 (R)	−2.61 .011	−.504 (R)	.327 .001
−0.28 .394	−.088 (R)	3.21 .002	.472	0.96 .180	.221	0.88 .192	.149	−0.25 .403	−.056	.291 .004
0.81 .219	.248 (R)	3.42 .001	.495	0.49 .320	.115	−1.61 .059	−.266 (R)	−0.60 .276	−.133 (R)	.216 .008
0.00 .500	0.00 (R)	1.92 .032	.305			0.96 .173	.162 (R)	0.93 .182	.204 (R)	.236 .008
6 symptoms 6 controls		19 symptoms 19 controls		10 symptoms 10 controls		21 non-symptoms 15 controls		11 non-symptoms 11 controls		(excludes laugh cases)

[c]Migraine used only AA's ratings.
[d]Absence (petit mal) used about 30 words before the symptom.
[e]PVC used the 60 s before the symptom (a mean of 161 words).
[f]Laughs used the thought unit before the symptom (Unit Number 3).
[g]Effect size summary: correlations and probability values were obtained using Rosenthal's (1991) techniques for combining effect sizes. Laugh cases excluded.

TABLE 3
Summary of Effect Sizes (ESs) for Seven Symptoms for Rated Variables
and Scored Variables

Rank	Rated variable	ES	p	Rank	Scored variable[a]	ES	p
1	Hopelessness	.530	.000				
2	Lack of Control	.530	.000				
3	Anxiety	.523	.000	5	Anxiety (GG)	.149	.064
4	Blocked	.515	.000				
5	Helplessness	.470	.000	1	Helplessness manual (LL)	.345	.000
6	Supplies	.405	.000				
7	Hostility to Therapist	.310	.000				
8	Involvement with Therapist	.236	.001	3	Reference to Therapist (LL)	.178	.038
9	Depression	.327	.001	6	Hostility-Inward (G-G)	.110	.093
10	Guilt	.291	.004				
11	Hostility to Others	.216	.008	7	Hostility-Outward (G-G)	.207	.100
12	Separation Concern	.236	.008				
				2	Schizophrenia (G-G)	.245	.012
				4	Cognitive Disturbance (LL)	.187	.043
				8	Total Hostility (G-G)	.080	.136
				9	Covert Hostility (G-G)	.020	.284
				10	Hostility ambivalent (G-G)	.060	.326
				11	Hostility overt (G-G)	.040	.397
				12	Speech Disturbance	.040	.397
				13	Cognitive Impairment (G-G)	−.030	.348

Note. The ranks are for the probability value of the effect sizes.
[a]The listing is arranged with the scored variables on the same row as the intended-to-be similar rated variables.

Intercorrelations of Rated Variables

Table 5 shows the intercorrelations of the 12 most used rated variables with each other across the seven cases with different recurrent symptoms. The intercorrelations tended to be low, except for a few variables. The low intercorrelations indicate that my findings reflect more than one broad negative affect variable, but instead a variety of more specific variables.

I note a few of the most related variables among the intercorrelations: (a) The terms *Helplessness* and *Hopelessness*, as they have been used throughout these chapters, tended to be correlated: The mean intercorrelation across the seven symptom cases was .75, which was the highest intercorrelation throughout the matrix. (b) Helplessness and Hopelessness tended to be correlated with Lack of Control (Helplessness = .66 and Hopelessness = .68). (c) Helplessness and Hopelessness tended to be related to Feeling Blocked (Hopelessness = .62 and Helplessness = .45). (d)

Helplessness was somewhat related to Anxiety (Helplessness and Anxiety = .42, Hopelessness and Anxiety = .20).

Although only a few variables showed up as being related across all cases, a few showed moderately high intercorrelations that applied only to one case. For example, for the PVC patient, Blocked correlated with Depression at .68.

Table 4: A Meta-Analysis of Scored Variables for Recurrent Symptoms

Like the rated variables, the scored variables also showed a trend toward significant discrimination of symptom segments versus control segments, but only for relatively few of the symptom cases. Some of the most discriminating scored variables (summarized in Table 3) were: the Helplessness manual was discriminating in two of the seven cases (effect size = .35), Schizophrenia (G-G) in two of the five cases (effect size = .25), Cognitive Disturbance in two of seven cases (effect size = .19), and Reference to the Therapist in one of seven cases (effect size = .18). The rest of the variables had even smaller effect sizes.

These results show that my fond hopes and expectations of finding or developing scored versions of the rated variables that would give better discrimination of the symptom versus control segments than the rated variables had given were not met. These dashed hopes can be seen in the skeletonized results in Table 1 and again in the more detailed results in Tables 2–4. In fact, wherever a comparison can be made between a rated variable and its related scored variable (as in Tables 1 and 3), the result for the scored variable was always less, never more. Therefore, my main presentation of results in this book is in terms of the rated variables.

Other Findings for the Seven Symptom Cases

- *The symptom-context studies are the only ones demonstrating that the patient's words immediately before symptoms reveal some of the symptom's preconditions.*

The crucial findings about the qualities in the patient's words just before symptoms need to be seen from the perspective of what has been done in this field of studies in the past: There is nothing in the literature yet in which the words before recurrent symptoms have been systematically analyzed.

- *Each of the graded series of methods of data analysis for each symptom shows some overlap and some distinctiveness in their results: clinical review, sortings, ratings, and scorings.*

The clinical review method, as expected, is the broadest because it is an impressionistic summary of the essential qualities of the symptom segments.

TABLE 4
Summary of Symptom-Context Scored Variables for the 50-Word Unit Before the Symptom Versus Control

	7 Symptom cases							
	Momentary forgetting[a]		Depression[b]		Phobia[c]		Stomach Pain[d]	
Scored variable	t/p	r	t/p	r	t/p	r	t/p	r
Helplessness manual (Difference score LL)	N/A N/A	N/A	0.59 .286	.218	2.65 .017	.578	1.38 .095	.252
Schizophrenia (G-G)	0.13 .45	.027					−0.37 .36	−.070
Reference to Therapist (LL)	1.43 .113	.280	−0.25 .407	−.094	0.00 .500	.000	0.00 .500	.000
Cognitive Disturbance (LL)	−0.82 .213	−.165	1.01 .160	.357	−0.44 .331	−.117	0.57 .287	.107
Anxiety (G-G)	−0.88 .20	−.177					0.57 .28	.107
Hostility-Inward (G-G)	−0.73 .24	−.147					0.53 .30	.100
Hostility-Outward (G-G)								
Hostility total (G-G)	−0.52 .31	−.106					1.26 .11	.232
Hostility covert (G-G)	1.79 .05	.343					0.44 .33	.083
Hostility ambivalent (G-G)	−0.27 .40	−.055					1.05 .15	.195
Cognitive Impairment (G-G)	−0.15 .44	−.031					−0.45 .33	−.085
Hostility overt (G-G)	−1.97 .03	−.373					1.39 .08	.254
Speech Disturbance (GM)	−2.00 .034	−.378	2.03 .041	.609	−0.94 .191	−.244	0.36 .366	.068
Instances compared	13 symptoms 13 controls		4 increases 5 decreases		8 increases 8 controls		15 symptoms 15 controls	

continues

Note. A negative t value indicates a smaller symptom than control. All probability values are one-tailed. Gottschalk-Gleser (1969). The correlations are translations of the t values.
[a]Momentary forgetting (LL) is for the 50 words before forgetting. Momentary forgetting (GG, scored by computer) is for the 300 words before forgetting.
[b]The 100-word unit just after the shift to increased depression. The t is for increased versus decreased depression segments.
[c]The Phobia ts, ps, and rs represent a comparison of 8 increases with 8 controls.
[d]Gottschalk-Gleser scoring was done by hand by Julia Hoigaard for stomach pain.

TABLE 4 *(Continued)*

7 Symptom cases						2 Nonsymptom cases				
						Laughing[h]				
Migraine[e]		Absence (petit mal)[f]		PVC[g]		Ms. CC		Ms. SS		ES summary[i]
t/p	r	t/p	r	t/p	r	t/p	r	t/p	r	r/p
1.41 .093	.407	1.84 .042	.293	1.34 .098	.301	N/A N/A	N/A	−1.00 .170	−.218	.345 .000
2.10 .03	.553	2.59 .01	.396	1.10 .15	.251					.245 .012
1.63 .089	.458	0.92 .205	.152	1.97 .060	.421	3.03 .002	.461	−0.42 .339	−.094	.178 .038
1.80 .041	.495	0.90 .187	.148	1.74 .046	.379	0.78 .221	.133	1.36 .092	.291	.187 .043
0.48 .32	.150	2.32 .025	.361	1.27 .11	.287					.149 .064
0.56 .29	.174	2.99 .003	.446	−0.16 .44	−.038					.110 .093
		1.32 .10	.215							.207 .100
−0.82 .21	−.251	2.40 .025	.371	0.61 .28	.142					.080 .136
−1.5 .09	−.429			0.40 .35	.094					.020 .284
1.33 .10	.388	0.21 .42	.035	−1.35 .10	−.303					.060 .326
0.75 .24	.231	0.28 .39	.047	−1.34 .10	−.301					−.030 .348
0.78 .22	.239			0.24 .41	.056					.040 .397
1.14 .146	.339	−1.53 .085	−.247	0.23 .410	.054	1.87 .052	.305	2.05 .040	.417	.040 .397
6 symptoms 6 controls		19 symptoms 19 controls		10 symptoms 10 controls		21 non-symptoms 15 controls		11 non-symptoms 11 controls		(Excludes laugh cases)

[e]Migraine used the new sample. Gottschalk-Gleser scoring was done by hand by Julia Hoigaard for Migraine.
[f]Absence (petit mal) used about 30 words before the symptom. Gottschalk-Gleser scoring (which did not include all the contexts) was done by hand by Carolyn Winget for petit mal.
[g]PVC used 60 s before symptom (about 161 words). Gottschalk-Gleser scoring by computer (Gottschalk & Bechtel, 1995). Unreported units scored by hand by Julia Hoigaard.
[h]Laughs used the thought unit (3) before symptom. N/A; indicates that no comparison was possible because both standard deviations were 0. Reference to therapist was rated (laughs only).
[i]Effect size summary: rs and ps obtained using Rosenthal's (1991) techniques for combining effect sizes. Laugh cases excluded.

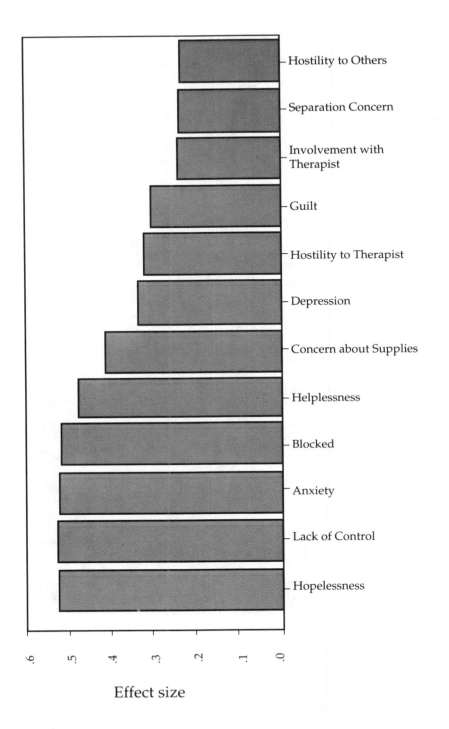

Figure 1. Effect sizes for 12 rated variables for the 50-word unit before symptom across 7 symptom cases.

TABLE 5
Mean Intercorrelations of Rated Variables Across the 7 Symptoms

Variable	1	2	3	4	5	6	7	8	9	10	11	12
1. Helplessness	—	.75 (.12)	.42 (.21)	.45 (.22)	.34 (.41)	.10 (.41)	-.08 (.27)	.09 (.31)	.10 (.45)	.11 (.23)	.66 (.22)	.22 (.19)
2. Hopelessness		—	.20 (.30)	.62 (.21)	.38 (.28)	.12 (.29)	-.09 (.22)	.06 (.28)	.19 (.54)	.07 (.15)	.68 (.16)	.31 (.35)
3. Anxiety			—	-.05 (.26)	.12 (.44)	.02 (.38)	.07 (.41)	.05 (.39)	.00 (.44)	.18 (.35)	.37 (.26)	-.01 (.39)
4. Blocked				—	.55 (.17)	.19 (.38)	.04 (.38)	-.10 (.29)	.04 (.44)	.17 (.25)	.42 (.14)	.03 (.43)
5. Supplies					—	.27 (.52)	-.08 (.57)	-.06 (.39)	.02 (.47)	.21 (.13)	.26 (.40)	.02 (.46)
6. Hostility to Therapist						—	.23 (.14)	.54 (.43)	-.21 (.14)	-.13 (.26)	-.02 (.37)	-.11 (.29)
7. Hostility to Others							—	.06 (.40)	-.01 (.33)	.11 (.20)	-.01 (.39)	.01 (.25)
8. Involvement with Therapist								—	-.38 (.15)	.04 (.37)	-.19 (.27)	.20 (.41)
9. Depression									—	.02 (.11)	.01 (.57)	-.16 (.43)
10. Separation Concern										—	.08 (.11)	.05 (.22)
11. Lack of Control											—	.14 (.23)
12. Guilt												—

Note. The top numbers are the mean intercorrelations. Numbers in parentheses are the standard deviations of the intercorrelations.

Although the other methods offer more precise confirmations than the clinical review, they still do not capture some of the richness of the clinical review. It remains an agenda worth trying to develop ratings and scorings for more of the trends uncovered in the clinical review.

The sorting method is a convenient variant of the rating method. The judge has only to sort samples of symptom and control segments, first with no guidance and then with several kinds of clues as guidance. The method has been tried successfully with three different symptoms: with the context for stomach ulcer pains (see chap. 7), with the context for bursts of electroencephalographic (EEG) paroxysmal episodes (see chap. 9), and with the context for PVCs of the heart (see chap. 10). For all three symptom cases, the sorting could not be done significantly without guidance, but the provision of specific clues made the discrimination of symptoms and controls possible at highly significant levels. These clues were then examined further in the form of ratings and scorings.

The rating method is based only on a definition and a graded scale for each variable. Yet, it achieved more discrimination of symptom segments versus control segments than the scoring systems.

The scoring method, despite my efforts to move to a reliance on such measures, did not improve on the discrimination of symptom segments versus control segments on the basis of the ratings, although the results by the scored measures were in the same direction as those by the rated measures. In discussions with L. A. Gottschalk (personal communication, June 1995), we agreed on two likely explanations: (a) The scoring systems may have overrestricted the judge's range of acceptable evidence for the variable and (b) the segments to be scored in the symptom's context tended to be short, and scored measures fare better with longer segments.

■ *Within each symptom case there is a unique ordering of the degree of discrimination of each variable for symptom segments versus control segments.*

The order of discriminating variables for each case appears to make sense clinically, although some of it could have been influenced by chance. (The degree of discrimination of each variable can be found in each chapter as well as in Tables 2 and 4 in this chapter.) The meaningfulness of this order tends to be supported when the list is examined along with the clinical review.

A couple of examples will make clearer the probable meaning of the ordering of the variables. For momentary forgetting (the list of discriminating variables can be found in Table 3 of chapter 3 and in the first column of Table 2 in this chapter). Involvement with the therapist had the most significant discrimination of symptom and control segments. This was followed by Rejection, but this variable is not in Table 2 because the table includes only the 12 most frequently used variables among the cases in the book. The next most discriminating variables were Hopelessness,

Helplessness, Anger to the Therapist, and Separation Concern. As the clinical review shows, in Session 20 in the 50 words before the forgetting, the patient says, "You [may] have had to tell me that we couldn't continue treatment anymore because it wasn't doing me any good. Or, that you judge my case not to be amenable to the treatment." The forgetting occurs just at that instant. Clearly, this segment reflects Involvement with Therapist. The patient inferred from her perception about the therapist that she had been rejected by the therapist. She then felt Helpless and Hopeless; it can be further inferred that she felt Angry about it and felt Separation Concern and Anxiety about the Separation Concern. What is especially revealing in this sequence is that her Involvement with Therapist was about her feeling of Rejection.

A similar analysis can be made of the ranked list of discriminating variables in other cases. Table 1 in chapter 8 on migraine-like headaches illustrates the unique constellation that applies to this symptom. The most discriminating variable in the ranking of variables rated by AA (the principal judge) was Blocked. The patient also felt Lack of Control, Hopelessness, Helplessness, and Angry at the Therapist. The clinical review illustrates this vividly in chapter 8. In the first instance of a headache in Session 104, the patient was talking about his wish to go south to work in the voter registration drives. He said, "But the thought that made me dismiss it was I realized that I would be coming here," meaning that he perceived the therapist and the treatment as blocking him. At that point he noticed that "I am starting to get a little minor headache," which developed into a major headache in its usual progression.

- *There is a time trend before symptoms. The psychological antecedents before a symptom tend to show progressively greater prominence the closer the segment is to the symptom.*

The time trends for each case for the significance of differences between symptom segments and control segments generally peak as the symptoms come closer to expression. These time trends can be seen easily in the graphs for the ratings of such symptoms. The 50-word unit closest to the symptom tended to reveal the largest within-case differences because the significance levels for each symptom tended to show larger differences as the symptom approached. However, the results would have been only slightly less for an adjacent unit, such as 100–200 words before the symptom appeared.

- *There is a time trend after symptoms. The psychological sequelae of the symptom tend to show progressively less prominence the further the segment is from the symptom.*

The time trends after the symptoms for the significance of the differences in the ratings tended to show gradual declines in the intervals after the symptom. This pattern was true for most symptoms, although a few declined more slowly than they increased before the symptom.

- *The psychological antecedents for the three psychological symptom cases tend to be similar to the four somatic symptom cases.*

Whether a symptom is psychological or somatic (or psychosomatic) does not make much difference in terms of the types of antecedents, so that many of the same variables are found across both types of symptoms.

- *The psychological antecedents tend to be similar across symptom cases regardless of whether the patient reports the symptom or the symptom is a physiological marker that is measured independently of patients' reports.*

This is an important comparison for understanding the results because it suggests that my results were not a product of self-reports.

As a possible alternative explanation, instead of my concept that the antecedents set the stage for the symptom to appear and create the catastrophe of symptom formation, one could suppose that the patient gradually senses that a symptom is about to appear; therefore, in the antecedent period there is gradually increasing helplessness and related qualities as the appearance of the symptom comes closer. One could imagine that this could occur before the patient's report of depressive shifts, stomach ulcer pain, and migraine headaches. But that supposition could not apply for the absence (petit mal) episodes or for the PVC because these did not involve the patient's verbal report of the symptom; it also could not apply to momentary forgetting because the thought that was in awareness dropped out of awareness and could not be reported. Yet, I found that the Helplessness, Hopelessness, and related qualities also were evident before the absence episodes (petit mal), the PVC, and the momentary forgetting symptoms.

- *The psychological antecedents tended to differ, as expected, for the seven recurrent symptom cases versus the two nonsymptom recurrent behavior cases.*

A natural and needed comparison for the symptom contexts examined in this book is between the antecedents for the seven recurrent symptoms of momentary forgetting, depressive shifts, phobic behavior, stomach ulcer pain, migraine, absence epilepsy [petit mal], and PVC versus the antecedents for the recurrent nonsymptom behaviors, such as the recurrent laughing.

The results for the two cases with recurrent laughing are in the end columns of Table 2. These were the only available cases in which recurrent nonsymptom behavior was analyzed in a way similar to the seven recurrent symptom cases. For these two cases, the results appear to be different, as would be expected, from the seven symptom cases. (The case with recurrent crying in chap. 2 could not be used as a nonsymptom comparison because crying was too closely associated with the patient's symptoms.) The set of symptoms showed the usual antecedents of Helplessness, Hopelessness, and related qualities. The set of nonsymptom recurrent behaviors, especially the two laugh behavior cases, were different in the antecedents that are usual in the symptom cases. Of course, more of the recurrent nonsymptom behavior cases need to be examined.

- *The set of psychological antecedents in the immediate context tends to show parallels with the set in the background context.*

The immediate contexts of the recurrent symptoms were always evaluated by a clinical review and then by ratings and scorings. By contrast, the background context used a greater variety of assessment methods, but most often the CCRTs of the sessions. Comparisons of some of these are given in the following:

In the CCRT measure, one type of analysis of the background context was based on a comparison of two grand themes: the symptom-context theme versus the CCRT. The symptom-context theme for each patient was discovered to have parallels with the CCRT. A parallel was first seen in the momentary forgetting case (see chap. 3) and then again in the other cases. I summarized these two grand themes for each of the seven recurrent symptom cases and found that there were parallels between them, particularly for the CCRT's response of self.

As an example of the parallels for Mr. Alton in Session 17 (see chaps. 6 and 16), the CCRT in which the symptom appeared included Wish 1, to assert independence. This wish conflicted with Wish 2, to give help and to please and not to hurt. The satisfaction of Wish 1 also conflicted with the Response from Others to dominate and to control. The resolution of these conflicts appeared in the Responses of Self, which included Anger, which appeared in three of four narratives; Anxiety, which was part of the symptom and appeared in two of four narratives; phobic behavior, which also was part of the symptom and appeared in two of four narratives; and feeling Helpless, which appeared in two of four narratives.

The parallels of the CCRT with the symptom-context results are impressive, even though a more precise method for doing the comparisons is needed. The part that is most clear was the parallel between the responses of self and the antecedent variables for phobic behavior (listed in Tables 2 and 4 under the Phobia column). These rated variables included, in order of significance, Helplessness, Concern about Supplies, Anxiety, Feeling Blocked, and Hopelessness; the outstanding variables that showed the parallel were Helplessness, Hopelessness, and Anxiety.

- *The conditions for symptom formation that are revealed through retrospective accounts may sometimes overlap with the conditions that are revealed through direct observation.*

I found, to my surprise, that for recurrent phobic behavior, the psychological antecedents for the accounts of past outside-of-session phobias were much like those for the six other types of symptom cases that always directly appeared in the session.

Other researchers have had similar surprises. Hodgins, el-Guebaly, and Armstrong (1995) expected that negative mood would have a greater precipitating effect on relapses among alcohol-dependent people when assessed with retrospective mood ratings rather than prospective mood ratings. Their results did not support their hypothesis: No evidence was found of a strong systematic negative attributional bias in retrospective reports.

But some findings from retrospective versus current methods can sometimes be amazingly divergent. An example of a major disjunction of information from concurrent observation versus from retrospection was described by Stunkard, Foster, Glassman, and Rosato (1985). Reports of vomiting were compared by concurrent versus retrospective methods for the frequency of vomiting after gastric surgery for obesity. The concurrent reports of vomiting in the first month were 3.4 times per week; the retrospective reports were 8.4 times per week.

- *Symptom onset conditions tend to have a one-way direction. The frequency of associations between antecedents followed by a symptom are much less than the frequency of associations of symptoms preceded by the antecedents.*

The observation about a one-way direction was first made by Engel and Schmale (1967). When starting with the appearance of a symptom and then looking back at its psychological antecedents, the main antecedents were found with moderate frequency. Yet the degree of co-occurrence was much less when the direction of examination was by looking forward from certain psychological antecedents, such as helplessness, to the rate of appearance of the symptom.

In fact, by the "looking forward" method, one may find that all of the usual antecedents may build up and yet no symptom will appear. Why? Because the person tends to find ways to cope with the buildup of the antecedents. These ways of coping so that the symptom does not appear may involve (a) dealing directly with the danger and with the other preconditions included in the theory, such as finding a boyfriend who is not rejecting, as was the case for Sandy Smyth; (b) experiencing reassurance and support from the therapist; or (c) instituting a variety of defenses leading to a mastery of the anticipation of a danger situation (Grenyer & Luborsky, in press).

The low degree of co-occurrence of an antecedent and the appearance of a symptom—by the looking forward method—makes sense when the analysis starts from a high point of an antecedent and then the search is for the later appearance of a symptom. My colleagues and I conducted a preliminary study of a depressed patient, Mr. Quinn, on the degree of co-occurrence beginning with a high point of a helplessness peak to the appearance of symptoms in sessions (Alexander, Luborsky, & Peterson, 1975; see also chap. 5). We first identified peaks of helplessness as scored by the Helplessness manual. The scores of four individual raters were summed for each of five sessions to establish the pattern of peaks of helplessness over the course of the sessions. The judges were able to agree on these peaks of helplessness in four sessions. But we found that these peaks in helplessness were usually not followed by increases in depression.

- *The within-case analyses that are central to the symptom-context method may sometimes produce results that differ from the more conventional aggregate-of-cases analyses.*

In all cases but one, I have stayed with the within-case analyses. The one exception occurred in chapter 4. The chapter offers a revealing comparison of these two approaches: by an intraindividual analysis of the momentary forgetting case (see chap. 3) compared with the across-17-cases analyses of momentary forgetting (see chap. 4). The results for the forgetting case were sometimes different from results that appeared across the 17 cases of momentary forgetting. One of these differences was for Cognitive Disturbance. It was not significant for the forgetting case, but it was significant in the across-17-cases results. Another quality, Involvement with Therapist, was highly significant for the momentary forgetting case and for the 17 cases.

The New Symptom-Context Theory of Preconditions for Symptom Formation

My clinical–quantitative theory of onset conditions for symptoms did not appear fully formed all at one moment; instead, it grew through a series of saltatorily reforming, low-key eurekas. The new theory tries to fit all cases, but each patient has his or her own version of a somewhat similar set of preconditions. The most common version of the preconditions operates roughly in the sequence to be listed shortly and in Exhibit 1, as these are seen in the symptom-context studies in this book.

Precondition 1: The initiating immediate precondition is a glimmering of a perception of a potential current danger. The danger tends to be "perceived" as external, but it also is internal.

Precondition 2: The danger is typically perceived in current involvements with people, with the therapist as well as with outside-of-treatment

---

EXHIBIT 1
The Symptom-Context Theory of Symptom Formation

1. A perception of a potential current danger
2. The danger is in relation to people with whom the person is currently involved.
3. The activation of the Core Conflictual Relationship Theme (CRRT)
4. An increase in Hopelessness, Lack of Control, Anxiety, Blocked, and Helplessness
5. Increased cognitive disturbance (in a few patients)
6. The psychological changes are paralleled by physiological changes
7. The background state parallels the immediate state
8. A target symptom chosen by the biopsychosocial disposition

relationships. As the point of eruption of the symptom comes closer, there may be a heightened insecurity about the involvement with and anticipated responses from the therapist. The here-and-now involvement with the therapist tends to be a more crucial precipitant than past involvement, as shown by Involvement with Therapist (in four of the seven cases) and Hostility to Therapist (in four of six cases), in contrast to Hostility to Others (in only one of six cases).

Precondition 3: There is an activation of the Core Conflictual Relationship Theme (CCRT). The activation involves the person's typical pattern of interaction with significant others, including the therapist. The pattern in the CCRT includes the most frequent types of three components: the Wishes, the Responses from Others, and the Responses of Self. Each person has one (or several) outstandingly frequent components in his or her CCRT, such as (a) Rejection by others, for the momentary forgetting patient, Rachael Apfel (see chap. 3), or (b) lowered Self-esteem, for James Quinn (see chap. 5) as a Response of Self to losing out in competition.

Precondition 4: A presymptom state is generated for dealing with the danger situation that combines feeling Hopeless, lacking Control, feeling Anxious, feeling Blocked, and feeling Helpless. This currently experienced state is often associated with similar remembered experiences.

Precondition 5: A buildup of a cognitively disturbed state (as shown on the cognitive disturbance scale) may appear in a few patients in the period before a symptom emerges.

Precondition 6: Changes on the physiological level, which often involve physical symptoms, parallel the psychological changes. Although little psychophysiological symptom-context research has been done, some exists for Helplessness and Hopelessness. As an example, Helplessness and Hopelessness appear to be part of a basic psychophysiological state. They show correlations with cerebral glucose metabolic rates with basically different cerebral correlates (Gottschalk, Fronczeck, & Buchsbaum, 1993). The cerebral region that involves feelings of hopelessness appears to be in the left temporal lobe. There also is a correspondence of learned helplessness and depression shown by brain chemistry and pharmacological similarities (Sherman & Petty, 1982).

Precondition 7: The background state parallels some of the qualities of the immediate state and includes a heightened prominence of the CCRT and may include a cognitively disturbed state.

Precondition 8: The choice of the target symptom is biopsychosocially predisposed for each patient. This general principle has long been recognized but is still little understood. My results show the rule of these two principles: consistency within each patient in the choice of target symptom and individual differences among patients in their choice of target symptom. (The term *target symptom* means that the symptom is recurrent in the session and becomes the target of the symptom-context analyses.)

The consistency within each patient means that one patient will respond to the preconditions with a target symptom in the gastrointestinal system, such as the stomach pain of the ulcer patient. Another patient will respond through the cardiac system, such as the PVC patient, and another in terms of the brain system, such as the patients with absence epilepsy (petit mal) episodes. The choice of a recurrent symptom often is related to a medical disorder, such as it was for the stomach pain patient and for the absence epilepsy episodes (petit mal) patients. Furthermore, just as there is consistency within each patient in the choice of the somatic symptom (Weiner, 1977), there also appears to be much consistency within each patient in the choice of the type of psychological symptom.

The Symptom-Context Theory Applied to an Example of the Onset of Momentary Forgetting

The best illustration of this set of eight preconditions for symptoms is from examples of actual symptoms that appeared in a session. Almost any symptom will do, but let us start with an instance of momentary forgetting from the momentary forgetting of Rachael Apfel in Session 36:

Precondition 1 was the initiating precondition listed in the set diagrammed in Exhibit 1, perception of a danger situation. In Session 36 (noted in chap. 3), it is clear that the danger situation that Ms. Apfel perceived was her interpretation of a noise by the therapist. She believed that the noise was caused by the therapist cleaning a spot from his trousers or sleeve rather than listening to her. She inferred further from it that the therapist could not like her.

Precondition 2 emerged in her thoughts. She experienced current heightened insecure involvement with a person—the therapist.

Precondition 3 appeared as part of her thoughts about the therapist and the attendant insecurity. There was an activation of the CCRT, a theme that has much in common with the symptom-context theme.

Precondition 4 was an increase in her experience of feeling Hopeless, Lacking in Control, Anxious, Blocked, and Helpless. Helplessness, as shown in Figure 2 of chap. 3, had a buildup that began about 200 words before the momentary forgetting and continued until 150 words after the momentary forgetting.

Precondition 5 was an increase in Cognitive Disturbance in a few patients. Although this variable applied to three of the seven symptom cases, it did not clearly show an upswing for Ms. Apfel, perhaps because she was already at such a high level of cognitive disturbance that it would have been hard to move to an even higher level.

Precondition 6 was an increase in related physiological disturbance. Although I do not have data on this for momentary forgetting, such an investigation should be fruitful.

Precondition 7, the background context for momentary forgetting, was examined in several ways. One assessment of this variable was in terms of the CCRT, where I found a parallel with the symptom-context theme.

Precondition 8 was the appearance of her target symptom of a momentary forgetting, a recurrent symptom that was much more frequent for Ms. Apfel than for any of the other cases. The patient said, "Now I have lost the other thing that I was going to say." After 7 s, however, she retrieved what she momentarily forgot and stated that she heard a sound the day before that she had interpreted as "brushing a spot off your trousers or your jacket sleeve" and "it struck me that you weren't really listening." Her choice of momentary forgetting as a recurrent symptom is not easily understandable, as is usual for choices of symptoms. What can be said is that she had a high level of cognitive disturbance, with momentary forgetting as one aspect of her cognitive disturbances.

The Symptom-Context Theory Dovetails With and Diverges From Other Theories

The preconditions in the new theory are somewhat consistent with Freud (1926/1959), are somewhat like the other classical theories in chapter 16, and are also somewhat special. The similarity is greatest in the centrality of helplessness and hopelessness and related variables, especially anxiety. In this aspect, the symptom-context research is a confirmation of Freud's (1926/1959) theory of the onset conditions for symptoms. Another precondition also is much like Freud's theory: the perception of a danger situation. The evaluation of the situation as presenting a danger situation seems like a fitting initial precondition, although it is still mostly clinically based and more evidence about it needs to be assembled. The dispositional determinants of the choice of the symptom, arrived at by the symptom-context method, also confirms part of Freud's theory. Freud's early training in Brücke's laboratory as a careful observer of specimens through the microscope clearly paid off in his 1926 helplessness theory of symptom formation. My examination of the facts of symptom formation for the seven symptom cases showed that his focus on helplessness and related qualities reflected accurate observations.

However, the symptom-context theory goes beyond Freud (1926/1959) and the other classical theories. It broadens, specifies, and conforms to tested knowledge about symptom formation, as in the effect sizes for qualities listed in Tables 2 and 3. The discoveries are easiest to see in this listing from the preconditions in the symptom-context theory:

- The emphasis on current rather than past triggers is special in the symptom-context theory.

- The emphasis on current involvement with and expected responses from people is greater in the symptom-context theory.
- The emphasis on the centrality of the activation of the CCRT is unique in the symptom-context theory.
- The centrality of helplessness and hopelessness in some of the classical theories of symptom formation (Freud; Engel and Schmale; and Seligman) has been tested and specified in the symptom-context theory. The specification highlights a special set of qualities: Hopelessness, Lack of Control, Anxiety, Blocked, and Helplessness (Tables 2 and 3).
- The distinction between hopelessness and helplessness is especially clear in the symptom-context theory, where hopelessness appears to be even more evident than helplessness. This distinction is not present in Freud (1926/1959); the distinction is present in Engel and Schmale (1967).
- The discovery of increases in Cognitive Disturbance in some patients is unique.
- The distinction between the immediate state and the background state and their parallels is special.

Finally, some unusual theories also may have something to add. The buildup of these eight preconditions can be seen as leading to the shift from a nonsymptom state to a symptom state, and this transition can be thought of as a catastrophe to the original state, as in the concept explicated by Berlinski (1978). This concept deriving from "catastrophe theory" suggests that when a symptom appears, there has been a buildup of preconditions destructive to the prior state until a catastrophe occurs and a new state emerges in the form of the symptom state. For example, this conceptualization fits my account of the sequence of states that leads to momentary forgetting. The state changes from one with the usual capacity to recall one's intended to-be-said thoughts to a state with a loss of capacity to recall such thoughts. For precipitous shifts in depression, the state changes from only a slightly depressed mood to a changed state with a more depressed mood.

Another theory that might well apply to understanding the catastrophes that appear as symptoms in the stream of a patient's expressed thoughts is called *chaos theory*. Gleick (1987) referred to an applicable idea of one advocate of this theory, Arnold Mandell, who argued for the importance of understanding physical and psychological symptoms as dynamic systems "capable of phase transitions" (p. 298). The changes in the seven symptom cases can be conceptualized as phase transitions in the midst of an apparently chaotic system. The concept is helpful because the symptom-context method can be seen as a guide to extracting from the apparent chaos of the flow of the patient's thoughts, a pattern that is most associated with the recurrent context of symptoms.

The set of preconditions in the symptom-context theory also can be organized at a more abstract conceptual level in terms of three contextual levels: immediate, broad background, and predisposition. If one groups the levels further and takes the broad background and the predisposition together as one superordinate set of variables, it is the interaction of the immediate state with this larger superordinate set that makes up the "two-condition" thesis to which I have referred.

LOOKING AHEAD TO THE METHOD'S FUTURE

This wind-up is a prognostic postscript to the account of the symptom-context method in chapter 2, but it was written after having become older and wiser through years of struggling with these studies.

1. The reliance of the symptom-context method on psychotherapy sessions will become generally recognized as a valid basis for testing theories of symptom formation. My studies based on psychotherapy sessions have made substantial discoveries, and they have done this through the guidance offered by the symptom-context method as applied to data collected during psychotherapy. With the controls built into the symptom-context method, the danger of invalid inferences is minimized; the most effective control method is provided by the degree of differentiation of symptom segments versus control segments.

However, it is timely to note here that Grünbaum (1984) and some others believed that researchers should not rely on data from psychotherapy sessions because sessions are inevitably contaminated by the therapist's impact on the patient (an argument that Freud (1926/1958) had tried to counter). Once, however, in 1988 at the Rapaport-Klein study group at the Austin Riggs Foundation, Grünbaum publicly announced a view that was inconsistent with his usual views: He thought it was appropriate to evaluate theories by the symptom-context approach using the material of psychotherapy sessions. His announcement came during a discussion at a conference on my symptom-context research on Freud's theory of helplessness as an antecedent to momentary forgetting. But he had never published anything about his exceptional announcement.

During the conference Grünbaum went on to limit his new view by adding to it the illogical restriction that the symptom-context method could not evaluate Freud's "grander" theories, only "the more minor ones." The examples in this book show that this restriction was not logical because, if the symptom-context method is able to evaluate Freud's helplessness theory, in Grünbaum's view a "minor" theory, it could also evaluate "grander" theories (Luborsky, 1986), for example, by studies of the greater presence of transference pattern material before symptoms versus before control points.

A general principle for future testing of Freud's theories emerges from the studies in my book: It is not required in testing Freud's theories to look outside the usual milieu of psychotherapy that Freud relied on. The current studies illustrate that it is appropriate and worthwhile to test Freud's theories by relying on the same type of data that he used. But, the studies also illustrate that the technical trick in achieving discoveries by testing Freud's theories is to go beyond clinical reviews by adding the clinical–quantitative methods used in this book.

2. Inevitably, discoveries will be made of even more basic conditions for each symptom. An impressive example is the discovery of the role of the bacterium, *Helicobacter pylori*, as another likely condition for the stomach ulcer pain in the patient described in chapter 7. As I discussed in that chapter, the new knowledge of the bacterium does not supplant the theory of the psychological conditions; instead, the psychological and physical conditions must contribute together. It is certain that more conditions will eventually be discovered, especially on the physiological level, just as that one was. Further basic discoveries will emerge to alter the understanding of other disorders as well.

The prediction just given is an obvious one: There will be more basic conditions discovered for each symptom. This one is less obvious, but highly likely: The discoveries will be based on a combination of clinical observation and physiological knowledge. That prediction fits the history of the development of neuroscience in the account by N. E. Miller (1995), in which he traced how the clinic suggested significant experiments for the laboratory. Specifically, the clinical and laboratory interactions have led to greater understanding of the role of the brain in mediating the greater health of the body.

3. The range of severity of symptoms and of measures of their antecedents will be enlarged in future studies. This book presents what I have learned so far from my unselected assemblage of the only available suitable set of recorded cases of recurrent symptoms. For the future, it is likely that more cases, more symptoms, and better measures will be added. Videos also will be viewed to add to the transcript-based analyses of the interactive facial and other expressions of the patient and therapist (Krause, Steimer-Krause, & Ullrich, 1992), as I also tried for one absence epilepsy episode (petit mal) case (see chap. 9). For both old and new cases, there will be improved systems for discerning the interaction of the psychological and the physiological levels (e.g., by event-related potentials as in Shevrin et al., 1992), leading to a better understanding of the mediating factors in creating these symptoms.

The seven symptom cases already differed considerably in the severity of their recurrent symptom. One major criterion of severity was the degree to which the symptom interfered with the conduct of the patient's life. It is interesting to note a likely correspondence of severity with the percentage of the 12 variables that showed significant differences between symptom segments and controls. The two symptom cases that were significant for only 50% or less of the variables, the stomach ulcer pain patient and the PVC patient, were not as severe in the sense that they were not impelled to get treatment by the severity of their symptoms.

4. Differences in the degree of each patient's self-disclosure will not prevent significant research findings. For several reasons, the findings reported in this book about consistency of certain variables in distinguishing symptom segments from control segments across types of symptoms were not entirely expected. One of the reasons was my concern that some patients would not reveal much about the preconditions for their symptoms in what they said; the more skimpy and opaque the patients' verbalizations, the less the preconditions would be evident. Contrary to this expectation, the fact is that enough was expressed by every patient, so that the preconditions for their symptoms discriminated between symptom segments and control segments.

5. Differences in the accuracy of locating the point of onset for each type of symptom will not prevent research findings. Each case differs in the exactness of the temporal concomitance of the symptom as measured and the actual time of its occurrence. The closeness of this concomitance appears to be fairly good for momentary forgetting, only moderately good for shifts in depression, fairly good for stomach pain (because of the acuteness of the pain), fairly good for migraine headaches, and very good for the absence epilepsy episodes (petit mal) and the PVCs (because these two symptoms possess measures that tap directly into the physical symptom so that verbal report is not required). Although there were such differences among cases in accuracy of measurement, it is noteworthy that the significance of differences between symptom segments and control segments for some variables was high across all symptoms.

6. More knowledge about mechanisms of interaction among the symptom context's qualities will be the aim of future research. My results so far are based on single variables, but the emergence of a symptom, whether psychological or psychosomatic, must require the interplay of a set of immediate and broad-context variables rather than single variables. This interplay is taken for granted in system theories, such as Gruen (1993), Swartz (1980), or J. G. Miller (1978). But so far, I have mainly relied on clinical reviews for understanding the interactions and sequence of the antecedents.

7. Temporal sequences will become thought of as causal sequences. Strictly speaking, one should remember that the findings from the symptom contexts are just concomitants; they are qualities that appear before symptoms and do not necessarily cause the symptoms. It is generally difficult to

move interpretatively from the frequency of an association of two events to the causation of one event by the other. Yet, temporal sequences are often a correct indication of causal association. And, from time to time, I have given in to that temptation here, especially for those qualities with the highest association with the appearance of the symptom, such as for helplessness and hopelessness. My concept of causation also shows in my use of the word *precondition* in the symptom-context theory of symptom formation.

Looking Ahead to the Application of Symptom-Context Methods in Clinical Practice

This section leads off with an imaginary conversation between Robert Waelder, a brilliant psychoanalytic clinician and theoretician, and me.

L: You said long ago that nothing more is learned from clinical–quantitative research than we already know clinically. Are the findings of the symptom-context studies beyond what you would have expected clinically?

W: No, what you've learned is what I've already seen clinically over the years.

L: [Thinking, I'll phrase the question another way] All of the symptom-context findings for the seven symptom-context studies show significant presymptom contexts for hopelessness or helplessness. Is that what you would expect clinically?

W: Yet, that is what I would have expected clinically.

L: What if none of the theories of symptom formation were confirmed by the symptom-context method? What would you have said?

W: I must admit, as a clinician I might have expected that too, because with such small samples of the session before the symptom, one might not expect to see the theories confirmed within the words just before the symptom.

L: So the findings from the symptom-context studies, you admit, do teach us something for clinical use that we did not know clinically?

W: It's true. They do.

L: And what about the eight preconditions that appeared in the symptom-context theory in the final chapter?

W: True, although they might have been partly expected clinically, there is, I must admit, more there than has been found out before and it should be considered in clinical work.

This imaginery conversation was a transparent wish fulfillment of my old wish: to have a fellow clinician of the caliber of Robert Waelder acknowledge that results from the symptom-context research have added to our knowledge and should be kept in mind in clinical work.

These broader meanings of the results for clinical practice are now to be expected.

1. The symptom-context studies confirm and expand on some clinical observations about the pervasiveness of Hopelessness, Lack of Control, Anxiety, Feeling Blocked, and Helplessness. Such studies indicate more about other preconditions before symptoms, especially in situations in which there is a perception of a danger from a current (and past) relationship with a person whose expected or perceived-to-be-actual responses cannot be coped with.

2. These results strongly support the value of a therapeutic focus on empowering the patient through working out the dynamics that lead to Hopelessness, Lack of Control, and so on (by techniques in chap. 15). The working through of the types of dynamics contained in the CCRT should enable the patient to achieve a greater sense of mastery and hopefulness, perhaps subsequent to periods of incipient hopelessness (which might then be called periods of "signal hopelessness" as a term parallel to "signal anxiety," as suggested by Engel & Schmale, 1967).

3. An expectable effect of my research should be to heighten psychotherapists' interest in symptoms and in symptom formation and to sensitize them to the conditions for their appearance. The effect of the symptom-context studies should be greatest on the concepts held by dynamically oriented practitioners. In recent issues of the *Journal of the American Psychoanalytic Association*, one can see that dynamically oriented practitioners tend not to be immediately concerned about focusing on the removal of symptoms. Rather, they attend to the patient's dynamics and to working out these dynamics by increasing the patient's self-understanding.

Behaviorally oriented practitioners, by contrast, already give focused attention to the symptom as the therapeutic target to be directly attacked and eliminated. Now, the symptom-context research also should have an effect on the concepts relied on by behaviorally oriented people; their concepts should grow to include more awareness of the dynamics within contexts that play a part in the genesis of the symptoms.

In connecting the dynamic and behavioral views, the central unit in the symptom-context data is the symptom with its surrounding context of thoughts and behaviors. This nodal unit can profitably be looked at from both a behavioral viewpoint and a dynamic viewpoint, as has been observed by others (Rhoads & Feather, 1972). In the associational point of view within behavioral theory, the thoughts and feelings surrounding the symptom are thought to appear there through the effects of past learning experiences; from a dynamic viewpoint, the thoughts and feelings surrounding the symptom are thought to appear there as a result of conflicting psychological forces, such as those that are estimated through the CCRT.

For practitioners from each orientation, I have shown that there are potential benefits from symptom-context studies and that the findings of this book should bring their interests closer together. Attention both to the symptom and to its context will reveal that it is around symptom outbreaks that the therapist and the patient are offered special opportunities to understand the symptoms and even for the patient, aided by the therapist, to become better able to master the symptoms.

REFERENCES

Alexander, K., Luborsky, L., & Peterson, C. (1975). *Prediction from peaks of help-lessness to depressive shifts.* Unpublished data.

Ambady, N., & Rosenthal, R. (1992). Thin slices of expressive behavior as predictors of interpersonal consequences: A meta-analysis. *Psychological Bulletin, 111,* 256–274.

Berlinski, D. (1978). Catastrophe theory and its applications: A critical review. *Behavioral Science, 23,* 402–416.

Cohen, J. (1994). The earth is round ($p < .05$). *American Psychologist, 49,* 997–1004.

Engel, G., & Schmale, A. (1967). Psychoanalytic theory of somatic disorders: Conversion, specificity and the disease onset situation. *Journal of the American Psychoanalytic Association, 15,* 344–365.

Freud, S. (1958). The dynamics of the transference. In J. Strachey (Ed. and Trans.), *The standard edition of the complete psychological works of Sigmund Freud* (Vol. 12, pp. 99–108). London: Hogarth Press. (Original work published 1912)

Freud, S. (1959). Inhibitions, symptoms and anxiety. In J. Strachey (Ed. and Trans.), *The standard edition of the complete psychological works of Sigmund Freud* (Vol. 20, pp. 87–174). London: Hogarth Press. (Original work published 1926)

Gleick, J. (1987). *Chaos: Making a new sign.* New York: Penguin Books.

Gottschalk, L., & Bechtel, R. (1995). Computerized measurement of the content analysis of natural language for use in biomedical and neuropsychiatric research. *Computer Methods and Programs in Biomedicine, 47,* 123–130.

Gottschalk, L., Fronczeck, J., & Buchsbaum, M. (1993). The cerebral neurobiology of hope and hopelessness. *Psychiatry, 56,* 270–281.

Gottschalk, L., & Gleser, G. (1969). *The measurement of psychological states through the content analysis of verbal behavior.* Berkeley, CA: University of California Press.

Grenyer, B., & Luborsky, L. (in press). Mastery of transference-related conflicts as an outcome of psychotherapy. *Journal of Consulting and Clinical Psychology.*

Gruen, R. (1993). Stress and depression: Toward the development of integrative models. In L. Goldberger & S. Breznitz (Eds.), *Handbook of stress: Theoretical and clinical aspects* (pp. 550–569). New York: The Free Press.

Grünbaum, A. (1984). *The foundations of psychoanalysis: A philosophical critique.* Berkeley: University of California Press.

Hodgins, D., El-Guebaly, N., & Armstrong, S. (1995). Prospective and retrospective reports of mood states before relapse to substance use. *Journal of Consulting and Clinical Psychology, 63,* 400–407.

Holzman, P., & Aronson, G. (1992). Psychoanalysis and its neighboring sciences: Paradigms and opportunities. *Journal of the American Psychoanalytic Association, 40,* 63–88.

Krause, R., Steimer-Krause, E., & Ullrich, B. (1992). The use of affect research in dynamic psychotherapy. In M. Leuzinger-Bohleber, H. Schneider, & R. Pfeifer (Eds.), *Two butterflies on my head: Psychoanalysis in the scientific dialogue* (pp. 277–291). New York: Springer.

Luborsky, L. (1986). Evidence to lessen Professor Grünbaum's concern about Freud's clinical inference methods. *Behavioral and Brain Sciences, 9,* 247–249.

Miller, J. G. (1978). *Living systems.* New York: McGraw Hill.

Miller, N. E. (1995). Clinical-experimental interactions in the development of neuroscience: A primer for non-specialists, and lessons for young scientists. *American Psychologist, 50,* 901–911.

Rhoads, J. M., & Feather, B. W. (1972). Transference and resistance in behavior therapy. *British Journal of Medical Psychology, 45,* 99–103.

Rosenthal, R. (1991). *Meta-analytical procedures for social research.* Newbury Park, CA: Sage.

Sherman, A., & Petty, F. (1982). Neurochemical basis of antidepressants on learned helplessness. *Behavioral and Neurological Biology, 30* 119–134.

Shevrin, H., Williams, W., Marshall, R., Hertel, R., Bond, J., & Brakel, L. (1992). Event-related potential indicators of the dynamic unconscious. *Consciousness and Cognition, 1,* 340–366.

Stunkard, A., Foster, G., Glassman, J., & Rosato, E. (1985). Retrospective exaggeration of symptoms: Vomiting after gastric surgery for obesity. *Psychosomatic Medicine, 47,* 150–155.

Swartz, G. E. (1980). Behavioral medicine and systems theory: A new synthesis. *National Forum of the Honor Society of Phi Kappa Phi,* 25–30.

Weiner, H. M. (1977). *Psychology and human disease.* New York: Elsevier.

AUTHOR INDEX

Numbers in italics refer to listings in reference sections.

Horowitz, L. M., 82, *103*
Horowitz, M. J., 168, *173*, 357, *364*
Houck, J., 133, *149*
Hutt, C., 310, *341*
Hutt, S., 310, *341*
Hyson, M., 309, 310, 311, 315, 318, *341*

Irwin, F. W., 91, 92, *103*
Isaacs, K. S., 344, *352*

James, W., 31, *62*
Janis, I. L., 9, 12, *27*
Jones, B., 310, 316, *341*
Jones, C., 193, *198*
Judd, C., 21, *27*

Kächele, H., 12, *27*
Katcher, A. H., 41, *62*
Kemph, J., 237, *242*
Kennedy, G., 269, *274*
Kenny, D., 21, *27*
Kimball, C. P., 70, *105*
Klein, G. S., 54, *62*
Kline, P., 91, *103*
Klohnen, E., 19, *28*
Knapp, P. H., *104*, *148*, *242*, *275*, *352*
Knight, R. P., 5, 8, 12, *26*
Knoblauch, D., 267, *274*
Kooi, K., 237, *242*
Kornfeld, D., 268, *274*
Krannich, S., *28*
Krause, R., 401, *406*
Kron, R., *104*

Lattin, G., 266, *275*
Leff, M., 109, *148*
Leigh, H., 244, 265, 268, *274*
Levy, L., *104*
Lown, B., 245, *274*
Luborsky, E., 297, 308, *341*
Luborsky, L., 3, 4, 5, 6, 8, 9, 17, 18, *26*,
    27, *28*, 31, 32, 33, 34, 35, 41,
    45, 49, 51, 55, 57, *62*, 63, 64,
    66, 69, 71, 76, 77, 79, 80, 81,
    82, 83, 89, *102*, *103*, *104*, 108,
    109, 110, 111, 112, 114, 115,
    123, 126, 137, *148*, *149*, 152,
    167, 170, 171, *172*, *173*, 180,

188, 189, 190, 193, *198*, *199*,
201, 214, *215*, 218, 222, 230,
239, 242, 244, 253, 265, *274*,
275, 288, 294, 295, 296, 297,
308, 336, *341*, 344, 352, 356,
360, 361, *364*, 394, 400, *405*,
406

Madakasire, S., 268, *275*
Madison, P., 91, *104*
Maher, B., 304, *308*
Mahl, G. F., 49, 57, *62*, 74, 76, 88, *104*,
    230, *242*
Maier, J., 108, *149*
Mark, D., 18, *26*, 148, 288, *296*
Markel, N., 133, *148*, *149*
Marmar, C., 357, *363*
Marshall, R., *105*, *406*
Mauck, H. P., Jr., 245, *274*
Mayerson, P., 267, *274*
McKinney, W., 108, *149*
McLean, H. V., 244, 264, *275*
McNeill, D., 92, *102*
Meisels, M., 133, *149*
Mellon, J., 18, *26*, 83, *104*
Mendels, J., 109, *149*
Mendelson, M., 109, 111, *149*
Merritt, H., 241, *242*
Mijoskovic, M., 41, *62*
Miller, C. K., 267, *275*
Miller, J. G., 402, *406*
Miller, M. L., 244, 264, *275*
Miller, N. E., 401, *406*
Milstein, V., 241, *242*
Mintz, J., 31, 33, *62*, 64, 69, 76, 80, *104*,
    189, 193, *198*, *199*
Minuchin, S., 298, 299, *308*
Mirsky, A. F., *104*, *148*, *242*, *275*, *352*
Mirsky, I., 365, *376*
Mlodnosky, L., 82, *105*
Molenaar, P. C., 193, *199*
Moran, G., 22, *26*
Moras, K., *296*
Morris, M., *341*
Mount Zion Psychotherapy Research
    Group, 19, *28*, *296*
Muran, J., 109, *149*
Murphy, D., 109, 145, *147*
Murray, J. B., 178, *199*

Neisser, U., 90, *104*
Nesselroade, J., 193, *198*, *199*

Todd, T. C., *104, 148, 242, 275, 297,*
308, 352
Tuason, V. B., *375, 376*
Twining, L., *149*

Uliana, R. L., 351, *352*
Ullrich, B., 401, *406*

Verrier, R., 245, *274*
Viney, L. L., 112, *149*
von Baeyer, C., 133, *149*

Wachtel, P., 359, *364*
Waelder, R., 6, *9*
Waggoner, R., 237, *242*
Waldo, A., 268, *275*
Weiner, H. M., 194, *199,* 365, 376, 397,
406
Weintraub, N., 134, *147*
Weisberg, P., 312, *341*
Weiss, J., 19, *28,* 82, *103,* 105, 281, *296*

Weiss, T., *104,* 245, 266, 269, *275*
Whybrow, P., 108, 144, *149*
Wiemer, M. J., *376*
Williams, R. B., Jr., 70, *105*
Williams, W., *105, 406*
Williard, H. N., 70, *105*
Wilner, N., 357, *363*
Winer, B. J., 43, 62, 131, *149*
Winget, C., 254, *274*
Winnicott, D., 310, *341*
Winston, A., *149*
Wolf, S., 244, 266, 267, 268, *274, 275*
Wolff, H. G., 244, *275*
Wolfson, A. W., 82, *103*
Wood, P., 193, *198*

Yildiz, M., 266, *275*
Younkin, D., *103*

Zander, B., 19, *28*
Zegans, L., 237, 238, *242*
Zimmer, J. M., 193, *199*

SUBJECT INDEX

EEG paroxysmal states, 217–242. *See also*
    Absence epilepsy
Effect sizes, 380–381, 384–385, 388
Empowerment, 404
Engel and Schmale's theory, 370–371,
    399
Enmeshment construct, 300
Epilepsy. *See* Absence epilepsy
Evoked potentials, 96
Explanatory style. *See* Negative
    explanatory style

Facial tension, 235–236
Factor analysis. *See* P-technique
Family context
    boundary issues, 300
    crying episodes, 297–308
    versus patient-as-unit variables, 304–
        305
Family therapy, 297–308
    crying context, 297–308
    parental conflict in, 300
    structural theory, 299–300
Feeling Blocked. *See* Blocked feelings
Focused attention, 238
Forgetting. *See* Momentary forgetting
Free associations
    and epileptic episodes, 343
    and mouth touching, 343–351
    symptom temporal sequences, 12
    unfreeness of, 350
Freud, Sigmund
    clinical method of, 4–5
    depression theory, 111–112
    phobia cases, 171
    repression theory, 91–92
    symptom-context theory, 398–401
    symptom formation theory, 366–370
    symptom temporal contiguity view,
        12

Galvanic skin response, 192
Gastric ulcer pain. *See* Stomach ulcer
    pain
Goldstein's symptom formation theory,
    371–372
Gottschalk-Gleser variables
    absence epilepsy, 222, 224
    depressive mood shifts, 111

momentary-forgetting scoring, 50
premature ventricular contractions,
    254–257, 262–264
Grünbaum's critique, 400–401
Guilt
    clinical review findings, depression,
        121–122
    depression theory, 111
    depressive mood shift ratings, 124–
        126, 130–133, 356
    and momentary forgetting, 81

Hand–mouth touching, 343–352
    adaptive function, 344, 351
    clinical review, 346–347
    and free associations, 347, 350
    scoring, 347–350
Headache. *See* Migraine-like headaches
Health Sickness Rating Scale, 66–67
Heart rate
    and premature ventricular
        contractions, 261, 264–266
    word segment context, 260–261
Helicobacter pylori, 193–195, 401
Helplessness
    coping effects, 394
    crying episodes, family context,
        299–301, 305
    depression relationship, 107–108,
        112–113
    and depressive mood shifts,
        124–126, 129, 134, 141, 146,
        356
        temporal association, 141–143
    Engel and Schmale's theory,
        370–371
    hopelessness distinction, 370–371,
        399
    intercorrelations, rated variables, 47–
        48, 384–385
    low degree of symptom co-
        occurrence, 394–395
    main findings, 380–385
    meta-analysis, 380, 382–384
    migraine headache context,
        209–210, 391
    momentary-forgetting ratings, 43–48,
        58, 90, 94
    time trends, 46
    phobic symptoms, 162–166

Helplessness (*continued*)
    physiology, 396
    stomach ulcer pain, 184–187
    in symptom-context theory, 399
    and symptom formation, 367–370
Helplessness manual
    depressive mood shifts, 126–127,
        130–136, 138, 142–144, 146
    meta-analysis, 385–387
    migraine headache scoring, 210–211
    momentary-forgetting ratings, 49
    phobic symptoms, 167
Hopelessness
    and absence seizures, 238
    depressive mood shift ratings,
        124–125, 130–133, 356
    effect sizes, 381, 384, 388
    Engel and Schmale's theory,
        370–371
    helplessness distinction, 370–371,
        399
    intercorrelations, rated variables, 48,
        384–385
    laughing context, 286
    main findings, 380–385
    meta-analysis, 380, 382–384
    momentary-forgetting ratings, 43, 58,
        90, 390–391
    and phobic symptoms, 162–164, 166
    physiology, 396
    and premature ventricular
        contractions, 251–252,
        262–263
    symptom-context theory centrality,
        399
    therapeutic focus, 404
Horton's headache, 202
Hostility-Inward
    and absence epilepsy, 222, 224
    and depressive mood shifts, 111,
        128–129
    premature ventricular contractions,
        254–257, 262–264
Hostility-Outward
    medical illness prognosis, 269
    and momentary forgetting, 50
    premature ventricular contractions,
        254–255
Hostility to Therapist
    intercorrelations, rated variables, 48
    laughing context, 287–288, 294
    migraine headache ratings, 209–210

momentary forgetting ratings, 43,
    56, 59
    theoretical aspects, 54–55
    time trends, 46
    and premature ventricular
        contractions, 251–252,
        262–263
    symptom onset precondition, 396
Hostility turned inward
    absence epilepsy antecedent, 222–
        225
    clinical review findings, 121–122
    depression theory, 111–112
    depressive mood shift ratings,
        127–129, 134
    helplessness relationship, 134
    premature ventricular contractions,
        254–257, 262–264

Individual therapy, 304–305
Inhibitions, 367
Interpersonal pattern. *See* Core
        Conflictual Relationship
        Theme
Interpretation
    and outcome, 359–360
    temporal sequences in, 12
    therapeutic alliance effect, 358
Intra-individual methods. *See* Single-case
        design
Intrapsychic variables
    crying context, 304–305
    versus social context variables,
        304–305
Involvement with Therapist
    crying context, 299–303, 307
    intercorrelations, rated variables, 48
    and laughing, 285–288, 294
    and momentary forgetting, 41–48,
        56, 61, 88, 94–95, 390–391
    symptom onset precondition, 396
Isoproterenol, 266

Laboratory studies, 91–92, 96–97
Lack of Control
    crying episodes, family context,
        299–301
    effect sizes, 388
    intercorrelations, rated variables, 384
    main findings, 380–385

Object attachment. *See* Blanket attachment
Object relations, 348
Observational studies
　blanket attachment, 312–315
　methodological problems, children, 335–336
　momentary forgetting, 65–66, 91–92, 96–97
　　versus laboratory studies, 91–92
　retrospective accounts overlap, 393–394
Oedipal conflict
　depressive mood shifts, 111–113, 124, 130–133, 146
　stomach ulcer pain, 187–188
One-tailed statistical tests, 20
Oral–passive urges, 345
Outcome factors
　comparative treatment studies, 360
　and mastery, 360
　in symptom interpretation approach, 359
　and working through symptom themes, 359–360
Outward Hostility. *See* Hostility-Outward

P-technique
　advantages, 192–193
　development of, 5–6
　limitations, 193
　psychotherapy applications, 193
　stomach ulcer pain context, 180, 192–193
Parasympathetic tone, 266–267
Peptic ulcer pain. *See* Stomach ulcer pain
Petit mal. *See* Absence epilepsy
Phobias, 151–173, 358
　CCRT results, 166–170
　　symptom-context theme comparison, 168–170
　clinical review, 153–159, 170–171
　comparative treatment studies, 360
　Little Hans case, 170–171
　modified symptom-context method, 151–173
　retrospective accounts versus direct observation, 393

symptom ratings, 159–165, 171–172, 382
symptom scoring, 166, 386
working through symptoms, and outcome, 359–360
Play behavior, 331–334
Positive affect, and absence epilepsy, 222–225
Premature ventricular contractions, 243–275
　activation mechanism, 266–267
　antecedent verbal segments, 247–250, 261
　　ratings, 250–253, 383
　antidepressant effects, 268
　brief psychotherapy implications, 267–268
　cognitive disturbances, 253–255
　conditioning paradigms, 245
　EKG recording, 246
　and emotional state, review, 244, 254–255, 264
　heart rate relationship, 261, 264–266
　high-risk affects, 268–269
　immediate psychological context, 245–273
　laughing episodes, antecedents, 259–260
　management, 268–269

　pronoun counts, 255–259
　suppression mechanism, 267
　and tranquilizers, 268
　word fluency relationship, 259
Process notes, and assessment, 19
Programmed electrical stimulation, 269
Pronoun counts, 255–259, 264
Psychosomatic symptoms, 367, 370–371
Psychotherapy
　Grünbaum's critique, 400–401
　symptom-context generation, 13, 378–379, 400–401
Psychotherapy outcome. *See* Outcome factors

Qualitative methods, 12. *See also* Observational studies
Quantitative methods, 6, 12

ABOUT THE AUTHOR

Over the past 50 years, the main theme in Lester Luborsky's research has been the shaping of clinical concepts into clinical–quantitative measures. He did not set out with that goal, but in fact as time went on, it became evident that that was his inclination. By now he has worked on about 36 different clinical concepts and tried to move them in the direction of operational measures. The one in this book is called the *symptom-context method* because, as the name implies, the context of each recurrent symptom is the focus of analysis in comparison with control points from the same patient where no subsequent symptom appeared.

His career was launched with a PhD in 1945 from Duke University, where he was much influenced by collaboration with Raymond Cattell on intra-individual studies of personality. He and Cattell left Duke in 1945 for the Department of Psychology at the University of Illinois. It was at Illinois that Luborsky began the symptom-context line of studies. In 1947 Luborsky became a research psychologist at the Menninger Foundation, whose staff he joined in order to get clinical training and combine it with research. For the next 13 years, he was a senior psychologist there, working as a research psychologist, psychotherapist, and eventually, a psychoanalyst.

His favorite clinical–quantitative measures include (a) the Health–Sickness Rating scale, which was first published in 1961 as an observer judgment method for estimating psychological health (now modified and included in the *DSM-IV* as Axis 5); (b) the Core Conflictual Relationship Theme method in 1976, which turned out to be the first reliable method of estimating the transference pattern; and (c) methods of judging the Helping Alliance in psychotherapy sessions in 1976.

His research output includes 345 articles and 8 books, with 6 of the 8 in the past dozen years. His recent awards include the 1995 American Psychological Association Award for "distinguished professional contribution to knowle'; and in 1996, the Hoch Award presented by the American Psychopathological Association.